STARTING POINT
1997

A WHOLE DIFFERENT KIND OF WALK

Dedication

STARTING POINT 1997 is dedicated to the clubs and individuals who have made Volkssporting possible in the United States.

DISCLAIMER: The AVA and its officers, members, and agents shall not be liable or responsible for, and shall be held harmless for and against any and all claims and damages to or loss of property arising out of or attributed to the operations of events conducted by the AVA.

Photo Credits:
Cover photo submitted by James T, Scofiled, Visalia, CA
Back Cover photo submitted by Helen S. Heimbigner, Denver, CO

D1597631

ISBN 0-9644794-2-7

Thank you for your purchase of the American Volkssport Association's (AVA) **STARTING POINT 1997.** **STARTING POINT** contains more than 1,100 listings of sporting events that are available on a daily basis for your personal physical fitness programs. Listings of events are provided by state in alphabetical order in this easy-to-read, compact book.

The following general information is provided to help get you acquainted with the AVA and our year-round walking events.

Who is the AVA? Founded in 1979, the AVA is a non-profit, tax-exempt, national organization dedicated to promoting the benefits of health and physical fitness for people of all ages. The AVA promotes physical fitness by sponsoring, through its affiliate clubs, non-competitive sports events in safe, stress-free environments.

What is volkssporting? A volkssporting event is an organized walk, bike, swim, or cross-country ski designed to appeal to everyone. Events are non-competitive, and participants exercise at their own pace.

Types of events: Most volkssport events are walks (referred to as volksmarches) that are 10 kilometers (6.2 miles) in length, however, the distance varies depending on the event. Bicycle events are 25 kilometers or more; swimming events are 300 meters or more; cross-country ski events are 10 kilometers or more. Other events may include rollerblading, ice skating or snowshoeing.

Weekend events: Sometimes referred to as "regular events," these events occur on weekends, usually both Saturday and Sunday, with published start and finish times. Participants may start an event individually or in a group at any time during a specified 3-5 hour time period and are allowed more than adequate time to finish. Many 5 kilometer walks are available for the beginner. Special provisions also allow for the physically challenged to participate in most events. Participation is open to the general public. A nominal fee is charged if a participant wishes to earn credit or to purchase an award. Weekend events are published in the AVA's bimonthly newspaper, *The American Wanderer*. Subscriptions are available through Volkssports Associate membership, see page 232.

Year-Round and Seasonal events: STARTING POINT features Year-Round events (YRE), which are events that are available any day of the year. There are some restrictions, most notably, closures during holidays at some locations. Seasonal events, as the name suggests, are open during a limited time frame (eleven months or less).

Trail Ratings:

1. Easy walk on pavement or a well-maintained trail. Usually suitable for wheelchairs and strollers.

2. A moderately easy walk on some pavement or some woodland or open field trails. No significant difficulty with hills. Possibly not suitable for wheelchairs and strollers.

3. A moderate walk in any setting with some difficult terrain, substantial hills and/or steps.

4. A more difficult walk. Most likely settings with natural paths and steep or hilly inclines.

5. A very difficult walk on rough terrain. Steep hills and high altitude trails. Unsuitable for persons not in good health.

Clubs: You are welcome to join one or more of our 550 + volkssporting clubs. Membership in these clubs is usually less than $10 per year. Of course, you may remain unaffiliated as AVA sporting events are open to everyone regardless of membership.

International Achievement Awards Program: A great incentive for participating in volkssporting is collecting "credits" for each event and distance accomplished. The AVA offers a voluntary International Achievement Awards program for those who wish to track their progress and credit. International Record Books are available for purchase at every regular event (and at some YRE events) for $5 each. An Event book is a record for the number of events in which you participate and a Distance book is a record of actual number of kilometers walked. When you register at an AVA sanctioned event, you indicate that you are walking "For Credit" and pay a small registration fee (not more than $2.00) and a nominal fee if you want to purchase an award, which is a memento of the event. At the finish, your record books are stamped. When your books are completed, you send them to the AVA Headquarters to receive your certificate, patch and pin. You earn your first Achievement Award after 10 events and/or 500 kilometers. You may order Event and Distance books at any time through the AVA National Headquarters.

Volkssports Associate: Information on **Volkssports Associate** membership is included on page 232. When you become an Associate, you receive the AVA's bi-monthly newspaper, *The American Wanderer*, travel discounts at **Choice** Hotels, **Alamo Rent-A-Car**, **Hertz** and **Avis** and special offers on AVA specialties. Your membership helps support the local clubs and the association overall as we can use Associate fees for Headquarters operations and development of volkssporting in the United States. To receive a free general information packet about volkssporting and the AVA call 1-800-830-WALK(9255) and leave your name, address and phone number.

Notes

Events in this book are sanctioned by the AVA in the IVV. Information was furnished by the sponsoring club. Updates to **STARTING POINT** are published in *The American Wanderer*. To join Volkssports Associates and receive a subscribtion, see page 232.

All participants must complete a Start Card & carry it with them throughout the event & must surrender the card upon completion of the event. Events are open to all persons.

You may walk an event for credit twice in the same day on the same start card for one fee. A new start card must be purchased each time you do a bike event for credit.

Anyone doing an event **other than a walk** must sign a waiver.

Participate during daylight hours only. Observe local laws regarding your pets.

If the club has more than one route available, check to make sure they have sanctions (look for the YR# in this book) on all trails. If not, you can only receive one event credit, even if doing all of the trails.

Remember to bring your books. Some YREs may not have them available for sale. You may order books from the AVA National Headquarters for $5.00 each including shipping & handling.

Top Ten Year Round Events for 1996

These events were voted as the best by volkssporters from all 50 states.
Visit them in 1997 and see if you agree.

They will be designated by **++** in the event listing.

1st Place: YR730, Boston, MA (Freedom Trail)
2nd Place: YR055, San Antonio, TX (Riverwalk)
3rd Place: YR171, Silverton, OR (Silver Falls State Park)
4th Place: YR497, Devils Tower, WY
5th Place: YR155, Santa Fe, NM (Historic Downtown)
6th Place: YR214, Niagara Falls, NY
7th Place: YR729, Newport, RI
8th Place: YR231, Washington DC (Mall Walk)
9th Place: YR736, Princeton, NJ
10th Place: YR037, West Point, NY

For additional information on volkssporting, please contact us at:

AVA National Headquarters
1001 Pat Booker Rd., Suite 101
Universal City, TX 78148
phone (210) 659-2112   fax (210) 659-1212

ALABAMA ===========================

Mobile - 10km Walk (YR338) Jan 1-Dec 31
Credit Only Event
Sponsoring Club: AVA-310, Magnolia State Volkssport Club
POC: William Sager, 334-653-1400. PO Box 636, Pascagoula, MS 39568

Start Point: Mobile Visitors Center (Ft Conde), 334-434-7304. From I-10 exit at Water St and follow the Fort Conde signs. Public parking across the street from the Fort.

Event Info: Daily, 8-5. Rated 1. Suitable for strollers & wheelchairs. Pets must be leashed. Trail travels through historic Mobile, past many homes listed on the Historical Register.

Montgomery - 11km Walk (YR323) **Jan 1-Dec 31**
B Awards available
Sponsoring Club: AVA-261, Capital City Wanderers
POC: Carolyn Harrison, 334-279-7012. 521 Fieldbrook Dr, Montgomery, AL 36117

Start Point: Racetrac, 1319 Eastern Blvd. Use Exit 6, Interstate 85. Drive South to the first intersection which is Carmichael Rd. Racetrac is on the Southeast corner of Eastern Blvd and Carmichael Rd.

Event Info: Start point is open daily 24 hrs. Walk during daylight hours only. Trail is rated 1, suitable for strollers but too many curbs for wheelchairs. Pets must be leashed. Walk is primarily on sidewalks and some streets, through two parks.

Montgomery - 10km Walk (YR398)   25km Bike (YR217) **Jan 1-Dec 31**
B Awards available
Sponsoring Club: AVA-261, Capital City Wanderers
POC: Elwood Hintz, 334-272-5986. 3914 Meredith Dr, Montgomery AL 36109-2312

Start Point: Embassy Suites Montgomery, 334-269-2493. 300 Tallapoosa St. Traveling North on I-65, exit Herron St (exit 172). Turn right (east) five blocks to Molton St. Turn left on Moulton. Embassy Suites is almost directly in front of you. Turn right on Tallapoosa.   Traveling South on I-65, exit at Downtown Clay Street exit (exit 172). After first traffic light turn left on Herron St. Cross the Interstate Bridge. Go five blocks to Molton St. Turn left on Molton. Turn right on Tallapoosa.

Event Info: Start point is open daily 24 hrs. Participate during daylight hours only. Bike is rated 1; very flat. Instructions to the bike course are contained in the Volkssport box at the Embassy Suites. Walk is rated 1+. An alternate route is available for strollers and wheelchairs. Mostly sidewalks with some hills. Bring a camera. Pets are allowed on a leash.

Tallassee - 10km Walk (YR129) **Jan 2-Dec 31**
B Awards available
Sponsoring Club: AVA-261, Capital City Wanderers
POC: Melvin Palmer, 334-514-0461. 77 Greenfield Place, Wetumpka, AL 36092

Start Point: Talisi Hotel, 334-283-2769. Sistrunk St. From I-85, exit #26. Drive North on Hwy 229 into downtown Tallassee. At stop light turn right on Hwy 14. Just before bridge, turn right on Sistrunk St. Hotel is at the end of the block on the right.

Event Info: Open daily, dawn to dusk. Closed major holidays. Trail is rated 3. Suitable for strollers but not wheelchairs. Pets must be leashed. Walk is on sidewalks and city streets all within the city limits.

Wetumpka - 10km Walk (YR574) **Jan 1-Dec 31**
B Awards available
Sponsoring Club: AVA-261, Capital City Wanderers
POC: Melvin Palmer, 334-514-0461. 77 Greenfield Place, Wetumpka, AL 36092

Start Point: Wetumpka Police Station; 334-567-5321. Corner of Main & Ready. Wetumpka is located 14 miles north of Montgomery. It can be reached on Hwys 231, 111, & 14. Easily accessible from I-65 via Hwy 14 or exit 173. PLEASE NOTE: The Police Station will be moving sometime between Jan & Mar 1997. Directions to the new location are: Turn left off Hwy 231 at McDonald's. The new location is on East Charles St (behind the Amoco station).

Event Info: Start point is open daily, 24 hrs. Participate during daylight hours only. Trail is rated 2, suitable for strollers but not wheelchairs. Pets must be leashed. Walk is on city streets and sidewalks with one steep hill and one cemetery.

ALASKA ━━━━━━━━━━━━━━━━━━━━━━━━━━━━━━━━━━━━━━━

Anchorage - 10km Walk (YR902) **May 20-Sep 30**
Credit Only Event
Sponsoring Club: AVA-754, The Over-The-Hill-Gang Volkssport Club
POC: Jack Maxcy, 206-927-4580. PO Box 23057, Federal Way, WA 98093

Start Point: Public Lands Information Center (Old Federal Bldg); 907-271-2737. 605 West 4th Ave, Suite 105. Located on the corner of 4th & F Streets on the first floor. From the airport, take Airport Road to Minnesota St. Turn left drive to 4th Ave, turn right to start.

Event Info: Jun 1-Aug 31: daily, 9-5:30. Sept 1-Sept 30: Mon-Fri only, 11-5:30. Trail is rated 1 along city sidewalks and groomed trails in downtown Anchorage and along the shore of the Captain Cook Inlet. One set of stairs will make it difficult for strollers or wheelchairs. Pets are allowed but must be leashed. Preregistration available by contacting POC at the PO Box above.

Juneau - 10km Walk (YR863) **May 1-Sep 30**
Credit Only Event
Sponsoring Club: AVA-754, The Over-The-Hill-Gang Volkssport Club
POC: Jack Maxcy, 206-927-4580. PO Box 23057, Federal Way, WA 98093.

Start Point: Galligaskin's Gift Shop; 907-586-8953. 219 S. Franklin St. From Cruise Ship Terminal: Exit on Franklin St. Turn left and walk to start point. From Airport: Drive South (towards town) on Egan Dr to Marine Dr. Stay on right side of road until you reach S. Franklin St. Turn left to start point. Drive is approximately nine miles.

Event Info: Daily, 9am-10pm. Trail is rated 3. Begins in the downtown area of Juneau which is a city of numerous hills. One stairway will make the trail difficult for strollers and wheelchairs. Pets are allowed. Pre-registration available by contacting POC at the PO Box listed above.

ARIZONA

Ajo - 10km Walk (YR1308) **Jan 1-Mar 31**
Credit Only Event
Sponsoring Club: AVA-498, Rogue Valley Walkers
POC: Loretta Carmickle; 520-387-6507. 320 Estrella Ave, Ajo, AZ 85321 or Shirley O'Hare; 541-479-7989. 199 S Gordon Way, Grants Pass, OR 97527

Start Point: Loretta Carmickle Residence, 320 Estrella Ave. Ajo is located on Hwy 85, 108 miles SW of Phoenix & 140 miles W of Tucson. From Phoenix take I-10 to Hwy 85 near Buckeye; south on Hwy 85 to Gila Bend, then further S on Hwy 85 to Ajo (follow the signs to Mexico). The start point is at a private residence three blocks from the central plaza. Estrella is one street S of the plaza. You may park at the plaza or on Estrella. The start box is in front of the house under a palm tree.

Event Info: Daily, dawn to dusk. Trail is rated 2; not suitable for strollers or wheelchairs. Pets are allowed. It is advisable to carry water and wear a hat. Ajo, a former copper-mining town, now a retirement community and "snowbird" destination is also the gateway for Organ Pipe Cactus National Monument & Sonora, Mexico. The route goes by a large open-pit copper mine, an organ pipe cactus forest, an earthen dam which was listed in the Guiness Book of World Records and several houses built in the early 1900's as well as several stretches of typical Sonoran desert habitat with sahuaro and organ pipe cacti. It is a moderately easy walk with some hills. It follows city streets but a few short sections have no sidewalks.

Bisbee - 10km Walk (YR669) **Jan 1-Dec 30**
A Award available
Sponsoring Club: AVA-746, Thunder Mountain Trekkers
POC: Wendy Breen; 520-378-1763/520-432-3931. 3288 Sky Hawk Dr, Sierra Vista, AZ 85635-6623

Start Point: Copper Queen Hotel, 520-432-2216. 11 Howell Ave. Take exit 303 off of I-10. Follow Hwy 80 through Tombstone to Bisbee. Take the Old Bisbee exit. Park in the lot on your left at the end of the exit (small fee). The Hotel is directly behind the Bisbee Mining and Historical Museum, which is across the street. (Walk across Naco Rd/Copper Queen Plaza along Brewery Ave. one bock to Howell. Go left for 1/2 block.)

Event Info: Daily, dawn to dusk. Trail goes through historic Old Bisbee. Experience first hand two sets of the town's famous stairs. Trail is rated 3+ (5300' elevation at start). It is not suitable for strollers or wheelchairs. Pets are allowed but must be leashed and are not allowed in the Hotel or any stores.

Glendale - 10km Walk (YR1310) **Jan 1-Dec 31**
A Award available
Sponsoring Club: AVA-332, Valley Volkssporters Association
POC: Bob Gary; 602-977-7432. 15202 N Agua Fria Dr, Sun City, AZ 85351

Start Point: Arrowhead Community Hospital Wellness Connection; 602-486-2105. 7700 W Arrowhead Towne Center, Suite 1261. From I-17 take Bell Rd exit west approximately 8 miles to Arrowhead Towne Center at Bell Rd & 75th Ave. Start Point (Wellness Connection) is located near the SW entrance between Dillards & Penneys.

Event Info: Mon-Fri, 7-5 (some days later dependant on available personnel. Call for specifics). Sat, 9-5; Sun 11-6. Closed Easter, Thanksgiving & Christmas. Trail is rated 1 and is suitable for strollers & wheelchairs. Pets are not allowed. Volkssporters can get a free blood pressure check at the start point. Please pay by check to VVA. Start point does not have funds or change. Ask or look for start box. Please be patient with the volunteers who run the start point. Option 1 is an indoor mall walk with air conditioned comfort ideal for the summer months. Option 2 will take you on an outside trail. Even though there are two trails, you can only receive one event credit per year.

Goodyear - 10km Walk (YR987) **Jan 1-Dec 31**
A Award available
Sponsoring Club: AVA-332, Valley Volkssporters Association
POC: Bob Gary; 602-977-7432. 15202 N Agua Fria Dr, Sun City, AZ 85351

Start Point: SAS Shoes, Wigwam Outlet Center; 602-935-0101. Suite B-7B, 1400 N Litchfield Rd. From I-10, north at exit 128 (Litchfield Rd/Goodyear). Start is at the Northwest corner of intersection. SAS Shoes is located near the food court. Start point is located on I-10 approximately 16 miles west of Phoenix going towards Los Angeles, CA.

Event Info: Open Mon-Sat 9-8; Sun 10-6. Early/late start box is located outside. Closed Thanksgiving, Christmas & Easter. Please pay by check to VVA. Trail is rated 1 and is an easy, flat walk along sidewalks, pathways and hard packed dirt areas along roads. It is suitable for strollers & wheelchairs. Pets are allowed but must be leashed.

Mesa - 11km Walk (YR025) **Jan 1-Dec 31**
A Award available
Sponsoring Club: AVA-332, Valley Volkssporters Association
POC: Hal Witter; 602-641-7577. 101 N 38th St #30, Mesa, AZ 85205-8526

Start Point: Mezona Best Western Motel, 602-834-9233/1-800-528-8299. 250 W Main. From I-10 go east on US-60 to Country Club. Go north two miles to Main St. Start is on the NE corner.

Event Info: Special motel rate for volkssporters. Ask upon checkin. Daily, dawn to dusk. Trail is rated 1+ and is a flat, easy route on sidewalks and dirt canal banks that pass several Mesa parks. Strollers & wheelchairs may have difficulty along the canal bank. Pets are allowed. Please pay by check to VVA.

Naco - 10km Walk (YR670) **Jan 2-Dec 30** This event goes into Mexico
A Award available
Sponsoring Club: AVA-746, Thunder Mountain Trekkers
POC: Wendy Breen, 520-378-1763/520-432-3931. 3288 Sky Hawk Dr, Sierra Vista, AZ 85635-6623

Start: Turquoise Valley Country Club (Pro Shop). 1791 W Newell St. Exit 302 off of I-10. South on Hwy 90 to Sierra Vista. Follow Hwy 90 By-pass to Hwy 92. Go South on Hwy 92 to Bisbee. Right on Naco Hwy (by Burger King) for 5 miles. Right on West Newell St on edge of Naco.

Event Info: Route goes into Mexico. All participants **must** sign the waiver. Identification needed to cross the border. Naturalized citizens & all aliens must have proof of citizenship, resident alien card or passport/visa. Trail is open daily, dawn to dusk. Closed New Year's Eve & Day, as well as Christmas. Trail is rated 1, suitable for strollers but not wheelchairs. It winds through these two very rural border towns. Five kilometers of the route is on each side of the border. **No** pets. Carry your own water

Phoenix - 10km Walk (YR139) 13km Walk (YR230)   25/50km Bike (YR452) **Jan 1-Dec 31**
A Award avaiable
Sponsoring Club: AVA-332, Valley Volkssporters Association
POC: Hal Witter, 602-641-7577. 101 N 38th St, #30, Mesa, AZ 85205-8526.

Start Point: MON THRU FRI: Norton House; 602-261-8443. 2700 N 15th Ave.
WEEKENDS/HOLIDAYS: Encanto Park Sports Complex, 602-261-8443. 2151 North 15th Ave. By the tennis courts at 15th Ave & Encanto Blvd. From I-10 take 7th Ave exit North to McDowell Rd. Turn left (West) on McDowell to 15th Ave. North to start.

Event Info: Mon-Fri, 9-5; Weekends & Holidays, 10-sunset. Trails are rated 1. Walks are flat, easy and go through historic neighborhoods, park areas and YR 230 goes to downtown Pheonix and returns. Walkers should wear hats and on all events you should carry water. The Bike is along city bike routes for the 25km and the 50km has an additional 25kms along canal bike paths that are mostly flat. Bikers MUST sign waiver. Please wear a helmet. Walks are suitable for strollers and wheelchairs but may have some difficulty with curbs. Pets must be leashed. Start has no change. Please pay by exact cash or local check.

Phoenix - 10km Walk (YR849) 11km Walk (YR851) **Jan 1-Dec 31**
A Award available
Sponsoring Club: AVA-332, Valley Volkssporters Association
POC: Hal Witter; 602-641-7577. 101 N 38th St #30, Mesa, AZ 85205-8526

Start Point: Phoenix Baptist Hospital Wellness Connection (inside Chris-Town Mall); 602-995-9355. 1703 West Bethany Home Rd. From I-17, take Bethany Home Rd exit. Go east one mile to Mall at 17th Ave. Start is near food court in Southeast section.

Event Info: Mon-Fri, 10-9; Sat, 10-7; Sun, noon-5. Closed Christmas, Easter & Thanksgiving. Call if in doubt. Trails are rated 1. **YR849** is inside the mall with outside laps permitted if desired. **YR851** passes through portions of the mall and out into and through the local neighborhood and returns. Both are suitable for strollers & wheelchairs. Pets are not allowed. Start has no money for change. Please pay by check to VVA. Free blood pressure checks at start point.

Phoenix - 10km Walk (YR848) **Jan 1-Dec 31**
A Award available
Sponsoring Club: AVA-332, Valley Volkssporters Association
POC: Hal Witter, 602-641-7577. 101 N 38th St #30, Mesa, AZ 85205-8526

Start Point: SAS Shoes (in Metro Market Place) 602-678-1668. 9201 N 29th Ave. From I-17, exit Dunlap Ave. Go west 1/4 mile to 29th Ave. Go north 1 block to start.

Event Info: Mon-Sat, 10-6; closed Sunday. (Early/late start box locate outside). Walkers must return during business hours for event stamp and awards. Closed Christmas, Easter, New Year's, 4th of July & Thanksgiving. Trail is rated 1 and is a flat walk along sidewalks and paved pathways along the canal and through park areas. Suitable for strollers and wheelchairs. Pets must be leashed. Please pay by check to VVA.

Scottsdale - Three 10km Walks(YR563, YR564 & YR850) 29km Bike (YR565) **Jan 1-Dec 31**
A Award available
Sponsoring Club: AVA-332, Valley Volksporters Association
POC: Hal Witter, 602-641-7577. 101 North 38th St #30, Mesa AZ 85205-8526.

Start Point: SAS Shoes in the Pavilions, 602-443-8091. 9180 E Indian Bend #F9. In Scottsdale, East to Pima & Indian Bend Roads. SAS Shoes is located near Best Buy in the Scottsdale Pavilions Shopping Center.

Event Info: Mon-Sat, 10-6. Closed Sundays, Thanksgiving, Christmas, New Year's, Easter & 4th of July. (Early/Late Start box located outside.) All trails are rated 1 and allow pets. **YR563** is a flat, easy walk on paved park pathways. Suitable for strollers & wheelchairs. There is a short drive from the SAS Store to the park where the walk begins is involved. **YR564** is a flat, easy walk on park pathways, sidewalks and canal banks. It goes through the expensive shopping areas and Scottsdale Mall (an open air mall with shops, fountains and the Scottsdale Civic Center) and back along park paths. It is suitable for strollers & wheelchairs but they may experience some difficulty with the canal bank. It also involves a short drive from the SAS Store to the park where the event begins. **YR850** is an easy, flat walk on sidewalks, dirt paths and canal banks. It crosses one dry wash which may flood but may be bypassed. Strollers & wheelchairs can complete this event if they bypass the wash. This event starts at the SAS Store. **YR565** is a flat, easy bike course on paved pathways & sidewalks. Bikers MUST sign a waiver. Please wear a helmet. A short drive from the SAS store to the park where the bike begins is involved. Pets are allowed on all courses. Participants must return to the store during business hours for the stamp, award and for payment. Please pay by check to VVA.

Sierra Vista - 11/12km Walk (YR447) 11/13km Walk (YR372) 12km Walk (YR499)
Jan 1-Dec 31
A Award available
Sponsoring Club: AVA-746, Thunder Mountain Trekkers
POC: Wendy Breen, 520-378-1763/520-458-8386. 3288 Sky Hawk Dr, Sierra Vista, AZ 85635-6623

Register: Registration for all events is at the Thunder Mountain Inn, 1631 S Hwy 92. Exit 302 off of I-10. South on Hwy 90 through Whetstone to Sierra Vista. Take Hwy 90 by-pass to Hwy 92 South. Motel is on the left at the top of the hill. You then drive to start locations shown below.

Start YR447-Coronado Nat'l Memorial: This event starts approximately 12 miles south of Sierra Vista (via Hwy 92 & Coronado Memorial Hwy). Trail is rated 5 (5300' elevation at start with 1600' gain/loss). Wear sturdy shoes with good traction. Carry plenty of water. Sun screen and hats are advisable. Pets are not allowed. Not suitable for strollers or wheelchairs. Trail follows Joe's Canyon Trail from the Visitor Center to Montezuma Pass and returns.

Start YR372-San Pedro: Walk start point is 6.8 miles east of Sierra Vista on Hwy 90. Trail is rated 2+ (4050' elevation at start). Not suitable for strollers or wheelchairs. Pets are allowed. Do not wear shorts. Please carry water. Sunscreen and hats are advisable. Trail goes through San Pedro Riparian Conservation Area using dirt roads, animal paths and a highway right-of-way. You will wade the river on the 13km route.

Start YR499-Fort Huachuca: Start point is approximately 5 miles west via Fry Blvd on Ft Huachuca. Trail is rated 1+ (4600' elevation at start). Pets are allowed and it is suitable for strollers & wheelchairs. Vehicles without a Department of Defense sticker must obtain a visitor's pass in order to enter the Fort. Valid driver's license, vehicle registration and proof of insurance or car rental agreement are needed to get the pass. The trail is on sidewalks and along residential streets through the Fort's National Historic District, past the cemetary to the post museum.

Event Info: Hotel is open 24 hours but participate only during daylight hours.

Sun City - 10km Walk (YR1311) Jan 3-Dec 31
A Award available
Sponsoring Club: AVA-332, Valley Volkssporters Association
POC: Bob Gary; 602-977-7432. 15202 N Agua Fria Dr, Sun City, AZ 85351

Start Point: SAS Shoe Store in the Promenade; 602-933-9286. 10001 W Bell Rd #124. From I-17 go west on Bell Rd to 99th Ave & Bell Rd. Start is in the SAS Shoe Store at the SW corner of the intersection.

Event Info: Mon-Sat, 9-5. Closed Sundays, New Years, Easter, July 4th, Thanksgiving & Christmas. Trail is rated 1 and is suitable for strollers & wheelchairs. Pets must be leashed. Please pay by check to VVA.

Tempe - 12km Walk (YR524) **Jan 1-Dec 31**
A Award available
Sponsoring Club: AVA-332, Valley Volkssporters Association
POC: Steve Bartley, 602-491-6017. 18 W Louis Way, Tempe AZ 85284

Start Point: Tyke's World Toys and Playcenter, 602-491-6017. 3136 S McClintock. From I-10 go east on US 60 to McClintock. North at McClintock to Southern. Start is at the left (northwest) corner of intersection.

Event Info: Mon-Sat, 9-6; Sun, 12-5. Closed January 1-2, Easter, Thanksgiving, & December 25 & 26. May also be closed on other major holidays. Call if in doubt. Trail is rated 1 and goes through residential areas to Arizona State University. A highlight is the Grady Gammage Auditorium, the last major work of Frank Lloyd Wright. It is a flat, easy walk on city sidewaks. Suitable for strollers & wheelchairs and pets are allowed. Please pay by check to VVA.

Tombstone - 10km Walk (YR986) **Jan 1-Dec 31**
A Award available
Sponsoring Club: AVA-746, Thunder Mountain Trekkers
POC: Wendy Breen, 520-378-1763/520-458-6194. 3288 South Sky Hawk Dr, Sierra Vista, AZ 85635-6623

Start Point: Circle K Store, Sumner & Bruce Sts. Exit 303 off of I-10. Follow Hwy 80 to Tombstone. Just after passing Boothill Cemetery Hwy 80 turns right & becomes Sumner. Circle K is on your left.

Event Info: Daily, dawn to dusk. Limited hours on holidays. Trail is rated 2+ and follows dirt/gravel roads, sidewalks and boardwalks. Goes past the O.K. Corral, Schieffelin Monument, Cochise County Courthourse and the Historic District. Pets are allowed. Trail would be difficult for strollers and wheelchairs should not attempt. Please carry plenty of water.

Tucson - 10km Walk (YR1309) 12km Walk (YR981) 31/44km Bike (YR459) **Jan 1-Dec 31**
A Award available
Sponsoring Club: AVA-374, Tucson Volkssport Klub
POC: Fred E. Barton, 520-298-4340. 270 S Candlestick Dr, Tucson AZ 85748-6743

Start Point: Tanque Verde Inn, 520-298-2300. 7007 E Tanque Verde Rd. Westbound I-10 exit at Kolb Rd. (exit 270) and go north approximately 11 miles to Tanque Verde Rd. Turn right and go approximately 3/ 4 mile to Sabino Canyon Rd. The Inn is on the northwest corner of this intersection. Eastbound on I-10 exit at Grant Rd (exit 256). Go east approximately 8.5 miles to Tanque Verde Rd. Turn left and the Inn is on the left approximately 3/4 mile.

Event Info: Daily, dawn to dusk. 12km walk is rated 2 and is a paved route that crosses Sabino Creek 7 times on stone bridges built by the WPA/CCC. The varied desert vegetation gives way to the relaxing riparian atmosphere of the stream and canyon as you gradually rise 600 ft and return. It is suitable for strollers and wheelchairs but pets are not allowed. 10km walk is rated 3 and is not suitable for strollers or wheelchairs, No pets are allowed. This walk is on paved road and desert trails in Saguaro National Park and is completely in the Sonora Desert. Bring your own water. The bike is rated 1+. After passing along the quiet residential streets of eastern Tucson, the route undulates along Old Spanish Trail bike path with its scattered homes set in desert surroundings. The optional 13km circles through Saguaro National Park. Bikers must sign a waiver. Please wear a helmet. Pets are allowed on this trail. Volkssporters can receive a discount at the Tanque Verde Inn.

Tucson - 10km Walk (YR321) **Jan 1-Dec 31**
A Award available
Sponsoring Club: AVA-374, Tucson Volkssport Klub
POC: Fred Barton, 520-298-4340. 270 S Candlestick Dr, Tucson, AZ 85748-6743

Start Point: Park Inn Hotel, 520-622-4000. 88 East Broadway Blvd. Take I-10 to Congress St exit (exit 258). Turn East into the center of downtown. Go six traffic lights to Scott Ave. Park Inn Hotel is on the southeast corner of Scott Ave & Broadway.

Event Info: Daily, dawn to dusk. Trail is rated 1 and meanders through historic Tucson to the University of Arizona. An information sheet will guide walkers past more than 50 significant, historical locations on this nearly flat walk on paved sidewalks. It is suitable for strollers & wheelchairs and pets are allowed. You should carry water & wear a hat. The Park Inn Hotel gives a discount to volkssporters.

ARKANSAS

Garfield - 10km Walk, (YR145) **Jan 2-Dec 31**
A Award available
Sponsoring Club: AVA-619, Ozark Hill Hikers
POC: Radine Trees Nehring, 501-787-5930. 11447 Wildwood Way, Gravette AR 72736-9318

Start Point: Register at The Buss Stop in Garfield, 3 miles east of Park entrance. Park is on Hwy 62 in Northwest Arkansas, East of Bentonville, West of Garfield and Eureka Springs. Start point is at the Visitors Center in the Pea Ridge National Military Park, 501-451-8122.

Event Info: Park will furnish map of trail. If you choose to walk any side trips, they are not sanctioned for added distance. Trail is rated 2 all paved with one medium hill. Suitable for wheelchairs and strollers with a strong pusher. Pets must be leashed. Park has a small admission fee. Carrying water is strongly recommended. Obey ranger's warnings about ticks, chiggers & poison ivy if you leave the paved road in summer. Par is open daily, 8-5.

Hot Springs - 11km Walk (YR979) **Jan 2-Dec 31**
Credit Only Event
Sponsoring Club: AVA-819, Arkansas OktoberfestVolksmarsch
POC: Gail Sears, 501-624-3383 x640   PO Box 1860, Hot Springs, AR 71902

Start Point: Fordyce Bathhouse Visitor Center, 501-624-3383. 369 Central Ave. Located on Central Ave or AR Hwy 7N in downtown Hot Springs. Parking is available nearby for a fee.

Event Info: Open daily, 9-5. Closed Thanksgiving, Christmas, New Year's and any other days Congress may declare if budget doesn't pass. Call if in doubt. Trail is rated 3+ and is not suitable for strollers or wheelchairs. Pets must be leashed. This walk covers parts of Hot Springs Mountain, North Mountain & West Mountain as well as much of the downtown historic district. Moderately steep areas with gentle slopes and level areas in between. You will have a chance to drink from several springs along the route. Bring a cup to enjoy these. Allow 4-5 hours to do this walk. Club prefers payment by check.

CALIFORNIA

Alameda - 10km Walk (YR620) 11km Walk (YR619) **Jan 2-Dec 31**
B Awards available
Sponsoring Club: AVA-575, Ye Olde Chico Walking Club
POC: Linda Detling, 916-343-7887. 1304 Arbutus Ave, Chico, CA 95926 or Diane Eatherly, 510-482-0817. 2634 Charleston St, Oakland, CA 94602

Start Point: Encinal Market, 3211 Encinal Ave at High St. Take I-580 or I-880 into Oakland. Exit off either at High St. Go SW on High St across the High St Bridge into Alameda. Contine on High St to Briggs St (just before Encinal Ave). Turn left, go past second house (#3206) turn right and park. Walk toward Encinal Ave and Market is on the right next to the Orchard Burger eating place.

Event Info: Mon-Sat, 9:15-9; Sun, 9:15-7. Closed on holidays. Trails are rated 1. Suitable for strollers & wheelchairs. Pets must be leashed and you must clean-up after them. To walk earlier or on a holiday, register the day before. Registration box is under the counter closest to Encinal Ave. YR619 is mainly paved and goes by parks, golf course, historical sites and offers a skyline view of San Francisco and the bay. YR620 is mainly paved with some gravel. It goes by parks, historical sites & old Victorian homes.

Campbell - 10/13km Walk (YR853) **Jan 1-Dec 31**
A Awards available
Sponsoring Club: AVA-338, South Bay Striders
POC: Jacquie Christensen, 408-356-3954. 16389 E. LaChiquita, Los Gatos, CA 95032

12

Start Point: Campbell Inn, 408-374-4300. 675 East Campbell Ave. From Hwy 17/880, take the Hamilton Avenue exit and go east to Bascom Avenue. Turn right and continue to Campbell Ave (Pruneyard Shopping Center on your right) and turn right again. Cross under the 17/880 Hwy and the Inn will be on your right.

Event Info: Daily, 8-dusk. Rated 1. Suitable for strollers & wheelchairs. Pets must be leashed and clean up is required. Inn Reservation No: 800-582-4449. Walk along the Los Gatos Creek Recreational paved trail and city sidewalks by the Campbell City Center. Many quaint shops & restaurants.

Capitola/Santa Cruz - 10km Walk (YR1183) 11km Walk (YR1182) **Jan 1-Dec 31**
Credit Only Events
Sponsoring Club: AVA-338, South Bay Striders
POC: Jacquie Christensen, 408-356-3954. 16389 E. La Chiquita, Los Gatos, CA 95032 or Margert Fitzgerald, 408-475-0857.

Start Point: Coffeetopia, 408-477-1940. 3701 Portola Dr. From Hwy 1, take the 41st Ave. Exit. Proceed on 41st Ave. south (towards the beach) and turn right onto Portola Dr. Coffeetopia is past 38th Ave. on your right.

Event Info: Daily, 6:30 a.m. - 9 p.m. Closed Thanksgiving & Christmas. Pets must be leashed on both events. **YR1183** is rated 2 and is not suitable for strollers or wheelchairs. Trail involves secret stairs and some hills. It goes along the ocean and through quaint town of Capitola. **YR1182** is rated 1 + and is not suitable for strollers or wheelchairs. It takes you along sidewalks, sandy paths and beach front sand. Ocean view and harbor.

Carlsbad - 10km Walk (YR200) 14km Walk (YR271) **Jan 1-Dec 31**
Credit Only Events
Sponsoring Club: AVA-392, San Diego County Rockhoppers
POC: Irja Graham, 619-758-5667. 1391 Broken Hitch Rd, Oceanside, CA 92056

Start Point: Ocean Palms Beach Resort, 619-729-2493. 2950 Ocean St. From I-5 N. or S., exit at Carlsbad Village Dr. Head west on Carlsbad Village Dr. Go to the end of Carlsbad Village Dr. (Ocean St.), turn right to Ocean Palms Beach Resort.

Event Info: Daily, dawn to dusk. Trails are rated 1+. Both events are along beach, residential and city streets. Strollers & wheelchairs are ok but the trail may prove challenging. Pets O.K. on leash. 10% discount on motel rates for volkssporters at Ocean Palms Beach Resort. Parking in front of motel for motel guests only. Both events go along the beach and residential and city streets.

Carmel/Point Lobos - Two 10km Walks (YR443 & YR445) **Jan 1-Dec 31**
A Awards available
Sponsoring Club: AVA-005, Monterey Walking Club
POC: Willis Sexton, 408-394-9503. 1213 Judson St, Seaside, CA 93955

Start Point: Power Juice Co., Crossroads Shopping Ctr behind Chevy's Restaurant. Take Hwy 1 South to Rio Rd in Carmel. Turn left at Rio Rd & right at Crossroads Shopping Center.

Event Info: Mon-Sat, 9-5; Sun, 10-5. **YR443**, Carmel is rated 1+ but is not suitable for strollers or wheelchairs. It has one hill with woodchips on path but otherwise is on city streets and sidewalks. **YR445**, Point Lobos is rated 3 and is not suitable for strollers or wheelchairs. It is on rough dirt paths thru pine forests and along the seacoast. Pets are not allowed on this event.

Cherry Valley - 10km Walk (YR543) **Jan 1-Dec 31**
A Award available
Sponsoring Club: AVA-285, Green Valley Gaiters
POC: Lois Wilson, 909-845-5872. 10315 Frontier Trail, Cherry Valley, CA 92223

Start Point: Vienna Liquor & Delicatessen, 38761 Cherry Valley Blvd off I-10, between Redlands and Palm Springs. From I-10 East and West, exit onto Cherry Valley off-ramp. Proceed east on Cherry Valley Blvd. for approximately 2 ½ miles. The Vienna Liquor and Deli is on the right side of the blvd.

Event Info: Daily, 9-5. Closed some holidays. Trail is rated 3+. Strollers and wheelchairs are not recommended. Pets must be leashed. Trail follows a scenic route through Cherry Valley noted for its fruit industry, particularly cherries. The walk is primarily in rural country with some residential housing. Please pay by check made out to "GVG". Employees will not handle cash.

Chico - 11km Walks (YR579) 33km Bike (YR700) **Jan 2-Dec 30**
Credit Only Events
Sponsoring Club: AVA-575, Ye Olde Chico Walking Club
POC: Linda Detling, 916-343-7887. 1304 Arbutus Ave, Chico CA 95926

Start Point: Fleet Feet Sports, 916-345-1000. 222 W 3rd St. From Hwy 99, take East First Ave exit and go west. Turn left at The Esplanade to West 3rd St. The Esplanade curves to the right and becomes Broadway. Go right on West Third St to the start.

Event Info: Mon-Fri, 10-6; Sat, 10-5; Sun, 12-4. Open Sundays Apr & May & Sept-Dec only. Closed major holidays. Pets must be leashed. Both trails are rated 1. Suitable for strollers. Wheelchairs will have some difficulty. **YR579** takes you by the Stansbury House, Bidwell Mansion, through the CSU Chico Campus, by Fraternity Housing & a small section of Bidwell Park. **YR700** takes you entirely through Lower Bidwell Park & part of Upper Bidwell Park & then follows a bike trail to the Chico Airport.

Chula Vista - 10km Walk (YR 982) **Jan 1-Dec 31**
Sponsoring Club: AVA-832, South Bay Roadrunners
POC: Herman H. Husbands, 619-287-0560. 6375 Elmhurst Dr, San Diego, CA 92120

Start Point: Rancho del Ray Information Center, 619-482-3171. 820 Paseo Ranchero. Travel I-805 Southbound to "H" St exit. Turn right on "H" St and travel for 2.7 miles. At Paseo Ranchero intersection light, turn left and proceed approximately 100 yards. On the left & prior to the intersection you will find the Information Center on the left. Parking & toilets are available.

Event Info: PST: Mon-Sun, 9-5. PDT: Mon-Fri 9-5; Sat & Sun 10-6. Closed Easter, Thanksgiving, Christmas & New Years. Trail is rated 1+ and pets are allowed. It is suitable for strollers but not wheelchairs due to sand trail. Carry water in warm/hot weather. Trail is on sidewalk except for horse trail which is hard packed sandy-like soil which is excellent for walking but not suitable for wheelchairs. Potential for wildlife sightings & views of the Pacific Ocean.

Citrus Heights - Three 10km Walks (YR224, YR289 & YR290) **Jan 2-Dec 31**
B Awards available
Sponsoring Club: AVA-575, Ye Olde Chico Walking Club
POC: Linda Detling, 916-343-7887. 1304 Arbutus Ave, Chico, CA 95926 or Jean Davis, 916-944-1087. 3253 Marshall Ave, Carmichael, CA 95608

Start Point: SAS Store, 916-722-7481. 7175 Greenback Ln. From Sacramento take I-80 N then East on Greenback Lane slightly over 2 miles to 7175. From US 50 go North on Sunrise then West on Greenback Lane. Store is located behind the Red Tomato Restaurant.

Event Info: Mon-Thurs & Sat, 10-6; Fri, 10-8; Sun, 12-5. Closed some holidays. Call ahead to verify. Trails are rated 1+ on surfaced roads with some slight hills. They are all suitable for strollers & wheelchairs. Pets allowed with clean-up. SAS will give volkssporters a 10% discount on the day of the walk.

Corona - 10km Walk (YR913) 27km Bike (YR1097) **Jan 1-Dec 31**
Walk has A Award available. Bike is a Credit Only Event.
Sponsoring Club: AVA-157, Low Desert Roadrunners
POC: Walk: Jean Vik, 909-737-8341; 19310 Ontario Ave, Corona CA 91719. Bike: Bob Gebo, 909-924-2208; 14786 Perham Dr, Moreno Valley CA 92553

Start Point: Corona Regional Medical Center, 800 S Main St.   From Eastbound 91, exit Main St. South in Corona. Turn right onto main. From Westbound 91, exit Main St. Turn left on Main St. From I-15, exit Corona or Beach Cities to 91 west. Then exit at Main Street and turn left. Travel south on Main to 8th. Turn right on 8th. Medical Center covers entire block. Please park on streets rather than in the lot. You must register here for the bike & travel by car to the start point (six miles).

Event Info: Daily, 8-5. Walk is rated 1+. Suitable for strollers & wheelchairs. Pets must be leashed. Trail goes through historic Corona, featuring diverse neighborhoods and residential areas. Bike is rated 2+ and goes along the Santa Ana River from Corona to Yorba Linda & return. It is on a well maintained, paved bike trail. There are some slight or gradual hills. Corona can be very hot. Carry water and participate early during the summer months.

Coronado - 12km Walk (YR352) **Jan 1-Dec 31**
Credit Only Event
Sponsoring Club: AVA-772, Coronado Beachcombers
POC: Elizabeth Soderholm, 619-437-4454. 20 Pine Court, Coronado, CA 92118-2723

Start Point: Tiffiny's Deli, 1120 Adella Ave. From I-5 take the Coronado Bridge (State Hwy 75) to Coronado. Follow the main artery from the bridge, which becomes Third St. Turn left at first light onto Orange Ave. Follow Orange to the light at Adella Ave and R.H. Dana Place. Turn left onto Adella and start is on the left.

Event Info: Daily, 8-5. Closed major holidays. Call ahead to confirm. Trail is rated 1+ and is suitable for strollers & wheelchairs with an alternate route. Leashed pets are allowed on the alternate route. Coronado is a walker's dream: Pacific Ocean, San Diego Bay, world famous Hotel del Coronado, historic homes and buildings - all in 12 km.

Dana Point - Two 10km Walks (YR1343 & 1344) **Jan 1-Dec 31**
Credit Only Events
Sponsoring Club: AVA-857, Laguna Turf & Surf Walkers of Orange County
POC: Bob Rothrock, 714-448-8345. 24191 Becard Dr, Laguna Niguel, CA 92677

Start Point: Natale Coffee & Cafe (next to Ralph's Market), 714-493-3088. 24847 Del Prado. North or South, San Diego Freeway #5 to beach cities turn off to coast Hwy 1. Turn left on Golden Lantern, left on Del Prado to Lantern Bay Village on this corner. Park in shopping center.

Event Info: Daily, 6am-8pm. Pets are allowed on both trails. **YR1343** is rated 2 and is suitable for strollers and wheelchairs. It goes through the village of Capistrano Beach to four viewpoint parks overlooking the beaches of San Clemente, Capistrano, Doneny and Dana Harbor. **YR1344** is rated 1+. It is suitable for strollers and wheelchairs. It goes through the city park to river bike traill, pass parks on black top trail to view mountains and nature. Return along the same trail. Please pay by check made payable to Laguna Turf & Surf Walking Club. Employees will not handle cash.

Davis - 10km Walk (YR404) 33km Bike (YR390) **Jan 1-Dec 31**
Credit Only Events
Sponsoring Club: AVA-556, Davis Dynamos
POC: Helen C. Green, 916-753-6821. 125 Jalisco Place, Davis, CA 95616

Start Point: Fleet Feet, 916-758-6453. 513 - 2nd St. Turn off Hwy 80 on the Davis turnoff (Richards Blvd). Go thru the underpass and continue on E St thru the first intersection to the next block (2nd

St). Go left 1/2 block to the start. Please park in free city parking lot located above movie theaters on F Street between 1st & 2nd Streets. Davis downtown parking is metered with a two hour limit and is policed regularly.

Event Info: Mon-Fri 10-7; Sat 10-5; Sun noon-5. Closed some holidays. Please park in free city parking lot located above movie theaters on F St between 1st & 2nd streets. David downtown is metered with a two hour time limit. Both trails are rated 1. The walk is suitable for strollers & wheelchairs and allows pets. Davis is very flat and has an abundance of separate bike paths, bike lanes and greenbelts throughout the city. The bike utilizes these and travels thru the University of California, Davis Arboretum. The walk goes through city streets, walking paths & the University of California, Davis Campus including the UCD Arboretum.

Fair Oaks - 11km Walk (YR559) **Jan 1-Dec 31**
B Awards available
Sponsoring Club: AVA-218, Sutter Strutters Volkssport Club
POC: Avis Showers, 916-988-7580. 5112 Sanicle Way, Fair Oaks, CA 95628

Start Point: Fleet Feet Sports, 916-965-8326. 8128 Madison Ave. Located in the shopping center at the corner of Madison Avenue & Fair Oaks Blvd.

Event Info: Mon-Fri, 10-8; Sat, 10-6; Sun, 12-5. Trail is rated 2; suitable for strollers & wheelchairs. Pets must be leashed.

Fairfield - 10km Walk (YR696) **Jan 1-Dec 31**
Credit Only Event
Sponsoring Club: AVA-376, Vaca Valley Volks
POC: Ruth A. Redd, 707-429-1899. 2000 Claybank Rd #E1, Fairfield, CA 94533

Start Point: North Bay Medical Center, 1800 Pennsylvania Ave (main lobby, old bldg). **From the East** (I-80) take Travis Blvd exit, turn left at the light, go straight past mall to Pennsylvania Ave. Turn left. Go about 2 blocks to B. Gale Wilson Dr. Turn right then left into hospital parking lot. **From the West** (I-80) take Travis Blvd East, continue past mall. Turn left at Pennsylvania Ave & follow directions above. The startbox (file cabinet) is in the old building (lobby) next to emergency entrance.

Event Info: Daily, dawn to dusk. Trail is rated 1+; suitable for strollers & wheelchairs. Pets must be leashed. Route goes through residential areas, past downtown businesses of Fairfield.

Fresno - 10km Walk (YR456) **Jan 1-Dec 31**
B Awards available
Sponsoring Club: AVA-371, Big Valley Vagabonds
POC: Mary L. Mott, 209-297-7685. 3212 E Tenaya Way, Fresno CA 93710-5925

Start Point: IHOP Restaurant, 3020 Tulare St. Take Hwy. 99 N, exit 41 to Yosemite. Then, take Tulare St. exit. Turn left across freeway overpass. Continue on Tulare to IHOP Restaurant (left side). Traveling south on Hwy. 99, exit Fresno St. Turn left and cross overpass. Continue to "R" St. Right on "R" St. to Tulare. Left on Tulare to IHOP (on right side).

Event Info: Daily, dawn to dusk. Trail is rated 1; suitable for strollers and wheelchairs. Pets must be leashed. If not accustomed to hot, dry weather, we suggest early morning walking and that you carry water. This is a city walk taking in the City Hall, St John Cathedral and many more historical experiences representing early Fresno and the Armenian community.

Fresno - 10km Walk (YR457) **Jan 1-Dec 31**
B Awards available
Sponsoring Club: AVA-371, Big Valley Vagabonds
POC: Mary L. Mott, 209-297-7685. 3212 E Tenaya Way, Fresno CA 93710-5925

Start Point: San Joaquin Suite Hotel, 209-225-1309. 1309 W Shaw. North on US 99 take 41 East to Shaw Exit. Turn left to 1300 block. Hotel on left. South on US 99, exit Shaw. Left across freeway to 1300 block. Hotel is on right side.

Event Info: Daily, dawn to dusk. Rated 1. Suitable for strollers if determined. No wheelchairs. An alternate route is available and better suited for wheelchairs. Pets must be leashed. Carry water during warm weather. Follows City Christmas Tree lane with lovely landscaped homes and shady trees.

Ft Bragg - 10km Walk (YR1096) **Jan 1-Dec 31**
Credit Only Event
Sponsoring Club: AVA-821, Mendocino County Meanderers
POC: Geri Lusnia, 707-459-4716. 24121 Sherwood Rd, Willits, CA 95490

Start Point: The Beachcomber Motel, 800-400-7873. 1111 N Main St. From the South, take Hwy 101 North to Hwy 128. Follow 128 to US 1. Turn right thru Mendocino to Ft Bragg. The Beachcomber is on left side of Highway north of town. From North, take Hwy 101 South to Willits. Turn right onto Hwy 20 to Hwy 1. Proceed as above.

Event Info: Daily, dawn to dusk. Trail is rated 2 and is okay for strollers but wheelchairs may have some difficulty (detour may be taken through parking lot). Pets are allowed but must be leashed. Route is on the Old Haul Road along the ocean. It is blacktop in poor repair. Once used by logging trucks, it is now a public walkway partly in Mackerricher State Park. A trail through the sand dunes parallels the road and may be used if desired. The Beachcomber offers a 20% off-season discount which coincides with whale watching season.

Galt - 10km Walk (YR1303) **Jan 1-Dec 31**
A Award available
Sponsoring Club: AVA-416, Delta Tule Trekker
POC: Bill Volkman, 209-745-2505. PO Box 714, Galt, CA 95632

Start Point: McDonald's, 324 Pine St. From Hwy 99, take central Galt Exit. Go west, turn left at "Welcome to Galt" sign. Please park in overflow parking while on walk.

Event Info: Daily, 6 a.m. - 11 p.m. Closed major holidays. Trail is rated 1 and is suitable for strollers and wheelchairs. Walk is along paved streets and sidewalks except for one area on "A" St. by railroad tracks. Trail is through historical Galt, surrounding the Water Tower on "C" St. Visit Spaans Cookie Factory. Note: Galt Outdoor Market is on Tuesdays/Wednesdays; park at McDonald's in the overflow parking lot. Ask about Volkssport Special of the month.

Huntington Beach - 10km Walk (YR899) **Jan 1-Dec 31**
B Awards available
Sponsoring Club: AVA-427, Hollywood Star Trekkers
POC: Tom Loppnow, 714-960-5339. 8855 Sutter Circle 517-C, Huntington Beach, CA 92646

Start Point: Grinder Restaurant, 714-536-1664. 21002 Pacific Coast Hwy (just south of pier). From the 405 Fwy, exit at Beach Blvd (Hwy 39). Go south on Beach Blvd approximately 5 1/2 miles until it dead ends into Pacific Coast Hwy (PCH). Turn right onto PCH and start is approximately 1/2 mile down on the right.

Event Info: Daily, dawn to dusk. Rated 1. Suitable for strollers but may be difficult for wheelchairs. Pets must be leashed and are not allowed on the beach path. They must stay on the sidewalk. Please do not interupt business customers. This is a city walk through various neighborhoods and along the beach front of Huntington Beach.

Ione/Jackson/Mokelumne Hill - Three 10km Walks (YR225, YR606 & YR378)
12km Walk (YR255) **Jan 1-Dec 31**
B Awards available
Sponsoring Club: AVA-575, Ye Olde Chico Walking Club
POC: Linda Detling, 916-343-7887. 1304 Arbutus Ave, Chico, CA 95926 or Dorothy Williamson, 209-274-4339. 2901 Coyote Ct, Ione, CA 95640

Start Point: Best Western-Amador Inn, 1-800-543-5221 (motel reservations only). 200 S Hwy 49. The start point is on Main Street which is also SH 49 & 88. It is on the SE corner where SH 88 turns NE and SH 49 continues SE. This is the registration for YR606 & YR225. After registering you will drive between 7 & 10 miles to start the events.

Event Info: If staying at the Inn, be sure to ask for the Volkssporter Discount. Daily, dawn to dusk. Pets must be leashed. Jackson events, **YR255 & YR378** are rated 2+. Strollers are okay but they are not suitable for wheelchairs. These events have a few hills but are mostly paved. **YR606** is rated 1+. Strollers ok but not recommended for wheelchairs. This trail has a few slight hills and is paved with some dirt & gravel. It is a town & country walk. **YR 225** is rated 2-3. It is not suitable for wheelchairs and strollers will have some difficulty. This walk goes by parks, historical sites, old & new homes and has several short, steep hills. B-awards available.

Laguna Niguel - 10km Walk (YR1342) **Jan 1-Dec 31**
Credit Only Event
Sponsoring Club: AVA-857, Laguna Turn & Surf Walkers of Orange County
POC: Bob Rothrock, 714-448-8345. 24191 Becard Dr, Laguna Niguel, CA 92677

Start Point: Ted's Place, 714-831-0061. 23990 Aliso Creek Rd. North or South on San Diego Hwy 5 to La Paz, South to Aliso Creek Rd. Turn right to first stop light (Dorine Rd).

Event Info: Mon-Sat, 6am-9pm; Sun 7am-9pm. Closed Christmas. Trail is rated 1; suitable for strollers & wheelchairs. Pets are allowed. Walk through parks, residential streets, bike trails, around the edge of a lake and along a creed bed.

Los Gatos - 25km Bike (YR241) **Jan 1-Dec 31**
B Awards available
Sponsoring Club: AVA-338, South Bay Striders

POC: Jacquie Christiansen, 408-356-3954. 16389 E LaChiquita, Los Gatos, CA 95032

Start Point: Los Gatos Cyclery, 408-356-1644. 15954 Los Gatos Blvd. From Hwy 17-880; in Los Gatos, take the Lark Ave exit & go east. At Los Gatos Blvd turn right & proceed to Blossom Hill Rd. Make a u-turn and turn right into shopping center. The start is near the center.

Event Info: Mon-Sat, 9-6; Sun, 11-5. Closed major holidays. Rated 1+. Participants must sign waiver. Pets must be leashed. The trail has several slight hills and takes you along the Los Gatos Creek Trail & through Vasona Park. It is a well shaded recreational path.

Los Gatos - 10km Walk (YR074) **Jan 1-Dec 31**
A Award available
Sponsoring Club: AVA-338, South Bay Striders
POC: Jacquie Christensen, 408-356-3954. 16389 E LaChiquieta, Los Gatos, CA 95032

Start Point: Village Inn, 408-867-3966. 235 W Main St. From Hwy 280 or 101 take I880 (SR17) south towards Santa Cruz. Take the Los Gatos-Saratoga exit (not east Los Gatos). At the signal, University Ave, turn left and proceed to the end. You will be at Main St. Turn right and go past the signal (Santa Cruz Ave) and the Inn is on the left. From Santa Cruz, take Hwy 17 to 1st Los Gatos exit. Left at signal (Main St) & look for Inn on the left.

Event Info: Daily, 8-dusk. Rated 1+. Suitable for strollers but difficult for wheelchairs. Pets must be leashed. This is a historic residential town walk with sidewalks and paved trails. It has a few short hills and is partially shaded.

Marina del Rey - 10km Walk (YR1084) **Jan 1-Dec 31**
Credit Only Event
Sponsoring Club: AVA-427, Hollywood Star Trekkers
POC: John Shirtz, 310-374-3189. 346 27th St, Hermosa Beach, CA 90254

Start Point: Best Western Jamaica Bay Inn, 310-823-5333. 4175 Admiralty Way at Palawan. From the 405 exit Marina Freeway (Hwy 90) West. Turn left on Mindanao. Continue to Admiralty Way, turn right. Motel is on the left approximately one mile down. Turn left at stop light at Palawan Rd.

Event Info: Daily, dawn to dusk. Trail is rated 1 and is suitable for strollers but not wheelchairs. Please do not interrupt hotel business customers. Pets must be leashed. This event goes through residential areas, along the strand & through the newly rebuilt canals of Venice.

Mariposa - 10km Walk (YR479) **Jan 1-Dec 31**
Credit Only Event
Sponsoring Club: AVA-371, Big Valley Vagabonds
POC: Jeannie Welling, 209-722-5493/Mary Mott, 209-297-7685. 3212 E Tenaya Way, Fresno, CA 93710-5925.

Start Point: Best Western Yosemite Way Station, 209-966-7545. Hwy 49 & 140. From Hwy 99 take Hwy 140 East to Mariposa (140 leaves 99 on the South side of Merced, CA). Follow 140 into town where it joins Hwy 49. The start is on the West side of this junction.

Event Info: Daily, dawn to dusk. Trail is rated 2; suitable for strollers if persistent but not wheelchairs. Pets are allowed but must be leashed. Best Western will give a discount to identified volkssporters when making a reservation. This is a historic town walk with short hills and a quiet river section. The Courthouse has been in continuous use since 1854. This is on one of the most scenic highways into Yosemite National Park.

Merced - 10km Walk (YR750) **Jan 2-Dec 30**
B Awards available
Sponsoring Club: AVA-371, Big Valley Vagabonds
POC: Mary L. Mott, 209-297-7685/Jeanne Welling 209-722-5493. 3212 E. Tenaya Way, Fresno CA 93710-5925.

Start Point: Mercy Hospital, 2740 "M" St. From US 99 take M.L. King exit. Go W to 13th St. Right on 13th to "M" St. Right on "M" to hospital. Please use parking lot off Bear Creek Road. If the lobby desk is not manned, the materials are in the cabinet. Get assistance for opening.

Event Info: Daily, 8-8. Closed Easter, Thanksgiving, Christmas & New Years. The trail is rated 1 and is suitable for strollers & wheelchairs. Pets must be leashed. This walk covers historical areas, quaint downtown and residential areas and a path along Bear Creek.

Mill Valley/Sausalito - 10km Walk (YR391) 12km Walk (YR392) **Jan 1-Dec 31**
B Awards available
Sponsoring Club: AVA-204, Bay Bandits Volksmarch Club
POC: Robert P. Glasson, 415-457-1073. 59 Convent Ct, San Rafael CA 94901

Start Point: Mill Valley Parks & Recreation Dept, 415-383-1370. 180 Camino Alto. From Hwy 101 North, take the Tiburon/Belvedere (131) East Blithedale exit. Turn right on E Blithedale & go 2 blocks to Camino Alto. Turn left for approximately 1 block. Turn left into parking lot of the Mill

Valley Parks & Recreation Dept. From Hwy 101 South take the Tiburon/Belvedere (131), East Blithedale exit. Turn left on East Blithedale Ave & follow above directions. Ample parking is available.

Event Info: Mon-Fri, 9-5; Closed Sat, Sun & Holidays. Pets must be leashed on both trails. **YR391** is rated 2; not suitable for strollers or wheelchairs. It is on paved city streets with two hills and one steep down grade. **YR392** is rated 1; suitable for strollers & wheelchairs. It is on flat city streets and a walk/bike trail.

Monterey - Two 10km Walks (YR019, YR1261) 25km Bike (YR020) **Jan 1-Dec 31**
A Awards available
Sponsoring Club: AVA-005, Monterey Walking Club
POC: Willis Sexton, 408-394-9503. 1213 Judson St, Seaside, CA 93955

Start Point: La Casa Bodega Deli, 500 Del Monte Ave. Take Hwy 1 South to Del Monte exit. La Casa Bodega is on left across from Fisherman's Wharf parking. Do not park in Casa Bodega parking lot.

Event Info: Daily, 9-5. **YR019 &YR020** are rated 1. Suitable for strollers & wheelchairs. Pets are allowed but must be leashed. **YR1261** is rated 1+ and is on some gravel and dirt paths with one hill, city sidewalks, and recreation trail. Route also goes through the world famous Hotel Del Monte, now the Navy Postgraduate School.

Morgan Hill - 10km Walk (YR328) 27km Bike (YR749) **Jan 1-Dec 31**
Credit Only Events
Sponsoring Club: AVA-338, South Bay Striders
POC: Jacquie Christensen, 408-356-3954. 16389 E La Chiquita, Los Gatos, CA 95032

Start Point: Breaktime Cafe, 408-778-9394. 614 Tennant Ave. From Hwy 101 take Tennant Ave exit West. After passing the RR tracks and stop light, turn left into the parking lot of the shopping center. You will drive from Cafe to start for bike event. The Breaktime Cafe is located between the C&M Comics and Breaktime Billiards.

Event Info: Daily dawn to dusk. Call if in doubt about holidays. The walk is rated 1+, suitable for strollers and wheelchairs. Pets must be leashed. Mostly paved through town, residential areas and parks. The bike is rated 1+. You will drive to the trail head; you are advised not to unload bike at start point. Carry water on the trail. It is partially shaded and mostly on a paved recreational trail that follows the Coyote Creek. Bikers must sign a waiver and should wear a helmet.

Orange - 10km Walk (YR1085) **Jan 1-Dec 31**
B Awards available
Sponsoring Club: AVA-427, Hollywood Star Trekkers
POC: Tom Loppnow, 714-960-5339. 8855 Sutter Circle 517-C, Huntington Beach, CA 92646

Start Point: SAS Comfort Shoe Store, 714-283-4950. 2332 North Tustin Ave (Mall of Orange). From Hwy 5 or Hwy 57, go east on Hwy 91 to Hwy 55. Go south on Hwy 55 & exit on Tustin Blvd. Go south on Tustin to the SAS Shoe store located in a separate bldg at the north end of the Mall parking lot. From the south, go north on Hwy 5 & then north on Hwy 55. Exit at Lincoln & go west to Tustin. Turn south on Tustin to the Mall. From the east or west, use Hwy 91 then go south on Hwy 55 to the mall. Watch for mall signs.

Event Info: Mon-Fri 10-9; Sat 10-6; Sun 11-7. Closed some holidays. Please call ahead to verify. Trail is rated 3. It is suitable for strollers & wheelchairs. Pets must be leashed. This is a city walk through the beautiful neighborhoods of Villa Park. There are several steep hills but the climb is well worth it.

Pleasant Hill - 10km Walk (YR537) **Jan 1-Dec 31**
Credit Only Event
Sponsoring Club: AVA-764, Walnut Creek Walk-A-Nuts
POC: Lorri Dane, 510-932-8965. 130 Sharene Lane #25, Walnut Creek, CA 94596

Start Point: The Shoe Walk (SAS), 1924 Contra Costa Blvd. From North on I-680, take the Gregory Lane exit. At the stoplight turn right onto Contra Costa Blvd then right into the shopping center. From South on I-680, take the Contra Costa Blvd exit & continue North. Just past Gregory Lane, turn right into the shopping center. In both cases, look for the Shoe Walk store on the right side of the shopping center.

Event Info: Mon-Sat 10-5:30; Sun 11-4. The trail is rated 1, suitable for strollers & wheelchairs. Pets are allowed but must be leashed. The trail is on sidewalks & a paved recreation trail.

Port Hueneme - 12/14km Walk (YR1337) **Jan 1-Dec 31**
Credit Only Event
Sponsoring Club: AVA-816, Channel Islands Volksmarchers
POC: Donald Hadd, 805-486-0322; dhadd@jetlink.net. 1249 Nautical Way, Oxnard, CAR 93030

Start Point: Channel Islands Bootery, 805-985-5080. 707 West Channel Islands Blvd. Take Victoria Ave exit off US 101. Follow signs to channel Islands Harbor. Turn left on Channel Islands Blvd. Turn left into first shopping center. Start Point is in the right corner of shopping center.

Event Info: Mon, 9-5; Tues-Sat, 9-6. Closed Sundays. Trail is rated 1+. A 5km trail is suitable for strollers & wheelchairs. Pets are allowed if leashed. This route takes walkers thru fields, along the beach and thru Channel Islands Harbor.

Redding - 10km Walk (YR133)   25km Bike (YR621) **Jan 1-Dec 31**
B Awards available
Sponsoring Club: AVA-645, Redding Road Ramblers
POC: Beverly Severance, 916-275-2793. 18251 Ranchera Rd, Redding, CA 96003

Start Point: Laboratory at Mercy Medical Center, Airpark Dr. From I-5 take Central Redding-Eureka-299 West exit. When 299 freeway ends, continue west on Shasta St for 7 blocks. Turn left at the light at Court St. Continue south for 11 blocks then turn right on Rosaline Ave and proceed up the hill. Turn left on Airpark Dr & follow signs to hospital parking lot or garage. Follow signs to the Main Entrance and ask for directions to the Laboratory at the Information Desk. The self-service Volkssport cabinet is located to the left of the reception counter in the Laboratory. From the west, enter Redding on Route 299 (Eureka Way). Turn right at the light on Court St and proceed south on Court St as above.

Event Info: Daily, dawn to dusk. **YR133** is rated 1+, suitable for strollers & wheelchairs. Pets are allowed if leashed. To do this trail, you must drive 2.2 miles to the start after signing in at the hospital. Please do not leave valuables exposed in your car when parking at the start of the Sacramento River Trail. This course follows the paved Sacramento River Trail west along the south bank of the Sacramento River to the suspension bridge over the river & returns along the north bank where there are a few short hills. **YR621**, the bike, is rated 2+. You must drive to the start. Please wear helmets. Bikers must sign waiver. This course follows the Sacramento River Trail west on the south bank to the suspension bridge, over the river, east on the north bank, then on wide residential streets, then follows the eastern portion of the Sacramento River Trail on the north bank to the end. You must follow this route in reverse to complete the distance.

Redlands - 10km Walk (YR584) **Jan 1-Dec 31**
A Award available
Sponsoring Club: AVA-285, Green Valley Gaiters
POC: Gerry Myers, 909-794-1534. 20 Maria Ct, Redlands, CA 92374

Start Point: Family Fitness Center, 700 E Redlands Blvd, #AA. Behind Thrifty Drugs. From I-10 (east and west bound), exit on Ford St. off-ramp. East bound exit, turn right onto Ford at off-ramp stop. Proceed to traffic light and turn right onto Redlands Blvd. West bound exit, remain on Redlands Blvd. Both exits, proceed West on Redlands Blvd. to the shopping center (on your left heading West) at the corner of Redlands Blvd. and Palm Ave. Park in the main parking areas only (not the green curbed area).

Event Info: Daily, 7am-5pm. Reduced hours on some holidays. This trail is rated 1+ & is suitable for strollers & wheelchairs. Pets are allowed but must be leashed. Please do not ask technical questions of the Center staff. Write checks payable to "GVG"; the staff will not handle cash. Also, allow the staff to wait on customers first. No restrooms available in the Center. A scenic 10 km walk through much of historic Redlands. Historical descriptions of houses provided. Redlands was the Palm Springs of 1880s and early 1990s.

Redondo Beach - Two 10km Walks (YR490 & YR491) **Jan 1-Dec 31**
Credit Only Events
Sponsoring Club: AVA-427, Hollywood Star Trekkers
POC: John Shirtz, 310-374-3189. 346 27th St, Hermosa Beach, CA 90254

Start Point: Best Western Sunrise Hotel, 310-376-0746. 400 N Harbor Drive. From 405 North, exit Rosecrans. Go west ton Rosecrans to Aviation. Turn left. Continue to Artesia, turn right. Continue to Pacific Coast Hwy (PCH). From 405 South, exit Artesia Blvd & go west to PCH. Turn left on PCH to herondo. Turn right on Herondo to Harbor Dr. Turn left. The Best Western will be on your left approximately 1/2 mile down. Please park in the back of the hotel.

Event Info: Please do not interrupt business customers. Daily, dawn to dusk. Pets must be leashed and are not allowed on the Redondo Beach Pier. An alternate is available for pets. **YR491** is rated 2+ and will be difficult for strollers. Wheelchairs should not attempt. There is a short drive from the hotel to the start point for this event. Pets must be leashed. It is above the coastline of lovely Lunada Bay & the magnificent cliffs of Palos Verdes. **YR490** is rated 2 and is suitable for strollers & wheelchairs. Pets must be leashed. It takes you to the Redondo Beach Pier, up the rolling hills of North Redondo Beach, through Hermosa & Manhattan Beaches and back along the beach walkway.

Roseville - 10km Walk (YR560) **Jan 1-Dec 31**
B Awards available
Sponsoring Club: AVA-218, Sutter Strutters Volkssport Club
POC: Avis Showers, 916-988-7580. 5112 Sanicle Way, Fair Oaks, CA 95628

Start Point: Fleet Feet Sports, 1730-3 Santa Clara Drive. Located in the shopping center at the corner of Douglas Blvd & Santa Clara Dr.
EFFECTIVE 2/1/97: Fleet Feet Sports, 916-783-4558. 1850 Douglas Blvd, Suite 700. Located in TJ Maxx Shopping Center. Just down the street about one block from previous address.

Event Info: Mon-Fri, 10-8; Sat, 10-6; Sun, 12-5. Pets must be leashed. Trail is rated 1+. Suitable for strollers & wheelchairs.

Roseville - 10km Walk (YR1241) **Jan 20-Dec 31**
A Award available
Sponsoring Club: AVA-686, Placer Pacers
POC: Peggy Plummer, 916-782-2725 or Peggy Swayne, 916-624-3907. PO Box 142, Auburn, CA 95678

Start Point: Antique Trove, 238 Vernon St. From Sacramento I-80 east, exit Douglas Blvd west. From Auburn I-80 west, exit Douglas Blvd., turning right on Douglas. Stay in right lane on Douglas to right turn on Judah, right on Oak, and right again on Washington into the public parking lot. Walk crossing Oak at Washington, turn right on Oak. Take paved path to immediate left which crosses the parking lot to the corner of Washington and Vernon. Cross Vernon and turn right into Antique Trove.

Event Info: Daily, 10-6. Closed major holidays. Trail is rated 1; suitable for strollers. Pets are not allowed. Roseville is a historical major railroad center. The route is on sidewalks & paved paths through Old Town and residential areas.

Sacramento - 11km Walk (YR003)   30/52km Bike (YR006) **Jan 1-Dec 31**
YR003 has an A Award available   YR006 is a Credit Only Event
Sponsoring Club: AVA-CA, California Volkssport Association
POC: Don Ratliff, 916-645-8280. 1515 Quail Rd, Newcastle, CA 95658

Start Point: Sandman Motel, 236 Jibboom St. From I-5 take Richards Blvd off ramp. Turn west & Richards Blvd runs into Jibboom St.

Event Info: Daily, dawn to dusk. Trails are rated 1. Carry water in hot weather. The walk is suitable for strollers & wheelchairs. Pets must be leashed and are not allowed in the Capitol Bldg. It is mostly on sidewalks through historic sites in old downtown Sacramento. Most sites are open 10-5. The bike is mostly level & follows the American River Bike Trail. Bikers must sign a waiver and should wear a helmet.

Sacramento - 10km Walk (YR558)   25/35km Bike (YR607) **Jan 1-Dec 31**
B Awards available
Sponsoring Club: AVA-265, Sacramento Walking Sticks
POC: Myrna Jackson, 916-481-6714. PO Box 660881, Sacramento, CA 95866

Start Point: Earth Alive, 4329 Arden Way (Arden Plaza). From Capital City Freeway, take Watt Ave south to Arden Way. Go left on Arden Way. From Hwy 50 take Watt Ave north to Arden Way. Turn right. Start is on the corner of Eastern Ave & Arden Way.

Event Info: Mon-Sat 9-6; Sun 12-5. Walk is rated 1 & is suitable for strollers & wheelchairs. The route follows city streets & sidewalks. The bike is rated 1+ & follows city streets & the American River Bike Trail. Pets are allowed but must be leashed. Bikers must sign a waiver and should wear a helmet.

Sacramento - 10km Walk (YR583) **Jan 1-Dec 31**
Credit Only Event
Sponsoring Club: AVA-265, Sacramento Walking Sticks
POC: Margaret Thornburg, 916-441-4403. PO Box 660881, Sacramento CA 95866

Start Point: Mercy General Hospital, Greenhouse Cafeteria, 4001 J St. West on Capital City Freeway, take J St exit. Go left on J St past 39th St one block; left into Mercy Hospital to parking lot. OR East on Capital City Freeway , take N St exit & continue ahead onto 30th St. Go 4 blocks to J St & turn right to Mercy Hospital.

Event Info: Daily, 6am-8pm. Pets must be leashed. Trail is rated 1; suitable for strollers and wheelchairs. This trail is mostly shaded & follows city sidewalks.

San Jose - 10m Walk (YR240) **Jan 1-Dec 31**
B Awards available
Sponsoring Club: AVA-338, South Bay Striders
POC: Jacquie Christensen, 408-356-3954. 16389 E LaChiquita, Los Gatos, CA 95032

Start Point: Best Western Inn, 408-298-3500. 455 South Second St. From Hwy 280, take the 7th St exit and go north on 7th. Turn left onto San Salvador and left again at 2nd St. (one way) to Best Western.

Event Info: Daily, 8-dusk. Pets are discouraged. Trail is rated 1 (flat). Suitable for strollers and wheelchairs. You will walk in historical downtown San Jose, on a river path, and paved walkways on the University campus.

San Leandro - 10km Walk (YR1068) **Jan 1-Dec 31**
B Awards available
Sponsoring Club: AVA-204, Bay Bandits Volksmarching Club
POC: Carrie/Ron Cutting, 516-569-6751. 1271 Timothy Dr, San Leandro, CA 94577

Start Point: P & D Market, 510-352-9396. 1011 Williams St. In San Leandro from either direction on I-880, take the Marina Blvd East exit. After the first signal at Wayne/Teagarden, you will pass two streets on the left & the third is Orchard. Turn left on Orchard Drive to the second stop sign. P & D Market is on the left at the corner of Orchard & Williams. Look for file cabinet just inside front door.

Event Info: Daily, 9-8. Open most holidays but check first. Trail is rated 1; suitable for strollers and wheelchairs. Pets are allowed. The trail is paved with one gravel area that is level and wide.

San Luis Obispo - 10km Walk (YR458) **Jan 1-Dec 31**
B Awards available
Sponsoring Club: AVA-371, Big Valley Vagabonds
POC: Ed Ritchie, 805-937-4719. 1650 E. Clark Ave #285, Santa Maria, CA 93455

Start Point: Holiday Inn Express, 805-544-8600. 1800 Monterey St. N on US101, take the Grand Ave exit and turn right to Monterey St. S on US101, Monterey St exit. Motel is on the corner of Grand Ave & Monterey St.

Event Info: Daily, dawn to dusk. Trail is rated 2 and is suitable for strollers & wheelchairs. Pets are allowed but must be leashed. This route includes Cal Poly University, historical residential & downtown areas with many interesting shops. Some moderate hills.

Santa Rosa - 10km Walk (YR1100) **Jan 1-Dec 31**
B Awards available
Sponsoring Club: AVA-720, Sonoma County Stompers
POC: Suzanne Gooch, 707-571-1839. 1055 W College Ave #274, Santa Rosa, CA 95401

Start Point: Louie's Restaurant. 1901 Mendocino Ave. From Hwy 101 take Steele Lane exit. Go east to Mendocino Ave & right on Mendocino Ave. Start is located in the small shopping center at the corner of Steele & Mendocino.

Event Info: Daily, 7am-9pm. Closed Christmas & may close earlier on other holidays. Trail is rated 1; suitable for strollers & wheelchairs. Pets must be leashed. Louie's Restaurant gives volkssporters a 15% discount. SAS Shoe Store in same shopping center gives a 10% discount. The route is on city streets. Burbank Gardens, Ripley's Church of One Tree and Julliard Park are among the highlights.

Stockton/San Joaquin - Two 10 km Walks (YR179 & YR1304) **Jan 1-Dec 31**
B Awards available
Sponsoring Club: AVA-416 Delta Tule Trekkers
POC: Robert S. Carlson, 209-951-7830. 8216 Manhattan Dr., Stockton, CA 95210

Start Point: Zoom Zoom's-A Place to Eat, 1304 E. Hammer Lane. Corner of Alpine & Alvarado Way. Walk #1 starts here but you must drive to the start of the #2 walk after registering. From Zoom Zoom's, go south on West Lane to Alpine. Turn west to Oak Park. Follow map with directions found in box at Zoom Zoom's.

Event Info: Daily, 7 a.m.-dusk. Closed major holidays. Both trails are rated 1 and are suitable for wheelchairs and strollers. Pets must be leashed. Routes are on paved streets and sidewalks through university campus and parks. Volkssporters may receive a Special of the Month at Zoom Zoom's.

Sun City - Two 10 km Walks (YR701 & YR1212)   11 km Walk (YR1213)
A Awards available
Sponsoring Club: AVA-157 Low Desert Roadrunners
POC: Rick Bundy, 909-678-3337. 21671 Darby St., Box 416, Wildomar, CA   92395

Start Point: Sun City Motel (main lobby), 909-672-1861. 27680 Encanto Dr. North or South on I-215, take the McCall Blvd. Exit and go east to Encanto (1 block). At Encanto Dr., turn left (north) to Sun City Motel.

Event Info: Daily, 8 a.m. to dusk.   **YR701** is rated 1 but will be difficult for strollers and wheelchairs. Pets must be leashed. After registration there is a .9 mile drive to start/finish. Walk is on city/residential streets. **YR1212** is rated 1 and is suitable for wheelchairs and strollers.   After registration, there is a 3.1 mile drive to the start/finish.   It is on city and residential sidewalks. **YR1213** is rated 2+ and is not suitable for strollers and wheelchairs.   After registration, there is a 4.7 mile drive to the start/finish.   This event is along county roads (some are dirt roads).

Sutter Creek - 10km Walk (YR103) **Jan 1-Dec 31**
B Awards available
Sponsoring Club: AVA-575, Ye Olde Chico Walking Club
POC: Linda Detling, 916-343-7887. 1304 Arbutus Ave, Chico, CA 95926 or Dorothy Williamson, 209-274-4339. 2901 Coyote Ct, Ione, CA 95640

Register: Gold Quartz Inn, (209-267-9155 Reservations Only) 15 Bryson Dr. Located on the south end of Sutter Creek. Turn east off SH 49 on Bryson Dr. Inn is 1/2 block down on the left. Drive to start point in town. Instructions are at the registration area.

Event Info: Event is open daily, dawn to dusk. The trail is rated 2+ and is not recommended for strollers or wheelchairs. Pets must be leashed with clean-up. This event goes by historical sites, old & new homes, shops & eating places. It is mostly paved with some dirt & gravel & a few short hills. The Inn is an elegant getaway in Queen Anne style. Afternoon tea & a generous breakfast are included in the tariff. A 10% discount is given to volkssporters.

Tahoma - 10km Walk (YR235) 25/49km Bike (YR389) **May 1-Nov 30**
Credit Only Events
Sponsoring Club: AVA-683, Sierra Nevada Striders
POC: Barbara Currie, 702-831-4356. PO Box 4344, Incline Village, NV 89450

Start Point: Norfolk Woods Inn, 916-525-5000. 6941 West Lake Blvd (Hwy 89). From I-80 take Hwy 89/Lake Tahoe exit in Truckee, CA to Tahoe City. Turn right in Tahoe City to continue on Hwy 89 South 8 miles to Tahoma. Inn will be on the right side. From Hwy 50; take Hwy 89 in South Lake Tahoe north 25 miles to Tahoma. Inn will be on the left.

Event Info: Daily, 8-dusk. Walk trail is rated 1+ due to altitude. Strollers are okay and an alternate route is available for wheelchairs. Pets are not allowed in the State Park. The route follows a flat, paved recreational trail along the shore of Lake Tahoe, including the beautiful Sugar Pine State Park. The bike is also rated 1+ due to altitude. Snow and/or ice cancels both events. The bike also follows a flat, paved recreational trail along the shore of Lake Tahoe including the beautiful Sugar Pine State Park. The extended bike route follows the bike trail adjacent to the Truckee River.

Tecopa - 10km Walk (YR1047) **Jan 1-Dec 31**
A Award available
Sponsoring Club: AVA-296, Las Vegas High Rollers & Strollers
POC: Aldine Wallace, 619-852-4580. PO Box 306, Tecopa, CA 92389 or Dick List, 702-438-0145. PO Box 30153, Las Vegas, NV 89036-1753

CALIFORNIA, cont.

Start Point: Desert Air Hostel, 619-852-4580. 2000 Old Spanish Trail Hwy. Hostel is 1.5 miles from the Post Office on Old Spanish Trail Hwy. Tecopa is 47 miles north of Baker or 62 miles west of Las Vegas, Blue Diamond exit off I-15 on 160 to Tecopa turn off (40 miles) and turn left to Tecopa.

Event Info: Daily, 7am-6pm. The trail is rated 3+ & is not suitable for strollers or wheelchairs. Pets must be leashed. You must carry water on this trail. Food is not readily available. Snacks & cold sandwiches are available at the Hostel & there is a Cafe in Shoshone (8 miles north) that is open daily 7 am-9pm. HI-AYH non-membership fees are discounted for overnighters at the Hostel. Please call ahead to insure trail is open. Free RV parking (no hook-ups) at the Hostel. Best to pre-register the day before for an early start. This trail winds through Amargosa Canyon. The majority of the trail is actually a 1 but the last 1.5 miles is climbing out of the canyon giving it the higher rating. Permanently marked trail plus map.

Truckee - 10km Walk (YR695) **May 1-Nov 30**
Credit Only Event
Sponsoring Club: AVA-489, Tahoe Trail Trekkers
POC: Gisela Steiner, 916-546-3452. Box 499, Tahoe Vista, CA 96148

Start Point: Sierra Mountaineering, Bridge & Jibbom St. Central Truckee exit off I-80. Coming from San Francisco/Sacramento, after exit drive along Donner Pass Rd to Bridge. Turn left to start point. Coming from Reno, go over overpass of I-80 and turn right at Bridge.

Event Info: Mon-Thurs 10-6; Fri 10-7; Sat 9-7 & Sun 10-5. This trail is rated 2, suitable for strollers with some difficulty. Not suitable for wheelchairs. Pets must be leashed with clean-up. Watch for traffic when crosswalks are not available. The trail is mostly flat with some hills at the beginning.

Vacaville - 11km Walk (YR331) **Jan 1-Dec 31**
B Awards available
Sponsoring Club: AVA-376, Vaca Valley Volks
POC: Ruth A. Redd, 707-429-1899. 2000 Claybank Rd #E1, Fairfield, CA 94535

Start Point: Vaca Valley Hospital, 1000 Nut Tree Rd (Main Lobby). From the East, take Mason St/Travis AFB exit and turn right at first light onto Elmira Rd. Continue to Nut Tree Rd and turn left on Nut Tree. Continue 2 more blocks & hospital is on the right side. From the West, take Peabody Rd/Elmira exit. Left at light; right at next light onto Elmira & follow above directions.

Event Info: Daily, dawn to dusk. Trail is rated 1 and is flat on sidewalks through a residential area and parks. It is suitable for strollers & wheelchairs. Pets must be leashed.

Ventura - 10km Walk (YR860) **Jan 1-Dec 31**
Credit Only Event
Sponsoring Club: AVA-861, Channel Islands Volksmarchers
POC: Marsha Polk, 805-339-9268. 1084 Britten Lane #104, Ventura, CA 93003-8207

Start Point: Vagabond Inn, 805-648-5371. 756 E. Thompson Blvd. Northbound on US 101 take California St exit to East Thompson Blvd, then right 2 1/2 blocks to Inn. From southbound on US 101, take Ventura Ave exit to East Thompson Blvd. Turn right and go 7 blocks to Inn.

Event Info: Daily, dawn to dusk. Rated 1+. Suitable for strollers and wheelchairs. Pets must be leashed and are not allowed on the pier. Inn will give a discount if you tell them you're a volkssporter when making reservations. Trail wanders thru historic Ventura by historic buildings such as City Hall and the Mission. It also goes along the ocean.

Visalia - 10km Walk (YR861) **Jan 1-Dec 31**
B Awards available
Sponsoring Club: AVA-371, Big Valley Vagabonds
POC: Jim Scofield, 209-734-5464. For Flyers: M. L. Mott, 3212 E Tenaya Way, Fresno, CA 93710

Start Point: Alpine Station, 209-627-2643. 610 W. Main St. From Hwy 99 take Hwy 198 East towards mountains. Turn left on Mooney Blvd, across the freeway Turn right on Main St.

Event Info: Daily, 6 a.m. to 10:30 p.m. Trail is rated 1; suitable for strollers & wheelchairs. Pets must be leashed. Walk includes early Visalia homes, some town area, lovely residential areas & significant "Trulli Blvd" located in Tulare County.

Walnut Creek - 10km Walk (YR852) **Jan 1-Dec 31**
Credit Only Event
Sponsoring Club: AVA-764, Walnut Creek Walk-A-Nuts
POC: Lorri Dane, 510-932-8965. 130 Shareen Lane #25, Walnut Creek, CA 94596

Start Point: The Walking Company, 510-210-1900. 1155 Broadway Plaza. From San Francisco take Hwy 24 East to the Walnut Creek exit. Stay on Mt Diablo Blvd. At North Main turn right. At Bothelo St turn left into the parking garage. After parking, walk past the Crate & Barrel, the California Pizza Kitchen & turn right. Start is on the right. From the South take Hwy 680 North to the S Main St exit. Turn into parking garage at Bothelo St & follow above directions. From the North take Hwy 680 South past Walnut Creek to the S Main St exit. Follow S Main & the above directions.

Event Info: Mon-Fri, 10-9; Sat, 10-8; Sun, 11-7. Trail is rated 1 and is suitable for strollers & wheelchairs. Pets must be leashed. This trail is on city sidewalks & a recration trail.

Weimar - 10km Walk (YR854) **Jan 1-Dec 31**
A Award available
Sponsoring Club: AVA-686, Placer Pacers
POC: Dave Davidson, 916-878-8470 or Herb Webber, 916-878-7023. PO Box 142, Auburn, CA 95604-0142

Start Point: Weimar Institute. 20601 W. Paoli Lane. From Auburn drive east on I-80 approximately 9 miles to West Paoli Lane exit. Turn left over the highway and right into the campus. From Colfax drive West on I-80 approximately 4 miles to West Paoli Lane, exit on around to the right into the campus. Park in visitors lot. Register at the Welcome Center at the main gate.

Event Info: Weekdays dawn to dusk but not earlier than 6:30am. Sat 9-dusk; Sun 8-dusk. Trail is rated 3 and has an elevation of 2200 ft. It is mostly wooded, dirt trails in the rolling Sierra foothills. Not suitable for strollers or wheelchairs. Pets must be leashed. NO SMOKING. Occasional snow or ice may temporarily close trails in winter. Call ahead. Trail is in an Oak, pine & manzanita forest; streams with wild grapes & berries in summer, wildflowers in spring. Good picnic spot at Checkpoint 1 with latrine close by. Carry water in summer & fall.

Willits - 10km Walk (YR1148) **Jan 1-Dec 31**
Credit Only Event
Sponsoring Club: AVA-821, Mendocino County Meanderers
POC: Geri Lusnia, 707-459-4716. 24121 Sherwood Rd, Willits, CA 95490

Start Point: Perko's Cafe, 707-459-3850. 1740 S Main St. Perko's is located in the Evergreen Village Shopping Center on Main St (Hwy 101). This is the first stop light North of San Francisco on 101 (140 miles). From the east take I-5 to Hwy 20 at Williams, turn right at 101, go north to Willits. From north go south on 101 to Willits, turn right into Evergreen.

Event Info: Daily, 6am-10pm. Closed at 2pm on Thanksgiving & Christmas Eve & all day Christmas. Trail is rated 1+ and is suitable for strollers & wheelchairs but some short distances where there is no sidewalk will require extra care. Pets are allowed but must be leashed. Walk is mostly through residential areas & a downtown business section.

CALIFORNIA, cont.

Yuba City - 11km Walk (YR111)   10km Walk (YR397) **Jan 1-Dec 31**
A Award available
Sponsoring Club: AVA-CA, California Volkssport Assn.
POC: Pat Lucero, 916-434-0205. 1951 Quail Rd, Newcastle, CA 95658-9493

Start Point: The Bonanza Inn, (Best Western), 916-674-8824. 1001 Clark Ave. From Sacramento, North on Hwy 99 to Hwy 20, in Yuba City. Right on Hwy 20 1/2 mile to Clark Ave. Left on Clark one block to Bonanza Inn. From I-5: At Williams, take Hwy 20 east to Yuba City. From intersection of Hwy 20 & Hwy 99, continue on Hwy 20 1/2 mile to Clark Ave. Left on Clark one block to Bonanza Inn. File cabinet is in staff "break room".

Event Info: Daily, dawn to dusk. Trails are rated 1. Suitable for strollers but not advised for wheelchairs. Pets must be leashed. YR397 is through residential, business & historic areas of Marysville. YR111 is through residential & business areas of Yuba City.

COLORADO

Aurora - 10km Walk (YR317) **Jan 2-Dec 30**
A Award available
Sponsoring Club: AVA-024, Rocky Mountain Wanderers
POC: Juanita Alseike, 303-340-2477. 914 Quari Ct., Aurora, CO 80011-6229.

Start Point: Helga's German Delicatessen, Hoffman Heights Shopping Village, 728 Peoria St. From I-225 exit onto 6th Ave (Exit #9) and proceed one mile west. Turn right onto Peoria St then right into Hoffman Heights Shopping Village. From I-70 esit onto Peoria St (exit 281) and proceed approx 3 miles south. Turn left into the Hoffman Heights Shopping Village. The Deli is on the north side of the village near the end.

Event Info: Mon, 8-8; Tue-Sat, 9-9; Sun, 11-8. Due to heavy lunchtime patronage, please avoid starting between 10am & 2pm. Closed all holidays. Trail is rated 1+ with an elevation of 5,500 ft. Suitable for strollers & wheelchairs with some difficulty with curbs in some areas. Pets must be leashed. Trail follows city streets and the Highline Canal which is a wide dirt trail.

Boulder - 10km Walk (YR826) **Jan 1-Dec 31**
A Award available
Sponsoring Club: AVA-024, Rocky Mountain Wanderers
POC: Kathryn Miller, 303-443-8898. 235 Linden Drive, Boulder, CO 80304-0472

Start Point: University Inn, 1632 Broadway. **From Cheyenne:** Travel south on I-25 to Hwy 52 (exit 235). Turn right (west) to Hwy 119 (Diagonal Hwy). Turn left & follow Hwy 119 through 28th St to Iris (end of road). Turn left 1 1/2 miles to Arapahoe. Parking available at Library one block west of Arapahoe & Broadway. Two hour parking on weekdays ($10 overtime parking ticket). University Inn on Arapahoe & Broadway. **From Denver:** Travel on Hwy 36 to Boulder. Exit on Baseline. Turn left (west) to Broadway, turn right for approximately 1 1/2 miles to University Inn at Broadway & Arapahoe. See above for parking information

Event Info: Daily, dawn to dusk. Rated 1+ with elevation of 5,344 ft. Suitable for strollers & wheelchairs with some difficulty due to curbs. Pets must be leashed. Do not interrrupt Inn keepers when they are busy with customers. This trail follows a creek, city streets and goes through the University.

Canon City - 11km Walk (YR277) **Jan 1-Dec 31**
A Award available
Sponsoring Club: AVA-072, Falcon Wanderers
POC: Richard Liphardt, 719-275-6669. PO Box 17162, Colorado Springs, CO 80935

28

COLORADO, cont. ━━━━━━━━━━━━━━━━━━━━━━━━━━━━━━━━━━━━

Start Point: Best Western Royal Gorge Motel, 719-275-3377. 1925 Fremont Dr. Entering Canon City from the East on US Hwy 50, the motel will be approximately 1 1/4 miles into the city on your right (north). Turn right (north) on Orchard St and then immediately left (west) onto Fremont Dr (Frontage Rd). Go 1/2 block & motel will be on your right.

Event Info: Daily, dawn to dusk. Rated 3. Not recommended for strollers or wheelchairs. Pets must be leashed. Trail is on well maintained dirt path along the Arkansas River with moderate hills.

Colorado Springs - 10km Walk (YR1329) **Apr 1-Dec 31**   10/14km Walk (YR1328) **Apr 1-Sept 30**
Credit Only Events
Sponsoring Club: AVA-119, High Plains Drifters
POC: YR1329: Jane Darling; 719-594-0791. 8029 Lexington Park Dr, Colorado Sprgs, CO 80920
YR1328: Kevin Ross, 719-597-5469. 2545 Rimrock Dr, Colorado Springs, CO 80915

Start Point: Albertson's Food & Drug Store, 455 E Cheyenne Mountain Blvd. Take I-25 (north or south) to exit 138 (S Circle Dr). Turn west on South Circle Dr & proceed to the Hwy 115 (Nevada Ave) interchange. Turn left (south) onto Hwy 115 & continue to Cheyenne Mountain Blvd. Start is on the SE corner of intersection.

Event Info: Daily, dawn-dusk. **YR1329** is rated 1+; suitable for strollers & wheelchairs. Pets must be leashed. This route is on paved streets and sidewalks in the Broadmoor section of Colorado Springs. There are many beautiful homes along the route, including the world-famous 5-star Broadmoor Hotel. **YR1328** is rated 4; not suitable for strollers or wheelchairs. Pets must be leashed. This route is on a dirt & gravel trail that is steep in some areas. It is in the North Cheyenne Canon by the Broadmoor section of Colorado Springs. Canyon & forest views are spectacular and at the midpoint of both distances area a series of waterfalls.

Colorado Springs - 11km Walk (YR095) **Apr 1-Dec 31**
A Award available
Sponsoring Club: AVA-072, Falcon Wanderers
POC: Pat Gray, 719-684-9462. PO Box 17162, Colorado Springs CO 80935

Start Point: 7-11 Store, 1011 S. 21st St. Take I-25 north or south to Colorado Springs and exit 141 (US Hwy 24). Turn left on US 24 West 1 1/2 miles to 21st St. Turn left & go one block to 7-11 on the left.

Event Info: Daily, dawn to dusk. Rated 3+ due to hills and altitude of 6500 ft. No strollers or wheelchairs. Pets are not allowed. Trail is on well maintained paths in a park. A 1km functionally disadvantaged trail rated 3+ due to a slight incline, altitude and uneven surfaces, is available.

Colorado Springs - 25km Bike (YR467) **Jan 2-Dec 31**
Credit Only Event
Sponsoring Club: AVA-072, Falcon Wanderers
POC: Pat Gray, 719-684-9462. PO Box 17162, Colorado Springs CO 80935-7162

Start Point: Ted's Bicycle, 719-473-6915. 3016 N Hancock Ave. Take I-25 North or South to Colorado Springs and Exit 145. Proceed east on Fillmore St 1.8 miles to Hancock Ave. Turn left & go 1/2 block to Ted's on the left. Do not park in small customer's lot.

Event Info: Mon-Sat, 9-6. Closed Sundays and most holidays except MLK Day, President's Day & Columbus Day. Open in AM only on Christmas & New Year's Eve. Trail is rated 2+ due to slight hills & altitude of 6,400 ft. Not suitable for strollers or wheelchairs. No pets allowed. Rental bikes are available. Remember to sign waiver. Helmets are required. Trail is on a paved road & hard packed natural surface.

Colorado Springs - 11km Walk (YR464) **Jan 1-Dec 31**
A Award available
Sponsoring Club: AVA-072, Falcon Wanderers
POC: Karen Seay, 719-475-1671. PO Box 17162, Colorado Springs CO 80935

Start Point: Garden of the Gods Trading Post, 324 Beckers Ln. From I-25 North or South take Exit 141 (Hwy 24). Turn left (west) on US 24 to the exit @ "Highway 24 Business Route, Manitou Ave" sign & turn left onto Manitou Ave. Turn left at first traffic light onto Beckers Lane. Continue on Beckers Lane to the Trading Post.

Event Info: Summer: daily, 8-8. Winter: daily, 9-4:30. Closed Thanksgiving & Christmas. Trail is rated 3 due to hills & an altitude of 6,412 ft. No strollers or wheelchairs. Pets must be leashed. Trail is all in the Garden of the Gods Park along dirt paths, sidewalks & park roads.

Colorado Springs - 10km Walk (YR465) **Jan 2-Dec 31**
A Award available
Sponsoring Club: AVA-072, Falcon Wanderers
POC: Deb Hillard, 719-748-3035. PO Box 17162, Colorado Springs CO 80935-7162

Start Point: Mountain Chalet, 226 N Tejon. From I-25 north or south, take exit 142 & proceed east on Bijou. Turn left at Cascade Ave. Proceed to Platte Ave & turn right. Go one block to Tejon & turn right on Tejon. Mountain Chalet will be on your right in the first block. There are parking meters along Tejon but just off Cascade there is free parking.

Event Info: Mon, Tues & Sat, 9:30-6; Wed-Fri, 9:30-8; Sun 11-5. Closed major holidays. Rated 1+. Suitable for strollers but not wheelchairs. Pets allowed but must be leashed. Trail is on dirt paths in city park & on residential sidewalks.

Colorado Springs - 10km Walk (YR777) **Jan 1-Dec 31**
Credit Only Event
Sponsoring Club: AVA-072, Falcon Wanderers
POC: Pat Gray, 719-684-9462. PO Box 17162, Colorado Springs, CO 80935

Start Point: 7-11 Store. 331 S Hancock Ave. Take I-25 north or south to Colorado Springs and exit 141. Turn right (east) on Cimarron St .6 miles to Wahsatch Ave. Turn left (north) 1 block to Costilla St. Turn right (east) .9 miles to Hancock Ave. 7-11 is on Northeast corner of intersection. Do not park in 7-11 parking lot.

Event Info: Daily, dawn to dusk. Rated 1+ (2+ for functionally disadvantaged) due to altitude of 6,200 ft. Suitable for strollers & wheelchairs. Pets must be leashed. Trail consists of a 2km loop around lake on a relatively flat, paved path except for 100 meters of light sand. Restrooms are available along the trail.

Colorado Springs - 10km Walk (YR1033) **Jan 1-Dec 31**
Credit Only Event
Sponsoring Club: AVA-119, High Plains Drifters
POC: Kevin Ross, 719-597-5469. 2545 Rimrock Dr, Colorado Springs, CO 80915

Start Point: Save Food Mart, 3960 Maizeland Rd. From I-25, going south, take exit 150A (Academy Blvd) & proceed south 7 miles to Maizeland Rd & turn left. From I-25 going north, take exit 135 (Academy Blvd) . Turn right and proceed north 7.7 miles to Maizeland Rd & turn right. Start is in the outdoor mall located on the NE corner of Maizeland Rd & Academy Blvd.

Event Info: Daily, dawn to dusk. Trail is rated 2; suitable for strollers but not wheelchairs. Pets are allowed but must be leashed. Walk is on roads in city park. There are moderate hills.

COLORADO, cont.

Colorado Springs/USAF Academy - 10km Walk (YR197) **Apr 1-Nov 30**
A Award available
Sponsoring Club: AVA-072, Falcon Wanderers
POC: Curt Converse, 719-591-8193. PO Box 17162, Colorado Springs, CO 80935S

Start Point: Loaf 'N Jug, 13854 Glen Eagle Drive. From I-25 north or south, take exit 156A (Gleneagle) & proceed east on North Gate Rd 1/4 mile to Gleneagle Dr. Turn left going 1/2 mile to Loaf 'N Jug. NOTE: Two volksmarches start at this location. Be sure to ask for the Academy Volksmarch Box.

Event Info: Daily, dawn to dusk. No walking in inclement weather. Rated 3+ due to hills & altitude of 7,280 ft. No strollers or wheelchairs. Pets must be leashed and owners must clean up after them. Trail is hilly with dirt trails, roadsides & sidewalks. A walking stick and hiking boots are recommended. Restrooms are available along the trail.

Creede - Four 10km Walks (YR128, YR209, YR355 & YR396) **Jun 14-Sep 28**
A Award available
Sponsoring Club: AVA-597, Upper Rio Grande Mountain Walkers
POC: BJ Myers, 719-658-2671. PO Box 272, Creede CO 81130

Start Point: Amethyst Emporium, 129 North Main St. Located across from the theatre.

Event Info: Mon-Sat 9-5; Sun, 10-5. Pets are allowed on all events. **YR128** is rated 4+ and is not suitable for wheelchairs or strollers. It follows a trail and 4x4 road. This walk travels through woods & Alpine meadows. Special attractions include two waterfalls & beaver ponds. **YR209** is rated 4. It is not suitable for strollers or wheelchairs. This walk is through woods & up a beautiful canyon, home to some of the best trout fishing in the Creede area. It is along a dirt road & Forest Service trail. **YR355** is rated 3+. It is not suitable for strollers or wheelchairs. It is along a dirt road & trail. The first half of this walk affords a panoramic view of the upper Rio Grande Valley. The second half follows a trail along Shallow Creek with excellent beaver ponds. Moose have been spotted along this trail. **YR396** is rated 3+. It is suitable for strollers and wheelchairs. It follows a dirt road through East Willow Creek Canyon. This walk introduces you to Creede's historic silver mining past. You will walk along East Willow Creek, through old North Creede & past a number of old mine sites.

Denver - 11km Walk (YR048) two 10km Walks (YR1051 & YR1083) **Jan 2-Dec 30**
YR048 & YR1083 have A Awards available   YR1051 is a Credit Only Event
Sponsoring Club: AVA-024, Rocky Mountain Wanderers
POC: Nancy Reisdorff, 303-343-3806. 303 S. Troy, Aurora, CO 80012

Start Point: Larry's Shoes, 175 Fillmore St. Exit I-25 at Colfax (exit 210A). Head east for .7 miles to Speer Blvd. Turn right & follow for 2.8 miles to Unviersity Blvd. (Speer Blvd turns into 1st). Turn left on University for 1 block to 2nd. Turn right for .4 miles to Fillmore.

Event Info: Mon-Fri, 10-8; Sat, 10-6; & Sun 12-5. All trails are rated 1+ with elevation of 5,280 ft. Suitable for strollers & wheelchairs with some difficulty due to curbs. Pets must be leashed. **YR48 & YR1051** are along city streets & through a park. **YR1083** goes past the capitol & through historic downtown Denver. After registering, you must drive to the start point for this event.

Evergreen - Two 10km Walks (YR195 & YR1307) **Jan 2 - Dec 31**
Credit Only Event
Sponsoring Club: AVA-671, Colorado High Country Hikers
POC: David J. Johnson, 303-674-0317. 31062 Wildwoods, Evergreen, CO 80439

Start Point: Paragon Sports, 303-670-0092. 2962 Evergreen Pkwy. From Denver go west on I-70 to Evergreen Pkwy. Take Evergreen Pkwy to Lewis Ridge Rd. Turn left to get on Frontage Rd. Follow Frontage Rd to Paragon Sports.

31

Event Info: Mon-Fri, 9-7; Sat 9-6; Sun 10-4. Both trails are rated 3; not suitable for strollers or wheelchairs. Pets must be leashed. No water is available on the trails. You must get directions to the trail head at Paragon Sports for YR195. Routes are on trails with altitude of 7,000+ ft. YR195 has a gain of approx 400'. YR1307 has minor elevation changes.

Fort Collins - 10km Walk (YR1273) **Jan 1-Dec 31**
Credit Only Event
Sponsoring Club: AVA-859, Northern Front Range Wanderers
POC: Gordan Thibedeau, 970-484-7123. 333 West Mountain Ave, Suite B, Ft Collins, CO 80521

Start Point: Fort Collins Club, 1307 East Prospect Rd. Take I-25 to Ft Collins. Exit at #278 (Prospect Rd). Proceed west on Propsect Rd for approx 2.5 miles. The Fort Collins Club is located on the south side of road.

Event Info: Mon-Fri, dawn-dusk; Sat, Sun & Holidays, 7am-8pm. Closed Christmas. Trail is rated 2; suitable for strollers & wheelchairs with assistance. Pet are allowed. Check in at main desk/counter inside Fort Collins Club. Refreshments are available at the Club. The walk follows the Spring Creek Trail and historic sited in Fort Collins.

Fountain - 11km Walk (YR153) **Jan 1-Dec 31**
B Awards available
Sponsoring Club: AVA-072, Falcon Wanderers
POC: Charles Baxter 719-390-7675/Bob Shute, 719-540-8755. PO Box 17162, Colorado Springs CO 80935

Start Point: Loaf 'N Jug Store, 7055 Alegre Circle. Take I-25 north or south to exit 132 & proceed east to Hwy 85/87. Go north (left) on 85/87 approximately 1/2 mile to Alegre St. Start is on the southwest corner of intersection.

Event Info: Daily, dawn to dusk. Trail is rated 2; not suitable for wheelchairs and strollers only with difficulty. Pets must be leashed & are not allowed on the Nature Trail Loop. This walk is on well maintained paths in a park.

Georgetown - 10km Walk (YR541) **May 24-Sept 30**
B Awards available
Sponsoring Club: AVA-024, Rocky Mountain Wanderers
POC: Dottie Baars, 303-237-9788. 2010 Kendall, Edgewater, CO 80214

Start Point: Hamill House. 3rd & Argentine Sts. 45 miles west of Denver on I-70, exit 228 Georgetown, left through underpass. Turn right at stop sign & proceed into Georgetown. Bear to the left at the fork in the road. At the stop sign turn left for one block, then right on Argentine St for 4 blocks to 3rd St. Turn right to Hamill House.

Event Info: Daily, 10-5. Trail is rated 3+ due to elevation of 8,519 ft. Not suitable for strollers or wheelchairs. Pets must be leashed. Walk is on streets and dirt trails through historic Georgetown. Overnight accomodations through Georgetown Chamber of Commerce, 303-569-2888.

Gleneagle - 10km Walk (YR1058) **Apr 1-Dec 31**
A Award available
Sponsoring Club: AVA-841, Black Forest Volkssport Club
POC: Linda Ford, 719-495-0769. 10955 Egerton Rd, Black Forest, CO 80908

Start Point: Loaf 'n Jug #61, 13854 Gleneagle Dr. Take I-25 and exit 156A (Gleneagle). Proceed east on North Gate Blvd. To Gleneagle Dr. Turn left & follow Gleneagle Dr to the start on your left.

Event Info: Daily, 7-7. Trail is rated 2+; not suitable for strollers or wheelchairs. Pets must be leashed. A map will be provided at the start/finish with directions to the trailhead. Restrooms are available at the trailhead but you must provide your own water. The walk is on dirt trails in a wooded area of the Black Forest.

Golden - 10km Walk (YR1052) **Jan 2-Dec 30**
A Award available
Sponsoring Club: AVA-024, Rocky Mountain Wanderers
POC: Dottie Baars, 303-237-9788. 2010 Kendall St, Edgewater, CO 80214

Start Point: Boettcher Mansion, 900 Colorow Rd. From the east take I-70 west to exit 256. From the exit ramp turn right, then turn left onto the frontage road. Follow the brown & white signs to the Nature Center. From the west take I-70 east to exit 254. From the exit ramp, turn left & cross over I-70. Turn right onto the frontage road & follow brown & white signs to the Nature Cener.

Event Info: The entrance to the Mansion is behind a small garage type building used for conferences. Mon-Sat, 8-5. Closed Sundays & major holidays. Trail is rated 3+ to 4 with elevation of 7,560 ft. It is not suitable for strollers or wheelchairs & pets are not allowed. The trail is on dirt/gravel paths & parts are rocky & steep.

Green Mountain Falls - 11km Walk (YR975) **Apr 1-Nov16**
Credit Only Event
Sponsoring Club: AVA-119, High Plains Drifters
POC: Robert McDuff, 719-260-8390. 488F West Rockrimmon Blvd, Colorado Springs, CO 80919

Start Point: The Market, 719-684-9874. 10398 Ute Pass Ave. From I-25 take exit 141 left (west) on US 24 to 1st Green Mountain Falls exit. Follow Ute Pass Ave to 3 way stop sign. Start will be on your right.

Event Info: Daily, 8-5. Closed major holidays. Call ahead if in doubt. Trail is rated 3+ due to some hills & altitude of 7300 ft. Strollers & wheelchairs are not recommended. Pets must be leashed. This walk is on dirt trails & town streets.

Loveland - 10km Walk (YR1053) **Jan 1-Dec 31**
A Award available (limited supply)
Sponsoring Club: AVA-024, Rocky Mountain Wanderers
POC: Carol Cross, 970-586-3504. PO Box 58, Glen Haven, CO 80532

Start Point: Village Inn, 1225 W Eisenhower Blvd. From I-25 exit 257B (Hwy 34). Proceed west 5.6 miles past Lake Loveland. Hwy 34 turns into Eisenhower Blvd. Start is on your right just past the Lake.

Event Info: Daily, dawn to dusk. Trail is rated 1+ with elevation of 6000 ft. It is suitable for strollers & wheelchairs with some difficulty from curbs. Pets are allowed but must be leashed. Walk is on city streets and paved trails through sculptured garden & around Lake Loveland.

Manitou Springs - 11km Walk (YR353) **Jan 1-Dec 31**
A Award available
Sponsoring Club: AVA-072, Falcon Wanderers
POC: Connie Duffy, 719-475-1671. PO Box 17162, Colorado Springs, CO 80935-7162

Start Point: Loaf 'N Jug, 137 Manitou Ave. Take I-25 north or south to Colorado Springs & exit 141 (US Hwy 24). Turn left on US 24 West & exit at the "Highway 24 Business Route/Manitou Ave" sign & turn left. Start will be on your immediate right.

Event Info: Daily, dawn to dusk. Rated 3+ due to hills and altitude of 6412 ft. No strollers or wheelchairs. Pets must be leashed. Trail is along city streets. Pass artistically unique retail stores, historical homes & many beautiful vantage points.

Monument - 11km Walk (YR466) 25km Bike (YR337) **Jan 2-Dec 31**
A Award available
Sponsoring Club: AVA-841, Black Forest Volkssport Club
POC: Mike Nelson, 719-495-0404. 5085 High Meadows Lane, Black Forest, CO 80908-3811

Start Point: High Country Feed Store, 243 Washington St. From I-25 take exit 161 (Hwy 105). Proceed west on 105 turn west onto 3rd street. Proceed to Washington St & turn left to the Feed Store.

Event Info: Mon-Fri, 8-6; Sat, 8-5; Sun, 9-5 except May to July. Pets must be leashed. Water not available at Start/Finish. Carrying water on trail is recommended. Restrooms available along the trail. **YR466** is rated 1 but is not suitable for strollers or wheelchairs. It is on a multiuse gravel trail on old railway grade & provides nice views of Monument Valley & Rampart Range. **YR 337**, the bike, is rated 2 and is on a multiuse gravel trail on an old railway grade. It provides nice views of the Air Force Academy & Rampart Range. Bikers must sign a waiver and should wear a helmet.

Pueblo - 11km Walk (YR480) **Jan 1-Dec 31**
A Award available
Sponsoring Club: AVA-072, Falcon Wanderers
POC: Bev Percival, 719-948-3156. PO Box 17162, Colorado Springs CO 80935-7162

Start Point: Loaf 'N Jug, 120 South Sante Fe. Take I-25 to exit 98B. Right on 1st St to Santa Fe Ave. Turn left on Santa Fe Ave. Start will be on your left.

Event Info: Daily, dawn to dusk. Trail is rated 2. Suitable for strollers but wheelchairs are not recommended. Pets must be leashed. Trail is along city streets.

Pueblo - 12km Walk (YR842) 26/38km Bike (YR1274) **Jan 1-Dec 31**
YR842 has an A Award available   YR1274 is a Credit Only Event
Sponsoring Club: AVA-072, Falcon Wanderers
POC: Bev Percival, 719-948-3156. PO Box 17162, Colorado Springs, CO 80935

Start Point: Loaf ' n Jug, 3639 Baltimore Ave. From I-25 take exit 101 (US Hwy 50 West) and go west 1.1 miles to the Loaf 'n Jug on the SW corner of Hwy 50 & Baltimore.

Event Info: Daily, dawn to dusk. Walk is rated 1+; suitable for strollers & wheelchairs. Pets must be leashed. This is a paved trail along the Arkansas River. A functionally disadvantaged trail is available that is rated 2+. The bike is rated 1+. It is along a paved trail along the Arkansas River. Bikers must sign a waiver and wear helmets.

CONNECTICUT ━━━━━━━━━━━━━━━━━━━

Cheshire - 10km Walk (YR1336) **Jan 1-Dec 31**
A Award available
Sponsoring Club: AVA-784, Connecticut Valley Volkssport Club
POC: Keith Robertson, 203-272-7368. PO Box 251, Glastonbury, CT 06033-0251 or Andrew Fal, 860-828-5750

Start Point: Richlin Store, 203-272-7642. 943 S Main St. From the west take I-84 to Cheshire exit 26. At the end of the ramp, go straight at light for approx five miles. At the top of the hill, go right onto Main St and proceed 4 blocks to the intersection with Rt 10. Take the right turn south for 1.5

miles to the Cheshire Shopping Center and Richlin Dept Store. From the east take I-84 to exit 27 (I-691). Proceed 0.25 miles to exit 3 Cheshire. Turn right onto Rt 10 south for 6.9 miles to the start point. From north or south take I-91 to exit 18 (I-691) to exit 3 Cheshire. Go left onto Rt 10 south for five miles to the start point.

Event Info: Daily, 8:30-7. Trail is rated 1+; not suitable for strollers or wheelchairs. Pets are allowed. The event follows city streets and sidewalks.

Farmington - 10km Walk (YR923) **Jan 1-Dec 31**
A Award available
Sponsoring Club: AVA-784, Connecticut Valley Volkssport Club
POC: Carol or Lee West, 860-721-1185. PO Box 251, Glastonbury, CT 06033-0251

Start Point: Farmington Inn, 860-677-2821. 827 Farmington Avenue. Follow I-84 exit 39, to Rt 4 West to Farmington Center. Farmington Inn is on the left after junction with Rt 10.

Event Info: Daily, dawn to dusk. Trail is rated 1+ and is suitable for strollers & wheelchairs. Pets must be leashed. Trail winds through this picturesque colonial village along the banks of the Farmington River and by the campus of Miss Porter's School for Girls.

Glastonbury - 10km Walk (YR925) **Jan 1-Dec 31**
B Awards available
Sponsoring Club: AVA-784, Connecticut Valley Volkssport Club
POC: Bob McDougall, 860-342-3062. PO Box 251, Glastonbury, CT 06033-0251

Start Point: Wawa Food Market, 860-659-3902. 103 New London Turnpike. Take I-91 to exit 25. Rt 3 to Glastonbury then take Rt 2 east to Hebron Ave exit. Turn right to light at New London Turnpike, turn right at light, Wawa is 1/2 block down on right.

Event Info: Daily, dawn to dusk. Trail is rated 1+ and is suitable for strollers & wheelchairs. Pets must be leashed. Trail includes many colonial homes and historic buildings.

Hartford - 12km Walk (YR567) **Jan 1-Dec 31**
A Award available
Sponsoring Club: AVA-784, Connecticut Valley Volkssport Club
POC: Bob McDougall, 860-342-3062. PO Box 251, Glastonbury, CT 06033-0251

Start Point: Ramada Inn, 860-246-6591. 440 Asylum Ave. From I-84 West, take the Asylum Ave Exit #48 & turn left at the end of the ramp onto Asylum Ave. From I-84 East, take the Asylum Ave Exit #48 & turn right onto Asylum. The Ramada Inn is one block past railroad overpass on the left.

Event Info: Daily, dawn to dusk. Trail is rated 1+ and is suitable for strollers & wheelchairs. Pets are allowed. Hourly parking is available from several commercial lots. State Capital walk.

Middletown - 10km Walk (YR1144) **Jan 1-Dec 31**
B Awards available
Sponsoring Club: AVA-784, Connecticut Valley Volkssport Club
POC: Bob McDougall, 860-342-3062. PO Box 251, Glastonbury, CT 06033-0251

Start Point: Dunkin Donuts, 860-344-0460. 170 Main St. From I-91 take Rt 9 South to exit 14 (DeKoven Dr), proceed straight at the stop sign and park in Metro Square on your right. Dunkin Donuts is on Main Street next to Burger King.

Event Info: Daily, dawn to dusk. Trail is rated 1 but is not suitable for strollers or wheelchairs. Pets are allowed. Trail features renovated Main Street & Wesleyan University.

CONNECTICUT, cont

Plantsville - 10km Walk (YR924) **Jan 1-Dec 31**
B Awards available
Sponsoring Club: AVA-784, Connecticut Valley Volkssport Club
POC: Carol or Lee West, 860-721-1185. PO Box 251, Glastonbury, CT 06033-0251

Start Point: Taylors Market, 860-628-6418. 44 W Main St. I-84 to exit 30. At end of ramp: from westbound turn left; from eastbound turn right. Taylor's Market will be on the right after the railroad crossing. Park in municipal parking across the street from the Market.

Event Info: Daily, dawn to dusk. Trail is rated 1+ and is suitable for strollers & wheelchairs. Pets are allowed. Trail passes through 19th century mill town and the Barnes Museum.

Portland - 10km Walk (YR254) **Jan 1-Dec 31**
A Award available
Sponsoring Club: AVA-784, Connecticut Valley Volkssport Club
POC: Bob McDougall, 860-342-3062. PO Box 251, Glastonbury, CT 06033-0251

Start Point: Dunkin' Donuts, 860-342-1490. 152 Main St. From I-91 north or south, take Rt 9 South to exit 16, Rt 17 North to Portland, after crossing the bridge.

Event Info: Daily, dawn to dusk. Trail is rated 2 and is suitable for strollers but not wheelchairs. It contains one long hill. Pets are allowed.

Wethersfield - 11km Walk (YR717) **Jan 1-Dec 31**
B Awards available
Sponsoring Club: AVA-784, Connecticut Valley Volkssport Club
POC: Bill Webb, 860-529-5577. PO Box 251, Glastonbury, CT 06033-0251

Start Point: Ramada Inn, 860-563-2311. 1330 Silas Dean Highway. Follow I-91 to exit 24. At end of ramp follow Rt 99 North. Ramada Inn is on the right one block north on Rt 99.

Event Info: Daily, dawn to dusk. Trail is rated 1+ and is suitable for strollers & wheelchairs if they use the alternate route. Pets are allowed. This walk covers a historic area with many museums. Inquire at the Ramada for discounts for volkssporters.

DC

DC - 11km Walk (YR157) **Jan 1-Dec 31**
B Awards available
Sponsoring Club: AVA-246, Walter Reed Wandervogel
POC: Klaus J. Waibel, 301-681-9084. 704 Bromley St, Silver Spring, MD 20902

Start Point: National Museum of Health & Medicine, Bldg 54, Walter Reed Army Medical Ctr. I-495 to Exit 31B (Georgia Ave). South on Georgia Ave 3 miles, right on Elder or Dahlia Sts into installation. Right again to follow road around hospital & up hill to bldg 54 (museum) on right.

Event Info: Daily, 10-2. Finish by 5. Closed Christmas. Trail is rated 3 & is not suitable for strollers or wheelchairs. Pets must be leashed. Weekday parking extremely limited. Recommend you use the Metro Red Line to Takoma Station. Females should consider walking with a partner. Half of event is on woodland trails through scenic Rock Creek Park & the other half is on pavement through affluent Maryland and DC neighborhoods.

Start Point: Morgan Memorial Hospital, 1077 South Main St. From I-20 eastbound from Atlant, take exit 51 (Hwys 129 & 441, Madison/Eatonton) and turn left at end of ramp. Follow signs to Hospital, turning left to South Main. Turn left on S Main, right on Cornwall and left into hospital parking lot. From I-20 Westbound, take exit 51, turn right at end of ramp and continue as above.

Event Info: Daily, 8-dusk. Trail is rated 1+; suitable for strollers but not wheelchairs. Pets must be leashed. Pre-paid envelopes are in the box for return of start card & money. The course is on roads & sidewalks through & around the historic district of Madison. Southern history & hospitality await you as you pass by the City's many antebellum and victorian homes & churches which escaped destruction during Union General William T. Sherman's infamous March to the Sea. Madison is now an internationally renowned destination for history, gardening, architecture and antique buffs.

McDonough - 10/12km Walk (YR1151) **Jan 1-Dec 31**
Credit Only Event
Sponsoring Club: AVA-280, McIntosh Trail Walkers
POC: Charles F. Lear, 770-631-8543. PO Box 2303, Peachtree City, GA 30269

Start Point: Holiday Inn (rear lobby), 930 Hwy 155 South. From Atlanta take I-75 South for 30 miles. Exit 69, State Hwy 155 South. Holiday Inn is on the right.

Event Info: Daily, dawn-dusk. Trail is rated an easy 1. Strollers & wheelchairs on the 10km route only. Pets are allowed. Carry a canteen or bottled drinking water. There is NO water or restroom along the route. This is a country walk and follows gently rolling terrain through isolated countryside. Trees line most of the unpaved road. Over 2/3 of the walk is on very lightly travelled unpaved roads.

Newnan - 10km Walk (YR1150) **Jan 1-Dec 31**
Credit Only Event
Sponsoring Club: AVA-280, McIntosh Trail Walkers
POC: Charles F. Lear, 770-631-8543. PO Box 2303, Peachtree City, GA 30269

Start Point: Holiday Inn Express (Entry Vestibule), 6 Herring Rd. From Atlanta take I-85 South for 40 miles. Exit 9, go west on SH34 (Bullsboro Rd). Turn right on Amlajack Blvd at 2nd traffic light. Follow signs to Holiday Inn Express. Register here and then drive to downtown Newnan to begin the walk. Directions are furnished at registration.

Event Info: Daily, dawn-dusk. Trail is rated 1, suitable for strollers & wheelchairs. Pets must be leashed. This is an Antebellum Walk. It follows tree-lined streets through historic neighborhoods past architectural masterpieces from the earliest settlement days through the twentieth century. Outstanding examples of period & contemporary arhitecture are found in this "City of Homes."

Peachtree City - Two 10km Walks (YR508 & YR1101) **Jan 1-Dec 31**
A Award available
Sponsoring Club: AVA-178, Georgia Walkers
POC: Duncan Brantley, 770-961-0109. 6524 Revena Dr, Morrow GA 30260

Start Point: Kroger Grocery Store (Pharmacy Dept), Braelinn Shopping Ctr, 564 Crosstown Dr. **From I-85** take exit 12 (Fairburn/Peachtree City) & follow GA74 south for 11 miles. Go straight and turn left at 2nd traffic light on Crosstown Dr. Go 0.3 miles to Kroger on left. **From I-75** take exit 80 (GA85) south for 13 miles. Turn right on GA54 for 10 miles & turn left on GA74. At 1st traffic light turn left on Crosstown Dr. Go 0.3 miles to Kroger on left. **From I-75 North,** take exit 76 (GA-54) and go west following GA-54 for about 25 miles to Peachtree City. Turn left onto GA-74. Go to traffic light & turn left on Crosstown Dr. Go 0.3 miles to Kroger on left in Braelinn Village Shopping Center.

Event Info: Daily, dawn to 3 hours before dusk. Both walks are rated 1, suitable for strollers & wheelchairs. They go through partial wetlands, residential, school & recreation areas. Most of the walks are on golf cart paths. Littering is strictly prohibited. All rules of Peachtree City must be strictly adhered to. Pets must be leashed.

Roswell - 10km Walk (YR096) **Jan 1-Dec 31**
A Award available
Sponsoring Club: AVA-178, Georgia Walkers
POC: Duncan Brantley, 770-961-0109. 6524 Revena Dr, Morrow GA 30260

Start Point: Courtyard by Marriott, 500 Market Blvd. From I-285 take Hwy 400 N to exit 7A, Holcomb Bridge Road. Bear right and take first right on Market Way to Courtyard by Marriott. Registration is handled at the registration desk of the hotel. You will be given a map & directions to the actual start point. You will need to drive to tha tpoint & return after you finish this event.

Event Info: Daily, dawn to 3 hours before dusk. Trail is rated 1 and is suitable for strollers but not wheelchairs. Pets are allowed. This trail will follow sidewalks & roads in Roswell's Historic District.

Roswell - 10km Walk (YR307) **Jan 2-Dec 30**   Four 10km Walks: (YR715) **Jan 2-Mar 31**; (YR837) **Apr 1-Jun 30**; (YR716) **Jul 1-Sep 30**; (YR1000) **Oct1-Dec 30**
B Awards available
Sponsoring Club: AVA-684, Roswell Striders
POC: Linda Nickles, 770-641-3760. 38 Hill St, Suite 100, Roswell GA 30075

Start Point: Roswell Area Park, Bldg A, 10495 Woodstock Rd. From I-285 go north on GA400. Take exit 7B. Go west on Holcomb Bridge Rd. At the 6th light turn left on "Pug" W L Marbry Hwy (Rt 9-Alpharetta Hwy). Turn right at next light (Woodstock Rd). Park is approximately 1 mile on the right.

Event Info: Daily 9-6. Closed Sundays & holidays. Pets must be leashed. All routes are rated 2+; suitable for strollers but not wheelchairs. All events are on walking trails in Roswell Area Park & on sidewalks through the historic district of Roswell.

Savannah - 10km Walk (YR051) 25km Bike (YR1257) **Jan 1-Dec 31**
B Awards are available
Sponsoring Club: AVA-717, The Happy Wanderers
POC: Richard Armitage, 912-877-5256. 727 S Main St Ap 8, Hinesville, GA 31313 or Alan & Elaine Brayton, 904-760-1410. 1212 Ryan St, Port Orange, FL 32119

Start Point: Wormsloe Historic Site, 912-353-3023. 7601 Skidaway Road. I-95 exit 16. Turn right -- 10.4 miles to Montgomery Crossroads. Right 3 miles to Skidaway Rd. It is less than one mile to Wormsloe Historic Site Gate. After entering park, go right approx 1 1/2 miles to parking lot. Volkssport Box is at the Gift Shop Desk. After registering for Bike Event, take map/directions and leave Wormsloe Gate.

Alternate Start Point: For Bike event. Skidaway Island State Park. From Wormsloe Gate, go left for 1/2 mile to Ferguson Rd. Travel along for 2.3 miles & you will arrive at Diamond Causeway. Left 2.8 miles to turn sign for Skidaway Island State Park. Register at Park Gate.

Event Info: Tues-Sat 9-5; Sun 2-5:30. Closed Mondays, Thanksgiving, Christmas & New Years Day. You must pay a fee to enter. Walk is rated 1. Strollers & wheelchairs may have difficulty. Pets are not allowed. It follows a wooded trail which features a beautiful Live Oak Ave and well-maintained dirt trails. It is a beautiful historic walk.   The bike event is rated 1. No pets are allowed. Bike helmets are strongly recommended. You must sign a waiver.

Stone Mountain Park - 10km Walk (YR387) **Jan 1-Dec 31**
A Award available
Sponsoring Club: AVA-178, Georgia Walkers
POC: Duncan Brantley, 770-961-0109. 6524 Revena Dr, Morrow GA 30260

Start Point: Stone Mountain Police Department, 922 Main Street. From Atlanta take I-285 to exit 30B (Stone Mountain Freeway, Hwy 78 East). Proceed on Hwy 78 to Hwy 10/Stone Mountain Village/Memorial Drive exit. From Hwy 10, take first right (East Ponce DeLeon/Stone Montain/Clarkson). At top of ramp, turn left and go over Hwy 78. Go straight through light on Main St to first parking lot on right by train station & gazebo. Police Department is at far end of train station.

Event Info: Daily, dawn to three hours before dusk. Trail is rated 2. Suitable for strollers & wheelchairs. Pets are allowed. You may walk into the park for free but if you drive there is a vehicle charge of $6.00. The trail will follow downtown Stone Mountain Village & into Stone Mountain Park for a walk around the mountain.

HAWAII ━━━━━━━━━━━━━━━━━━━━━━━

Honolulu - Two 10km Walks (YR988 & YR166) **Jan 1-Dec 31**
B Awards available
Sponsoring Club: AVA-456, Menehune Marchers
POC: John LeGoullon, 808-942-3748. PO Box 31102, Honolulu HI 96820

Start Point: New Otani Kaimana Beach Hotel, 2863 Kalakaua Ave. On the right side of Kalakaua Ave as you head towards Diamond Head between San Souci State Recreation Area & the Colony Surf Hotel. The bus (#2 Waikiki/Kapiolani Park) stops just before the hotel.

Event Info: Daily, 8-3:30. Both trails are rated 1+. Suitable for strollers. Wheelchairs with difficulty due to grade of hill. Pets are not allowed. **YR988** goes partly around Waikiki, along Diamond Head & thru the Kahala residential area. **YR166** wanders through Waikiki, around Diamond Head & returns along the Ala Wai Canal & back to hotel.

Honolulu - 10km Walk (YR097) **Jan 1-Dec 31**
B Awards available
Sponsoring Club: AVA-456, Menehune Marchers
POC: John LeGoullon, 808-942-3748. PO Box 31102, Honolulu, HI 96820

Start Point: McDonald's of Manoa Market Place, 2915 East Manoa Rd. H-1 Freeway, get off University Ave exit #24B. Proceed on to University Ave toward the mountain. At the complex intersection of University Ave/Oahu Ave/East Manoa Rd, turn right onto East Manoa Road to Manoa Market Place Shopping Center. OR: take Bus #6 (University-Woodlawn) from Ala Moana Center to Manoa Market Place McDonald's.

Event Info: Daily, dawn to dusk subject to operating hours of McDonald's. Closed Christmas & New Years. Rated 2. Strollers may encounter difficulty due to grassy shoulders and grades of three hills. No wheelchairs or pets. The walk wanders through the University of Hawaii, thru the residential areas of Manoa & past a chinese cemetery.

Honolulu - 10km Walk (YR1312) **Jan 1-Dec 31**
Credit Only Event
Sponsoring Club: AVA-456, Menehune Marchers
POC: Barbara L. Mateo, 808-247-5059. PO Box 31102, Honolulu, HI 96820

Start Point: Zippy's Restaurant, 59 N Vineyard Blvd. If coming from Ewa, take H1 (east) to exit 20B (Vineyard Blvd). Stay on (98) Vineyard Blvd until you get to Zippy's which will be on the right. From Waikiki, take (92) Ala Moana Blvd. You will be passing Ala Moana Center, Ward Warehouse and Restaurant Row. At Restaurant Row, Ala Moana Blvd becomes (92) Nimitz. Stay on Nimitz till you get to Smith St. Go right on Smith, left on Beretania then right on Maunakea St to Vineyard Blvd. Zippy's is on your right.

Event Info: Daily, 8-noon. Finish by 3. Closed New Year's & Christmas. Trail is rated 1; suitable for strollers but wheelchairs may encounter difficulty due to numerous curbs. Pets are not allowed. Route is on paved sidewalks. You will be passing many historical points including the State Capitol, Aloha Tower, Kawaiahao Church, Chinatown and the Chinese Cultural Center.

Kailua - 10km Walk (YR1149) **Jan 1-Dec 31**
B Awards available
Sponsoring Club: AVA-456, Menehune Marchers
POC: Maria Brasher, 808-261-3583. PO Box 31102, Honolulu, HI 96820

Start Point: Castle Medical Center, 640 Ulukahiki. From Like Like, Kamehameha Hwy (83) to Pali turn left to Kailua. Turn left at intersection where Castle Medical Ctr is on left & Kalanianaole Hwy (72) goes to Waimanalo. Enter CMC parking lot & proceed to main lobby. OR: The bus #56 & #57 from Ala Moana Center or downtown.

Event Info: Daily, dawn to dusk. Trail is rated 1+ and will be difficult for strollers. It is not suitable for wheelchairs. Pets are not allowed. Trail starts in a residential area passing Kawainui Swamp Regional Park, Ulu Po Heiau, Kailua Beach Park Scenic Lookout.

Kailua-Kona - 10km Walk (YR1181) **Jan 1-Dec 31**
Credit Only Event
Sponsoring Club: AVA-456, Menehune Marchers
POC: (In Honolulu, Oahu) Calei Ewing, 808-955-7185. PO Box 31102, Honolulu, HI 96820
(In Kona) Glenna Ewing 808-322-9145

Start Point: Kona Seaside Hotel, 76-5646 Palani Rd. If coming from the Keahole Airport, turn right onto Queen Kaahumanu Hwy (19). At intersection of Palani Rd (190) & Queen Kaahumanu Hwy (19), turn right. Hotel entrance will be on your left. Free parking lot located one block from hotel.

Event Info: Daily, dawn to dusk. Trail is rated 1 and is suitable for strollers but caution should be exercised on highway shoulders. Pets are not allowed. This walk goes through a quaint seaside village with unique character and stops at many historical sights along the route.

IDAHO ━━━━━━━━━━━━━━━━━━━━━━━━━━

American Falls - 11km Walk (YR118) **May 30-Sept 1**
B Awards available
Sponsoring Club: AVA-650, American Falls Volkssport Club
POC: Max Newlin, 208-548-2672. 3592 Park Lane, American Falls, ID 83211

Start Point: Massacre Rock State Park Visitor Center. 3592 Park Lane. Exit 28 on I-86 between American Falls & Burley at Visitor Center follow signs after getting off freeway.

IDAHO, cont. ━━━━━━━━━━━━━━━━━━━━━━━━━━━━━

Event Info: Daily, 9-5. Trail is rated 3 and is not suitable for strollers or wheelchairs. Pets must be on a short leash. Start early to avoid the heat. Route follows a native soil trail which is sandy and rocky. See the Oregon Trail ruts. Watch for deer and other wildlife. There are many views of the Snake River and the Visitor's Center has a permanent display.

Athol - 10km Walk (YR1205) **Apr 1-Sept 30**
B Awards available
Sponsoring Club: AVA-729, Selkirk Striders
POC: Lane & Ruby Lowe, 208-263-9639. 1812 Hickory St, Sandpoint, ID 83864

Start Point: Farragut State Park Hqs, 208-683-2425. E 13400 Ranger Rd.
Midway between Coeur 'd Alene and Sandpoint. From I90 take Hwy 95 exit at Coeur 'd Alene towards Sandpoint. North for 20 miles to Athol and turn right on Hwy 54 and travel 4 miles east to park headquarters.

Event Info: Daily 8-6 to Sept 14. Weekdays only from Sept 15-30. Trail is rated 3; not suitable for strollers or wheelchairs. Pets are allowed. A State Park Entrance Fee of $2.00 will be charged. Most of route follows foot trails and cross country ski trails. It has several short uphill and downhill sections.

Boise - Two 11km Walks (YR089 & YR1006) 12km Walk (YR613) **Jan 1-Dec 31**
A Award available
Sponsoring Club: AVA-766, Treasure Valley Volkssports
POC: George Wendt, 208-345-0668. 4818 Collister Dr, Boise, ID 83703 or Barbara Silverstein 208-939-7292. 3096 Holl Dr, Eagle, ID 83616

Start Point: Boise Family YMCA, 208-344-5501. N 11th St & W State St. Take I-84, City Center exit. Stay on left side of hwy. Turn left on 11th St. Proceed straight on 11th to State St & the YMCA will be on the right. YR089 and YR613 start at the YMCA. YR1006 registers at the YMCA. You will then go west (right) on State St to Veterans Pkwy (2 miles). Turn left & left again into Veterans Park.

Event Info: Mon-Fri 6am-9:30pm; Sat 7-5:30; Sun noon-4:30. Closed New Years, Easter, Memorial Day, 4th of July, Labor Day, Thanksgiving & Christmas. **YR089** is rated 1+, suitable for strollers & wheelchairs. Pets must be leashed. The walk goes along attractive residential streets & paved trails along the Boise River highlighting the Oregon Trail & historic Boise. **YR613** is rated 1+, suitable for strollers & wheelchairs. The trail goes through parks, along the Boise Greenbelt and attractive residential streets & the Old Idaho Penitentiary. Pets must be leashed. **YR1006** is rated 2 and is suitable for strollers & wheelchairs but use caution on hills. Pets may be prohibited in one of the parks due to spring nesting season--the distance involved is nominal. This trail goes through two of Boise's Greenbelt parks & up to a residential area overlooking the city. It is on paved trails & streets.

Coeur d'Alene - 10km Walk (YR780) **Apr 1-Oct 31**
A Award available
Sponsoring Club: AVA-475, Coeur d' Alene Volkssport Club
POC: Larry Strobel, 208-664-4904. PO Box 535, Coeur d'Alene, ID 83814

Start Point: The Coeur d'Alene Resort, 115 S 2nd St. Westbound on I-90 take exit 15 and turn left. Proceed to downtown area. Turn left on 2nd St and proceed to city parking area, Eastbound on I-90 take exit 11 and continue to Sherman Ave. Then turn right on 2nd St to city parking area.

Event Info: Daily, dawn-dusk. Rated 3 if doing Tubbs Hill around Lake Coeur d'Alene shoreline. This route is not suitable for strollers or wheelchairs. An alternate route which eliminates Tubb Hill is rated 1 and is suitable for strollers and wheelchairs. Pets must be leashed. Walk on paved streets through old residential areas, the City Park, Fort Sherman area and through the North Idaho College Campus. The Tubbs Hill portion is a 1.2 mile trail along a rustic shoreline.

Glenns Ferry - 10km Walk (YR1007) **Jan 1-Dec 31**
A Award available
Sponsoring Club: AVA-766, Treasure Valley Volkssports
POC: George Wendt, 208-345-0668. 4818 Collister Dr, Boise, ID 83703 or Barbara Silverstein, 208-939-7292. 3096 Holl Dr, Eagle, ID 83616

Start Point: Carmela Winery. From I-84 take either Glenns Ferry exit & follow the signs to Three Island Crossing State Park. Carmela Winery is just east of the park entrance.

Event Info: Daily, 9-5. Closed New Years Day, Easter, Thanksgiving and Christmas. Trail is rated 1+, suitable for strollers but not wheelchairs. Pets are allowed. The trail is through parts of Glenns Ferry, along the Snake River & through Three Island Crossing State Park.

Sandpoint - Two 10km Walks (YR732 & YR1067) **Apr 1-Nov 30**
B Awards available
Sponsoring Club: AVA-729, Selkirk Striders Volkssport Club
POC: Lane/Ruby Lowe, 208-263-9639. 1812 Hickory St, Sandpoint, ID 83864

Start Point: Edgewater Resort Motor Inn, 208-263-3194. 56 Bridge St. Exit Hwys 95 & 2 at Bridge St (downtown Sandpoint), to Edgewater Resort, adjacent to city beach. Self start registration cabinet is in the lobby.

Event Info: Daily, dawn to dusk. Trails are rated 1. **YR732** is the City Walk. This trail is suitable for strollers & wheelchairs. It is along paved city streets and walking paths traversing two city parks & our beautiful beach. **YR1067** is the Long Bridge walk. It is suitable for strollers & wheelchairs. It is on a bike path crossing a bridge over Lake Pend Oreille and back. Pets are not allowed in city parks or on the beach. Alternate routes available for pet owners. Call POC for information.

Sun Valley/Ketchum - 11km Walk (YR1008) **May 1-Sep 30**
A Award available
Sponsoring Club: AVA-766, Treasure Valley Volkssports
POC: George Wendt, 208-345-0668. 4818 Collister Dr, Boise, ID 83703 or Barbara Silverstein, 208-939-7292. 3096 Holl Dr, Eagle, ID 83616

Start Point: Ketchum Chamber of Commerce-Tourist Info Bldg, 800-634-3347. 4th St & Main St. From I-84 take Hwy 20 from Mountain Home to Hwy 75 (past Fairfield) or Hwy 75 from Twin Falls to Ketchum. The Visitors Information Bldg will be on the left side of main St (4th & Main).

Event Info: Mon-Sat 9-5. Closed Sundays until Memorial Day. Trail is rated 2, suitable for strollers & wheelchairs. Pets are allowed. Most of the route is on paved bike trails & city sidewalks. A few areas will require walking on dirt shoulders along roads.

ILLINOIS

Belleville - Four 10km Walks: (YR226) **Jan 1-Mar 31** (YR1011) **Apr1-Jun 30** (YR1012) **Jul 1-Sep 30** (YR1013) **Oct 1-Dec 31**
A Awards available
Sponsoring Club: AVA-047, Illinois Trekkers Volkssport Club
POC: Dick Parle, 618-632-8390. 111 Stacy Dr, Fairview Heights, IL 62208

Start Point: Shrine Motel of our Lady of the Snows, 618-397-6700. 9500 West Hwy 15. From I-64, I-55 or I-70, take I-255 South to exit 17 onto Illinois Hwy 15. Follow Hwy 15 to the entrance of the Shrine on your right. Once on the grounds, follow signs to Motel. From Belleville, taKe Rt 15 West to entrance.

Event Info: Daily, dawn to dusk. Trails are rated 1+, suitable for strollers & wheelchairs with some difficulty. Pets must be leashed. Walks are on paved streets with some gradual hills. They are tree lined with beautiful landscaping, etc.

Belleville - 10km Walk (YR904) **Jan 1-Dec 31**
A Award available
Sponsoring Club: AVA-047, Illinois Trekkers Volkssport Club
POC: Doug Leith, 618-451-2980, 2216 Terminal Ave, Granite City, IL 62040

Start Point: St. Elizabeth Hospital Main Lobby Visitors Desk. 211 S 3rd St. From I-64 take exit 12. Turn right (south) on IL 159. Continue through Swansea into Belleville. After crossing RR tracks continue to Fountain (Main St). Turn right and go three blocks to 3rd St; then left one block to Hospital.

Event Into: Daily, dawn to dusk. Trail is rated 1+; suitable for strollers & wheelchairs. Pets must be leashed. Walk is on paved streets through historic Belleville.

Champaign - 10km Walk (YR1195) **Jan 2-Dec 31**
B Awards available
Sponsoring Club: AVA-609, Ridgewalkers Walking Club
POC: Mike Balogh, 217-355-1704 or David Bradley, 217-355-6811. 1911 North Duncan Rd, Champaign, IL 61821

Start Point: Hometown Pantry, 217-359-5156. 2402 West Springfield Ave. At the junction of I-57 and I-72, go east on Univeristy Ave. At the first traffic light, turn right on Country Fair Dr. Turn right on Springfield Ave and the start is a short distance down on the right.

Event Info: Daily dawn-dusk. Closed New Years, July 4th, Thanksgiving, & Xmas Day. Trail is rated 1, suitable for strollers but not wheelchairs. Route includes four parks and two small lakes.

Chicago (Frankfort) - 10km Walk (YR831) **Jan 1-Dec 31**
A Award available
Sponsoring Club: AVA-722, Wewalkits Volksmarching Club
POC: Tom O'Donnell, 708-339-8909. 3901 West 155th St, Markham, IL 60426

Start Point: Always Open Convenience Store, 6 West Elwood. From I-80 take exit 145A (Rt 45 LaGrange Rd/96th Ave). Go south to Frankfort. Just past stoplight at Rt 30, turn left onto White St (Historic Area). Start is on corner of White & Elwood.

Event Info: Daily, 8am-6pm. Trail is rated 1+, suitable for strollers, no wheelchairs. May be slippery or icy during winter months if snow hasn't been cleared away. Pets must be leashed. Trail wanders through historic Frankfort, rich in German heritage as well as new areas of a growing community.

Collinsville - 10km Walk (YR249) **Jan 2-Dec 31**
A Award available
Sponsoring Club: AVA-047, Illinois Trekkers Volkssport Club
POC: Andrew/Helen Knopik, 618-482-5225. 3012 N 60th St, Fairmont City, IL 62201

Start Point: Cahokia Mounds Historical Site, Interpretive Center. From I-55/70 take exit 6. Proceed south & follow signs to Cahokia Mounds. From I-255, take exit 24 & proceed west on Collinsville Rd approximately 1 mile to the Cahokia entrance which will be located on your left.

Event Info: Daily, 9-4:30. Closed New Years, ML King Day, President's Day, Veteran's Day, Thanksgiving & Christmas. Trail is rated 1. It is accessible to strollers & wagons but you may experience some difficulty. Pets must be leashed. Trail is on dirt paths which may become muddy during rainy weather. The trail is flat but provides an option of climbing Monk's Mound.

Glen Carbon - 11km Walk (YR903) **Jan 1-Dec 31**
Credit Only event
Sponsoring Club: AVA-682, S.M.T.M. Volkssport Society
POC: Gary Staley, 618-288-2804. 1300 New Florissant Rd, Florissant, MO 63033-2122

Start Point: Hardee's, 4207 S SR 159. Glen Carbon is located just south of I-270 between IL Hwy 157 & 159. From I-270, exit IL Hwy 159 (exit 12) and go north about one mile. Hardee's is on your left.

Event Info: Daily, dawn to dusk. Closed Thanksgiving & Christmas. Trail is rated 1. Suitable for strollers & wheelchairs. Pets must be leashed and cleanup must be provided. Flat, paved rails-to-trails route.

Hillsboro - 10km Walk (YR232) **Jan 2-Dec 31**
B Awards available
Sponsoring Club: AVA-146, Railsplitter Wanderers
POC: Roger Mollett/Randy Mollett, 217-546-8137/532-5455. 837 S. Columbia Ave, Springfield IL 62704

Start Point: Red Rooster Inn, 217-532-6332. 123 East Seward St. From Rt 127 turn east on Seward St. Go around the Courthouse. Inn is just east of courthouse.

Event Info: Mon-Sat, 8-5; Sun, 8-1:30. Closed New Years & Christmas. Pets must be leashed. Trail is rated 1.5. Difficult for strollers or wheelchairs. The trail follows city sidewalks, paved roads & the shoulders of asphalt roads.

Lockport - 10km Walk (YR625) **Jan 1-Dec 31**
A Award available
Sponsoring Club: AVA-722, Wewalkits Volksmarching Club
POC: Tom O'Donnell, 708-339-8909. 3901 W 155th St, Markham, IL 60426

Start Point: White Hen Pantry, 1134 State St. Exit I-80 at Briggs St North to Division St. Left (west to State St, then right to the White Hen or exit I-55 at Joliet Rd South to Rt 53 to Rt 7 Lockport, then (after railroad tracks) turn right on State St to White Hen.

Event Info: Daily, 8-5. Trail is rated 2. Not recommended for strollers or wheelchairs. Pets are allowed but must be leashed. Winter storms can bring ice & snow which can make the trail slippery. Part of the trail is along the historic Illinois & Michigan Canal, generally flat & shaded. Remainder of the trail is through parks & along streets through historic areas & beautiful architecture from times past.

Oak Lawn - 10km Walk (YR593) **Jan 1-Dec 31**
A Award available
Sponsoring Club: AVA-722, Wewalkits Volksmarching Club
POC: Ken Stoffregen, 708-422-3034. c/o Color Key Printing, 9517 S Cook Ave, Oak Lawn, IL 60453

Start Point: Oak Lawn Community Pavillion, 94th & Oak Park Ave. Exit I-294 at 95th St East. Turn left (north) at stop light on Oak Park Ave (approximately 1/2 mile). Pavillion is one block on right.

Event Info: Daily, 8-5. Trail is rated 1+. It is suitable for strollers but not wheelchairs. Pets must be leashed. Trail is on city streets passed historic sites, beautiful parks, shops, restaurants & more. Only 35 minutes from downtown Chicago. For public transportation from downtown Chicago, please call.

Oak Park - 10km Walk (YR1194) **Jan 2-Dec 31**
Sponsoring Club: AVA-722, Wewalkits
POC: Ken Stoffregen, 708-422-3034. 9517 S Cook Ave, Oak Lawn, IL 60453

ILLINOIS, cont. ━━━━━━━━━━━━━━━━━━━━━━━━━━━━━━━━━━

Start Point: Oak Park Visitors Center, 708-848-1500. 158 Forest Avenue. Located 10 miles due west of Chicago's Loop. Take I-290 west to Harlem Ave (Ill 43) and exit north. Continue on Harlem to Lake St and turn right. Proceed to the northeast corner of Lake St and Forest Ave where you will find the Visitors Center. Parking is available adjacent to the Center. By Public Transportation from Chicago, call RTA/Metro at 312-836-7000 for schedule info.

Event Info: Daily 10-1. Must be off the trail by 4pm. Closed Thanksgiving, Christmas and New Years. Trail is rated 1 and is suitable for strollers and wheelchairs. Pets must be leashed. This route goes through Oak Park and River Forest. These two communities boast one of the finest collections of late 19th and early 20th century American architecture in the US. Oak Park contains the largest collection of Frank Lloyd Wright-designed buildings in the world--30 in all--including Wright's own home and studio and his first public building, Unity Temple. Visit the Hemingway museum and birthplace, Pleasant Home Mansion and Cheney Mansion.

Oregon - 10km Walk (YR1347) **Apr 5-Dec 31**
B Awards available
Sponsoring Club: AVA-802, Rock River Valley Volkssporters
POC: Debbie Leffelman, 815-732-3101. 304 S 5th St, PO Box 237, Oregon, IL 61061

Start Point: Nash Recreation Center; 815-732-3101. 304 S 5th St. At intersection of Rts 2 & 64 go south 2 blocks. Turn right on Madison and go 1 block to start point on the left at the corner of 5th & Madison. Start box is located at the reception desk. Plenty of parking available.

Event Info: Mon-Fri, 6:30 to dusk; Sat 7:30-3:30; Sun 1-5. Closed May 26, July 4, Sept 1, Oct 4 & 5, Nov 27, Dec 24, 25 & 31. Walk is rated 2, suitable for strollers but not recommended for wheelchairs due to curbs and some streets with no sidewalks. Pets must be leashed and are not permitted in buildings. The route includes historical points of interest, quaint shops, parks & residential areas. Terrain consists of sidewalks, residential streets and paved park trails on fairly flat ground plus one hill.

Rock Island - 10km Walk (YR731) **Jan 1-Dec 31**
A Award available
Sponsoring Club: AVA-407, Mississippi River Ramblers
POC: Ralph Krippner, 309-797-8157. 1109 3rd St, Moline, IL 61265

Start Point: US Army Corps of Engineers, Mississippi River Visitor's Center, 309-794-5338. Lock & Dam 15, Arsenal Island. Take exit 11B on I-280 to downtown Rock Island (approximately 3 miles). Turn left at sign onto Arsenal Island. Turn right at second entrance to the Aresenal. Visitors Center is the first left past the guard shack.

Event Info: Mid May-mid Sep, 9-9. Rest of year, 9-5. Closed Christmas & New Year's. Trail is rated 1. Suitable for strollers & wheelchairs. Pets must be leashed. Headphones may not be worn on the Island. Highlights of the trail include beautiful views of the Mississippi River, the Corps of Engineers Visitor Center at Lock & Dam 15, and the Rock Island Arsenal Museum which displays the history of Rock Island Arsenal, from Indian times to the present. Other highlights include the Confederate Cemetery, the National Cemetery & the oldest house in the Quad Cities.

Springfield - 10km Walk (YR058) **Jan 1-Dec 31**
B Awards available
Sponsoring Club: AVA-IL, Illinois Volkssport Assn.
POC: Ken Stoffregen, 708-422-3034(w) 708-422-2985(h) 708-422-3038(fax). 9517 S Cook Ave, Oak Lawn, IL 60453

Start Point: Best Inns of America Motel, 500 North First St. Take I-55 to Springfield. Exit on SR125 west (Clearlake Ave). Follow thru to 1st St. Turn right on 1st and start point is between 1st and 2nd streets on Carpenter. For reservations call 217-522-1100 and ask for room discount for volksmarchers.

Event Info: Daily dawn to dusk. Closed Christmas. Trail is rated 1, suitable for strollers and wheelchairs with bypass options. Snow and/or ice may not be removed from the trail which could make the trail less suitable for wheeled participants. This route passes many historical sites: Lincoln's Tomb, Illinois Vietnam Veterans Memorial, State Capital, Dana Thomas House and Lincoln's Home.

INDIANA ━━━━━━━━━━━━━━━━━━━━━━━━━━━━━━━

Anderson - 10km Walk (YR149) 11km Walk (YR453) **Jan 1-Dec 31**
B Awards available
Sponsoring Club: AVA-045, White River Ramblers
POC: James R. Bratton; 317-789-6683(new area code 2/1/97, 765) 840 N Main St, Albany, IN 47320

Start Point: Shadyside Marina, 317-649-9025(new area code 2/1/97, 765). 1117 Alexandria Pike. From Indy, take I-69 to SR 9N (Exit 26). Take SR9 thru Anderson (4.8 miles) to Lindberg Rd. Left on Lindbert to Alex Pike. Right on Alex Pike (.4 miles) to Marina. From Ft Wayne take I-69S to SR 32W (Exit 34). SR 32W to Anderson. At SR32/9 intersection, turn right onto SR 9N and go to Lindberg Rd (.5 miles). Left onto Lindberg Rd to Alex Pike. Right on Alex Pike (.4 miles) to Marina.

Event Info: Daily, 8-6. Closed major holidays. Trails are rated 1+. Suitable for strollers and wheelchairs. Pets must be leashed & are not allowed in buildings. Free parking available. Restaurant in the Marina. **YR149** winds around Shadyside Lakes, Killbuck Wetlands, and includes the boardwalks of the White River & Indian Trail Riverwalk. Also includes part of downtown Anderson. Wildlife abounds along this trail. **YR453** introduces the walker to Anderson University with its tree-lined campus & red brick buildings. Part of the river walk & Shadyside lakes are included on this trail.

Auburn - 10km Walk (YR374) **Jan 1-Dec 31**
B Awards available
Sponsoring Club: AVA-750, Auburn Duesey Walkers
POC: Edna Scott, 219-925-4272. 312 N McClellan St, Auburn, IN 46706

Start Point: Auburn-Cord-Duesenberg Museum, 1600 S Wayne St. Take I-69 to exit 129 (also SR 8). Go eat on SR 8 to VanBuren St. Go south on Van Buren to Museum. (Follow ACD Museum signs.)

Event Info: Daily 9-5. Closed Thanksgiving, Christmas and New Years. Trail is rated 1+ and is suitable for strollers and wheelchairs. Pets are allowed. Trail will take you past homes that were owned by the innovators, engineers & craftsmen of the automobile industry.

Columbus - 10km Walk (YR266) **Jan 1-Dec 31**
A Award available
Sponsoring Club: AVA-357, Columbus Wellness Walkers
POC: Charles Chinn, 812-376-3828. 3121 13th Street, Columbus, IN 47201

Start Point: Tipton Lakes Athletic Club, 812-342-4495. 4000 W. Goeller Blvd. From I-65 exit #68 (SR46) go west one mile to first traffic light (Goeller Blvd) turn left then right at first corner (Mimosa). Start is on your right.

Event Info: Daily, 6am-9pm. Closed all national holidays. Call to check if in doubt. Pets must be leashed. Trail is rated 1+ & portions of trail are not suitable for wheelchairs or strollers; however, a bypass option is available. This walk is routed through the Tipton Lakes community with views of serene lakes, thick woods & beautiful homes. The route consists of sidewalks, paved walkways & nature trails.

Ft Wayne - 10km Walk (YR907) **Jan 1-Dec 31**
A Award available
Sponsoring Club: AVA-062, Three Rivers Strollers
POC: Bob Geldien, 219-493-2473. 3914 Scarborough Dr, New Haven, IN 46774

Start Point: Veteran's Hospital, 2121 Lake Avenue. Take I-69 to Hwy 30. Go east on Colisum Blvd (US30) to Lake Ave. Turn right and go several blocks. The hospital is on the right. The parking lot and entrance is off Randallia Drive. Go into the mainlobby, turn right & go to the information desk. Ask the information person for the "walk" box.

Event Info: Daily, 8-dusk. Rated 1+, not suitable for strollers or wheelchairs. Pets must be leashed. Trail is mostly on sidewalks with some grassy areas, going through residential areas, parks & downtown.

Indianapolis - 10km Walk (YR091)   25km Bike (YR1110) **Jan 1-Dec 31**
A Awards available
Sponsoring Club: AVA-089, Indy "G" Walkers
POC: Clarence Wright, 317-357-8464. PO Box 16001, Ft Harrison IN 46216 or Paul Mullen, 317-545-9061. 7919 White Lane, Indianapolis, IN 46226

Start Point: Eagle Creek Park, 71st Street Gatehouse. From I-65 exit at 71st St & turn west to the gate house approximately .25 miles. From I-465 exit onto 71st St & turn west for approximately 1.5 miles. 71st St runs right to the parks gate house which is the start point.

Event Info: A Park entrance fee is required to do these events. Daily, 9-dusk. Closed Thanksgiving & Christmas. Trails are rated 3. No strollers or wheelchairs. Pets must be leashed. No water available November through April. A Concession stand is open at the Marina during the summer months. Numerous picnic tables are also available. **YR091** (walk) winds through a scenic forest setting with wild flowers. Eagle Creek Park is the nations largest city park. **YR1110** (bike) is on a road which makes two loops through a scenic forest setting. There are some hills. Bikers must sign waiver & wear a helmet.

Indianapolis - 11km Walk (YR259) **Jan 1-Dec 31**
A Award available
Sponsoring Club: AVA-089, Indy "G" Walkers
POC: Clarence Wright, 317-357-8464. PO Box 16001, Indianapolis, IN 46216 or Paul Mullen, 317-545-9061. 7919 White Lane, Indianapolis, IN 46226

Start Point: White River State Park Visitors Center, the "Pumphouse", 801 W Washington St. From the north on I-65 S to exit 114. South on Dr M.L. King/West St to Washington St. Turn right on Washington St. From the east on I-70 West to I-65 N to exit 114 & follow directions above. From the west on I-70 E use exit 79A. North on Missouri/West St to Washington St. Turn left on Washington. From the south on I-65 N to I-70 W to exit 79A. Then follow the West directions above. Once on Washington St, the entrance is the second driveway/street on the right. The road is a dead end. The start point is 200 meters up and on the left.

Event Info: Mon-Fri, 8-5; WEEKENDS: Apr-Oct, 12-5; Nov-Mar, Closed on weekends. Also closed 1/1, 1/20, 3/31, 5/26, 7/4, 9/1, 10/13, 11/10, 11/27, 11/28, 12/24, 12/25 & 12/26. Rated 1, suitable for strollers and wheelchairs with some difficulty with curbs. Pets must be leashed and are not allowed in bldgs. You must clean up after your pet. Be flexible at all times because of construction. This walk wanders throughout the scenic downtown area of Indianapolis.

Marion - 11km Walk (YR373) **Jan 1-Dec 31**
B Awards available
Sponsoring Club: AVA-487, Marion Fussganger
POC: Bob Marrs, 317-662-7798. 1124 West 3rd St, Marion, IN 46952

Start Point: Holiday Inn, 501 East 4th St. From I-69 go east on SR18 to Holiday Inn. From SR9, 37 or 15, go west on 4th to the Holiday Inn.

Event Info: Daily, dawn to dusk. Trail is rated 1+ and is suitable for strollers, wagons & wheelchairs. Pets must be leashed. Walk through downtown Marion & along the beautiful, scenic river walk along the Mississinewa River, winding through the newly renovated Matter Park, make a loop & come back along the river walk to downtown area.

Marshall - 10km Walk (YR909) **Jan 1-Dec 31**
A Award available
Sponsoring Club: AVA-615, Wabash Wanderers
POC: Karen Summers, 317-474-5630. 1323 S 19th, Lafayette, IN 47905. Susan Tapia, 317-474-0881. 3123 Rubble Way, Lafayette, IN 47905

Start Point: Turkey Run Inn. Located in a park in Parke County nestled along SR 47 southwest of Crawfordsville IN just off I-74.

Event Info: Daily, dawn to dusk. Trail is rated 3 & is not suitable for strollers or wheelchairs. Pets are allowed but must be kept on a leash no longer than six ft. Carry your own water. The only water/restrooms available is at the Start. This trail includes paths that are uneven & narrow steps & inclines.

Mitchell - 10km Walk (YR1325) **Apr 19-Dec 31**
A Award available
Sponsoring Club: AVA-453, Bedford Hiking Club
POC: Rowena Mount, 812-279-4862. 1428 14th St, Bedford, IN 47421 or Andrew Kluender, 812-275-2564. 2315 30th St, Bedford, IN 47421

Start Point: Spring Mill State Park Inn, 812-849-4081. Hwy 60 East. On SR60 approximately 18 miles west of Salem and 3.4 miles east of SR37/SR60 junction just south of Mitchell.

Event Info: Daily, dawn to dusk. Trail is rated 3 and is not suitable for strollers or wheelchairs. Pets must be kept on a leash no longer than 6 ft. Carry water. This shaded trail includes uneven paths, steep steps and inclines. It passes thru a virgin forest, a restored pioneer village & grist mill, goes along a stream, sinkholes, caves, a nature center and around a lake.

Muncie - Two 10km Walks (YR092 & YR906) **Jan 1-Dec 31**
B Awards available
Sponsoring Club: AVA-045, White River Ramblers
POC: James R. Bratton, 317-789-6683 (new area code after 2/1/97, 765). 840 N Main St, Albany, IN 47320

Start Point: **(YR092)** Hotel Roberts, 317-741-7777. (New area code effective 2/1/97, 765) 420 S. High St. From Indy/Ft Wayne, take I-69 to exit 34 (SR32). Take SR32 east to center of Muncie. Right on High St. The Hotel Roberts is 3 blocks on your left.

(YR906) Family Kitchen Restaurant, 288-2097 (new area code effective 2/1/97, 765) 1617 N. Wheeling Ave. From Indy/Ft Wayne, take I-69 to exit 41(SR 332). Take SR 332 into Muncie (9 miles) to Wheeling Ave which is the 7th stop light. Turn right on Wheeling. Family Kitchen is on the right just after going through first stop light. From Richmond/Ohio, take SR 35 North to Muncie. Take McGilliard Rd west into Muncie to Wheeling Ave (7th stop light) and turn left (into center of Muncie). Family Kitchen is on your right, just after the 1st stop light on Wheeling.

Event Info: Daily, dawn to dusk. Both trails are rated 1+, suitable for strollers and wheelchairs. Pets are allowed but not in the store. Free parking is available & the restaurant in the hotel features a menu that includes breakfast through dinner. Ask for the volkssport discount at the Hotel Roberts for lodging reservations. **YR092** starts in downtown Muncie, the route includes the banks of the White

River, Ball State University campus, Minnetrista Center & other historic neighborhoods. Shopping, food stops & sightseeing opportunities along the trail. **YR906** focuses on Ball State University. Included on the trail is Christy Woods, campus shops, bookstores, duck pond, shady quads, fraternity/sorority houses & local neighborhoods.

South Bend - 10km Walk (YR291) **Jan 1-Dec 31**
A Award available
Sponsoring Club: AVA-723, Hoosier Hikers
POC: Janice Bella, 219-277-9682. C/o Jamison Inn, 1404 North Ivy Rd, South Bend, IN 46637

Start Point: Jamison Inn, 219-277-9682. 1404 N Ivy Rd. Located at the intersection of Ivy Road, SR 23 (South Bend Ave) & Edison Rd. It may be reached by travelling south on SR 23 from Toll Rd exit 83 or by travelling east on Angela Blvd from its intersection with US 33. Register at the Front Desk. Ask for the "Volksmarch Box".

Event Info: Daily, dawn to dusk. Trail is rated 2 and would be difficult but not impossible for strollers and wheelchairs. No dogs allowed. The trail includes paved & gravel roadways & paths that are entirely located on the Campus of the University of Notre Dame.

West Lafayette - 10km Walk (YR908) **Jan 1-Dec 31**
B Awards available
Sponsoring Club: AVA-615, Lafayette Wabash Wanderers
POC: Karen Summers, 317-474-5630, 1323 S 19th, Lafayette, IN 47905

Start Point: Snowbear Frozen Custard, 620 West Stadium Ave. From I-65 exit onto SR25 to Lafayette. At US52 go right. Cross Wabash River to West Lafayette. At Northwestern Ave turn left. Turn left at Stadium, the Snowbear is on the left. From US 231 & points south, enter Lafayette & follow SR26 west. Cross Wabash River into West Lafayette. At Grant St turn right. At Northwestern turn left, at Stadium turn right. There is a very noticeable McDonalds & stop light at the intersection of Northwestern & Stadium.

Event Info: Mon-Sat, 10am-11pm; Sun 11-10. Closed major holidays and the week between Christmas & New Years. Trail is rated 1+. It would be difficult for strollers & is not recommended for wheelchairs. Pets must be leashed & you must cleanup after them. The walk includes sidewalks, residential streets & paths that can be uneven in spots. Most of the walk is on the Purdue Campus.

IOWA ═══════════════════════════════════

Akron - 10km Walk (YR504) **Apr 1-Sept 30**
B Awards available
Sponsoring Club: AVA-160, Prairie Wanderers
POC: Marlene Krause, 712-568-2600. 440 N 7th, Akron, IA 51001

Start Point: Casey's General Store, 79 South St. Corner of Iowa Hwys 3 & 12. From I-29 take the Akron/Spink exit #31. Go east on SD Hwy 48 for 13 miles. Turn right at the stop sign onto Hwy 12 for 0.7 miles to Casey's located on the left.

Event Info: Daily, 7am-dusk. Trail is rated 2 and is not suitable for strollers or wheelchairs. Pets must be leashed. The trail follows the Akron Trail System through the Dunham Prairie Preserve & Nature Trail, then through Akron. There is free seven day camping in Akron City Park.

Bloomfield - 10km Walk (YR812) **Apr 1-Oct 31**
B Awards available
Sponsoring Club: AVA-851, Ottumwa Area Walkers
POC: Charles J. Bates, 515-682-5870. 407 East Rochester Rd, Ottumwa, IA 52501

IOWA, cont.

Start Point: Pioneer Ridge Nature Center, Admin Bldg, 515-682-3091. 1339 Hwy 63. From Junction of Hwys 34 & 63 at SE edge of Ottumwa follow Hwy 63 south 6 miles. Large identification sign on east side of Hwy 63 Pioneer Ridge Nature Center. Staffed by Wapello County Conservation Officers.

Event Info: Mon-Fri, 8-5. Closed most Saturdays and Sundays. Call Charles Bates at 515-682-3091 or 515-682-5870 to arrange to walk these days. Trail is rated 2, not suitable for strollers & wheelchairs. Pets must be leashed. Summer walk could be very warm and advised for only very healthy experienced walkers. Route follows a trail of short cut grass through rolling hills and woods. Beautiful natural setting. Spring flowers and fall leaf colors are best seasons for walking.

Council Bluffs - 10km Walk (YR1099) **Jan 2-Dec 31**
B Awards available
Sponsoring Club: AVA-016, NE Wander Freunde Trailblazers
POC: Jim/Sheila Goeltz, 712-323-5874. 508 Lori Lane, Council Bluffs, IA 51503

Start Point: Barn'rds Restaurant, 1131 N. Broadway. From West & North: I-80 & 29 to Manawa exit 3, turn left on 192. North to Kanesville (1 block north of Broadway). At Kanesville, turn right (east) to North Broadway. Turn left 1/2 block to start. From East & South: I-80 & 29 to Manawa exit 3, turn right & follow 192 N to Kanesville (1 block north of Broadway). At Kanesville, turn right (east) to North Broadway. Left 1/2 block to Barn'rds.

Event Info: Daily, 10:30-9. Closed major holidays. Trail is rated 2+, not suitable for strollers or wheelchairs. Pets must be leashed. You may get your startcard on the previous afternoon or evening so you can start early in the morning. Checks only, please. Trail is on city streets, some hills, many historical sites.

Cresco - 10km Walk (YR772) **May 1-Oct 31**
B Awards available
Sponsoring Club: AVA-812, Northeast Iowa Volkssport Association
POC: Teresa Steffens, 319-864-7112. RC&D for NE Iowa, Inc. PO Box 916, Postville, IA 52162

Start Point: Cresco Motel, 319-547-2240. 620 2nd Ave Se (Hwy 9 East). Call for more specific directions.

Event Info: Daily, 8-5. Trail is rated 1, suitable for strollers or wheelchairs. Pets must be leashed. Trail highlights historic Beadle Park & Milwaukee Rd Railroad enigne & cars.

Davenport - 10km Walk (YR974) **Jan 1-Dec 31**
A Award available
Sponsoring Club: AVA-407, Mississippi River Ramblers
POC: Ralph Krippner, 309-797-8157. 1109 Third St, Moline, IL 61215

Start Point: Best Western Riverview Inn, 309-324-1921. 227 LeClaire St. From I-80 eastbound, take I-74 eastbound (exit 298). Exit I-74 at the last Iowa exit (exit 4). Turn right at the second signal (Grant St, US67). Stay on US67 for 2.7 miles until you get to the start. From I-74 westbound, take the first Iowa exit (exit 4). Turn left at the second signal (Grant St, US67). Stay on US67 for 2.7 miles until you get to start.

Event Info: Daily, dawn to dusk. Trail is rated 1 and is suitable for strollers but not wheelchairs. Pets must be leashed. The trail is on city sidewalks & paved bike paths & is mostly flat. the portion of the trail on the riverfront bike path provides many scenic views of the Mississippi River. The walk also goes through the 60 square block Village of East Davenport, Iowa's largest historic district.

Davis City - 10km Walk (YR814) **Apr 1-Oct 31**
Credit Only Event
Sponsoring Club: AVA-250, Greater Des Moines Volkssport Assn.
POC: Peggy Welter, 515-795-3800. 509 N Kennedy, Madrid, IA 50156

Start Point: Nine Eagles State Park. 10 miles from I-35, Lamoni/Davis City exit. East on Hwy 69 to J66. Follow park signs to ranger station.

Event Info: Daily, dawn to dusk. Trail is rated 3+, not suitable for strollers or wheelchairs. Pets must be leashed. Trail is mostly nature trails covered with grass or woodbark. A walking stick may be useful. Trail condition is dependent on the weather. Water & restrooms are available only at the start/finish.

Decorah - 10km Walk (YR774) **May 1-Oct 31**
B Awards available
Sponsoring Club: AVA-812, Northeast Iowa Volkssport Association
POC: Teresa Steffens, 319-864-7112. RC&D for NE Iowa, Inc., PO Box 916, Postville, IA 52612

Start Point: Vesterhiem Norwegian-American Museum Gift Shop, 502 W Water. Call 319-382-9681 for specific directions.

Event Info: Mon-Sat 9-3; Sun 10-3. Trail is rated 2 and is suitable for strollers but questionable for wheelchairs. Pets must be leashed. Water & restrooms are available at various businesses & parks along the route. The trail is on city sidewalks & streets. For more information, contact the Decorah Parks & Recreation Dept @ 319-382-4158.

Des Moines - Four 10km Walks (YR021) **Jan 1-Mar 31** (YR531) **Apr 1-Jun 30** (YR533) **Jul 1-Sep 30** (YR540) **Oct 1-Dec 31**
A Award available
Sponsoring Club: AVA-250, Greater Des Moines Volkssport Assn.
POC: Angie Anderson, 515-241-5902/277-9534. 1804 27th, Des Moines, IA 50310

Start Point: Des Moines Botanical Center, 909 E River Dr. Located on the East bank of the Des Moines River. The dome is visible from I-235. Signs indicate most direct routes. There is free parking on site.

Event Info: Daily, 10-5. Closed Christmas, New Year's & Thanksgiving. Rated 1+, suitable for strollers & wheelchairs with some difficulty with curbs & one set of railroad tracks. Please no pets. Paid walkers are allowed to tour the Dome at no cost. The trail will be mostly city sidewalks & bike trails on flat terrain. Just one gradual hill up to the State Capital Bldg. Route is marked with permanent signs.

Humboldt - 10km Walk (YR1066) **Jan 1-Dec 31**
B Awards available
Sponsoring Club: AVA-845, Humboldt County Hikers
POC: Steve Mitchell, 515-332-2707. 808 5th Ave N., Humboldt, IA 50548

Start Point: Humboldt County Memorial Hospital, 1000 N 15th. Hwy 169 N to Hwy 3 Intersection. Turn left (west) on Hwy 3 approximately 1/4 mile to 15th St N. Turn right on 15th St then left at first intersection into Hospital parking lot. Start/finish is at the information desk.

Event Info: Daily, 7-5. Trail is rated 1+, suitable for strollers but wheelchairs may have difficulty with some parts. Pets must be leashed. Route follows paved roadways and gravel walks/trails.

Indianola - 10km Walk (YR813) **Apr 1-Oct 31**
Credit Only Event
Sponsoring Club: AVA-250, Greater Des Moines Volkssport Assn.
POC: Rhonda S. Heim, 515-274-4321. 3601 Center St, Des Moines, IA 50312-3230

Start Point: Lake Ahquabi State Park Ranger Station, 6 miles south of Indianola on Hwy 69/65. Enter through the South entrance to the park.

Event Info: Daily, dawn to dusk. You must be off the trail by dusk. Trail is rated 3+, not suitable for strollers or wheelchairs. Pets must be leashed. Walking sticks are recommended. You are encouraged to carry water. This is a beautiful trail around the lake & through prairie lands. Some hills & inclines will be encountered.

McGregor - 10km Walk (YR1211) **May 25-Oct 31**
Credit Only Event
Sponsoring Club: AVA-250, Greater Des Moines Volkssport Assn.
POC: Peggy Welter, 515-795-3800. 509 N Kennedy, Madrid, IA 50156

Start Point: Pikes Peak State Park. Located 3 miles SE of McGregor on IA340. Start is at the concession stand in the park.

Event Info: Daily, 11-7. You must be off the trail by 7pm. Trail is rated 4+. No strollers or wheelchairs. Pets must be leashed. Food, water & restrooms are available at the start/finish only. Pike's Peak, one of the highest bluffs on the Mississippi River is in the heart of one of the nation's most picturesque regions. It offers a unique combination of scenic beauty, history, and outdoor recreation. The trail will follow woodland paths through the park. Hills and inclines will be encountered as well as steps. A walking stick is highly recommended.

Pella - 10km Walk (YR 1186) **Jan 1-Dec 31**   25km Bike (YR1185) **Apr 1-Oct 31**
B Awards available
Sponsoring Club: AVA-250, Greater Des Moines Volkssport Assn.
POC: Janet Eggerling, 515-628-3827. 2165 Idaho Dr, Pella, IA 50219-0003

Start Point: Pronto Market, 209 Oskaloosa St. East edge of town on Business 163.

Event Info: Daily, dawn to dusk. Pets must be leashed. The walk is rated 1+ and is suitable for strollers & wheelchairs. It is on city sidewalks. The bike is rated 2 and is on an asphalt bike trail near Red Rock Dam.

Polk City - 10km Walk (YR810)   25km Bike (YR1245) **May 30-Sept 30**
Credit Only Events
Sponsoring Club: AVA-250, Greater Des Moines Volkssport Assn.
POC: Mary Jo Lippold, 515-274-2651. 5608 Franklin, Des Moines, IA 50310

Start Point: Big Creek State Park, two miles north of Polk City. Approximately 8 miles from I-35 at the concessionaire stand at the beach. After Labor Day call Concession stand to be sure they are open (984-6083)

Event Info: Daily, dawn to dusk. Be off the trail by dusk. Walk is rated 1+, suitable for strollers & wheelchairs. Pets must be leashed. Food, water & restrooms are available at the start/finish only. Walk along the lake on paved multi-use trails. A huge wooden play structure & beach is located adjacent to the trail for the young & the young at heart. The bike is rated 1 and follows a paved, multi-use trail. Bikers must sign a waiver and should wear a helmet.

Silver City - 10km Walk (YR1341) **Apr 1-Oct 31**
A Award available
Sponsoring Club: AVA-016, Nebraska Wander Freunde Trailblazers
POC: Bob & Elsie Olsen, 712-622-8397. RR1, Box 11, Pacific Junction, IA 51561

Start Point: Wabash Bar & Grill. From I29 (north or south) exit 35. Go east on Hwy 34 for 11 miles to Hwy 242 then left (north) for 6 miles to start point .

Event Info: Daily, 6:30-dusk. Closed major holidays as well as Memorial Day weekend and Labor Day weekend. Trail is rated 1 but is not suitable for strollers or wheelchairs. Pets must be leashed. Trail fee of $1.00 is included in award and/or credit price. Route follows a nature trail along an abandoned rail line. There is some gravel or fine rock.

Solon - 10km Walk (YR811) **May 26-Sept 7**
Credit Only Event
Sponsoring Club: AVA-250, Greater Des Moines Volkssport Assn.
POC: Angie Anderson, 515-277-9534 (eve) 515-241-5902 (day). 1804 27th, Des Moines, IA 50310

Start Point: Lake Macbride State Park, Hwy 382 West of Solon. I80 or 380 or Hwy 218 to Hwy 382 to Solon. MacBride State Park to boat rental area near the concession stand.

Event Info: Daily, 7-7. Trail is rated 2, not suitable for strollers or wheelchairs. Pets must be leashed. A 2,180 acre park offering much to the outdoor enthusiast. The trail will follow the lake on multi-use trails. All park trails offer opportunities for the sights & sounds of Iowa at its best.

Spillville - 10km Walk (YR1030) **May 1-Oct 31**
B Awards available
Sponsoring Club: AVA-812, Northeast Iowa Volkssport Association
POC: Teresa Steffens, 319-864-7112. RC&D for NE Iowa, Inc, PO Box 916, Postville, IA 52162

Start Point: Bily Clocks, 319-562-3569. 323 N Main St. Call for more specific directions.

Event Info: Call ahead for hours of operation. Trail is rated 2. Strollers & wheelchairs would be questionable on portions of the walk. Pets must be leashed. This is a town & country walk and also goes along the Turkey River.

Strawberry Point - 10km Walk (YR1210) **May 25-Sept 2**
Credit Only Event
Sponsoring Club: AVA-250, Greater Des Moines Volkssport Assn.
POC: Peggy Welter, 515-795-3800, 509 N Kennedy, Madrid, IA 50156

Start Point: Backbone State Park. Located 4 miles SW of Strawberry Point on IA410. Start at the beach concession bldg.

Event Info: Daily, 7-7. You must be off the trail by 7pm. Trail is rated 3+ and is not suitable for strollers or wheelchairs. Pets must be leashed. Water & restrooms are available at the start/finish only. Backbone is Iowa's first state park and remains one of the most significant. It is named for the high ridge of rocks in the center of the 1750 acre park. This feature is bounded by the Maquoketa River and is aptly named Devil's Backbone. The route follows hiking trails through the park. There are some hills and inclines so a walking stick is recommended.

West Branch - 10km Walk (YR1244) **Apr 1-Oct 31**
Credit Only Event
Sponsoring Club: AVA-250, Greater Des Moines Volkssport Assn.
POC: Bill Willcox, 319-643-2541 or 319-643-5301. C/o Herbert Hoover National Historic Site, Parkside Dr, West Branch, IA 52358

Start Point: Herbert Hoover National Historic Site, 319-643-2541. Parkside Dr. From I-80 take exit 254 and follow signs.

Event Info: Daily, 9-5. Closed Thanksgiving, Christmas & New Year's Day. Trail is rated 2 and is not suitable for strollers or wheelchairs. Pets are not allowed. Route is on city streets, trails through the historic site and 76 acre restored tall-grass prairie as well as the Hoover bike trail.

KANSAS

Abilene - 11km Walk (YR282) **Apr 5-Dec 31**
Sponsoring Club: AVA-234, Sunflower Sod Stompers of Topeka
POC: Terri Tyler, 913-233-4385/Betty Augustine, 316-327-4124. PO Box 2576, Topeka, KS 66601

Start Point: West's Plaza Country Mart, 1900 N Buckeye; 913-263-2285. From I-70 exit 275. Proceed south on K-15 or N. Buckeye approximately 2 blocks to West's Plaza Country Mart which is on the right. Please park towards the east end of the lot. Registration is located at the Service Counter.

Event Info: Daily, dawn to dusk with limited hours on Easter & Christmas. Trail is rated 1, suitable for strollers & wheelchairs with some difficulty with surfaces & curbing. Pets must be leashed but should not be taken if participant is planning on visiting any museums and/or businesses. Please be considerate of your pet's health in extreme heat conditions. This course will lead through shaded residential areas of Abilene as well as business areas. Numerous historical sites will be located along the route. The trail is mostly city sidewalks or paved streets on flat terrain. This is a credit only event.

Arkansas City - 10km Walk (YR310) **Jan 1-Dec 31**
A Award available
Sponsoring Club: AVA-211, Wichita Skywalkers
POC: Sharon Regnier, 316-442-1018. Rt 5, Box 322-5, Arkansas City, KS 67005

Start Point: Chaplin Nature Center, 316-442-4133. Rt 1, Box 216 (5 miles NW of Arkansas City). From north or south, take I-35 to exit 4. From west exit 4, go east on US Hwy 166 13.5 miles to gravel road. From east (intersection of US Hwys 77 & 166 in Arkansas City) go west on Hwy 166 3 miles to gravel road. Look for Chaplin Nature Center sign at gravel road. Go north on gravel road 2 miles to the entrance.

Event Info: Tuesday-Saturday 9-5; Sunday 1-5. Closed Mondays. Trail is rated 2 and is not suitable for strollers or wheelchairs. Pets are allowed. If there have been steady or heavy rains, some of the trails will be impassable. Call ahead to the Nature Center to verify the status of the trails. Course is on maintained nature trails through woodlands, prairies, and wetlands and along the sandy beaches of the Arkansas River in Chaplin Nature Center, a magnificent 230 acre preserve filled with the flora and fauna of SC Kansas.

Atchison - 10km Walk (YR778) **Jan 2-Dec 31**
B Awards available
Sponsoring Club: AVA-037, Kansas Jaywalkers of Ft Leavenworth
POC: Barbara Wood, 913-985/3708/evenings. PO Box 3136, Ft Leavenworth, KS 66027

Start Point: Atchison Santa Fe Depot Visitors Center & Museum. 200 South 10th St. Located at the intersection of Hwy 59 & Hwy 73. Go 2 blocks north on Hwy 73 to Santa Fe Depot Visitors Center on the right.

Event Info: Mon-Fri, 9-5; Sat, 10-4; Sun, noon-4. Must finish before office closes. Closed Easter, Thanksgiving, Christmas & New Years. Trail is rated 2+, suitable for strollers & wheelchairs. Pets must be leashed. Go past beautiful old victorian and gothic homes to include Amelia Earhart's. Also go through Benedictine College.

Council Grove - 11/12km Walk (YR1206) **Apr 6-Dec 31**
A Award available
Sponsoring Club: AVA-234, Sunflower Sod Stompers
POC: Terri Tyler, 913-233-4385/Betty Dutton, 316-767-5610. PO Box 2576, Topeka, KS 66601-2576

Start Point: The Cottage House Hotel-Motel, 25 North Neosho. For reservations: 1-800-727-7903. Council Grove is located at the crossroads of US56 and Kansas 177. The Cottage House is located one block west of the Madonna of the Trail Statue, just north of Main St (US56) on Neosho.

Event Info: Daily, dawn to dusk. Trail is rated 1+ but various surfaces will make it difficult for strollers or wheelchairs. Pets must be leashed and should not be taken if you are planning on visiting any museums and/or businesses. Please be considerate of your pet's health in extreme heat conditions. This course will lead through shaded, residential areas of Council Grove as well as the business district. Numerous historical sites will be located on the route highlighting the Santa Fe Trail. It is mostly city sidewalks or paved roads on fairly flat terrain. A portion of the route will be on highway shoulder with open spaces while ascending to Council Grove Lake.

Fort Leavenworth - Two 10km Walks (YR043 & YR263) **Jan 2-Dec 31**
B Awards available
Sponsoring Club: AVA-037, Kansas Jaywalkers of Ft Leavenworth
POC: Thomas N. Tesch, 913-651-3127(eves). PO Box 3025, Ft. Leavenworth, KS 66027

Start Point: Leavenworth Riverfront Community Center, 123 Esplanade. From Kansas City, take I-70 West to I-435 North to Hwy 24/40 West to Hwy 73 North to Delaware St. Right on Delaware for 3 blocks to start.

Alternate Start: YR263 is at Hoge Barracks on Grant Ave. From Kansas City, take I-70 West to I-435 North to Hwy 24/40 West to Hwy 73 North to Hwy 92 West to entrance of Ft Leavenworth (Grant Ave). Right on Grant, past Kansas Ave to Hoge Hall on the left.

Event Info: Mon-Fri 6am-9pm; Sat 9am-7pm; Sun 1pm-6pm. Closed all Federal holidays. **YR263** is rated 2 and is suitable for strollers but not wheelcharis. It goes through Ft Leavenworth on the Missouri River with numerous historic sites of significance & the Ft Leavenworth Frontier Army Museum. **YR043** is rated 1+; suitable for strollers and wheelchairs. Pets are allowed but must be leashed. The Pizza Hut offers volkssporters free bread sticks & the 7-11 will give you a free Big Gulp. It goes through Leavenworth on the Missouri River seeing numerous Victorian homes and the old business district. Also see the Leavenworth Historical Society County Museum.

Lawrence - 10km Walk (YR322)   25km Bike (YR555) **Jan 2-Dec 30**
B Awards available
Sponsoring Club: AVA-771, Free State Walkers
POC: Judith Galas, 913-842-4958; Email jgalas@aol.com. 1125 Vermont, Lawrence, KS 66044

Start Point: Eldridge Hotel, 701 Massachusetts. From I-70 take the east Lawrence exit. After you go through the toll booth, turn left at Hwy 59 and go toward Lawrence. Cross the river & continue on Vermont St to 7th St. Turn left at 7th. The start is on the next corner.

Event Info: Daily, dawn to dusk. **YR322** is rated 1+ but is not suitable for strollers or wheelchairs. It is a quaint historic town walk. Pets must be leashed. The bike, **YR555** is rated 1. It is in full sun almost all of the way. Carry your own water. Restrooms only at start/finish. It is on level, flat surfaces going through open country. Remote but peaceful. Bikers must sign a waiver and should wear a helmet.

Lenexa - 10km Walk (YR013) **Jan 1-Dec 31**
A Award available
Sponsoring Club: AVA-331, Heart of America Volkssport Club
POC: Gary or Sandy Chancellor, 913-788-9721. 6410 Roswell, Kansas City, KS 66104

Start Point: Lenexa Community Center, 13420 Oak St; 913-541-0209. Exit 95th St off of I-35 and proceed west to Pflumm Rd. Right on Pflumm then right on Oak.

Event Info: Daily, 8-dusk. Closed Thanksgiving & Christmas. Trail is rated 1+, suitable for strollers & wheelchairs. Pets must be leashed. The trail is fairly level with a few moderate hills. It runs through historic downtown Lenexa, through residential areas & partly on a bike-hike trail.

Lindsborg - 10km Walk (YR269) **Apr 5-Dec 31**
A Award available
Sponsoring Club: AVA-234, Sunflower Sod Stompers of Topeka
POC: Terri Tyler, 913-233-4385/Betty Augustine, 316-327-4124. PO Box 2576, Topeka, KS 66601

Start Point: Viking Motel, 446 Harrison/I-135 Business Loop. 913-227-3336. (Room information or directions only). Located on K-4. Also known as I-135 Business Loop. Coming from the north on I-135, use exit 78 & follow K-4 into Lindsborg. Use exit #72 when coming from the south. Please park so as not to interfere with motel business.

Event Info: Daily, 7 to dusk. Start cards may be picked up the night before if walking before 7. Trail is rated 1, suitable for strollers & wheelchairs with some difficulty from surfaces & curbing. Pets must be leashed. Pets should not be taken on the trail if you are planning on visiting museums and/or other businesses. Please be considerate of your pet's health in extreme heat conditions. This course will lead through shaded residential areas of Lindsborg as well as business areas & the campus of Bethany College. Numerous historical sites will be located along the route. The trail is mostly city sidewalks or paved streets on flat terrain.

Overland Park - 10km Walk (YR1048) **Jan 1-Dec 31**
A Award available
Sponsoring Club: AVA-331, Heart of America Volkssport Club
POC: Gary/Sandy Chancellor 913-788-9721. 6410 Roswell, Kansas City, KS 66104

Start Point: Prairie Life Center, 10351 Barkley. Take Metcalf North exit from I-435. Proceed north on Metcalf to 103rd St. Turn right on 103rd to Barkley. Turn right (south) to Prairie Life Center. Please park near the back of the lot.

Event Info: Daily, 8 to two hours before dusk. Closed Thanksgiving & Christmas. Trail is rated 1+, suitable for strollers & wheelchairs. Pets must be leashed. Be sure to finish before dark. Follows an asphalt bike-hike trail with some hills. Restrooms at start/finish & at or near the checkpoint.

Topeka - 10km Walk (YR008) **Jan 1-Dec 31**
A Award available
Sponsoring Club: AVA-234, Sunflower Sod Stompers of Topeka
POC: Terri Tyler, 913-233-4385/Margaret Harney, 913-272-4572. PO Box 2576, Topeka KS 66601

Start Point: Holiday Inn City Centre, 913-232-7721. 914 Madison. Coming into Topeka from the east on I-70, use the 10th Ave exit. If approaching from the west, exit at 8th Ave & proceed two blocks to 10th Ave. Turn left & cross-over the Interstate to the start.

Event Info: Daily, dawn to dusk. Checkpoint hours are usually 8-dusk. Checkpoints might be closed due to functions. Trail is rated 1, suitable for strollers & wheelchairs but some difficulty with curbs & brick sidewalks. Pets must be leashed. Holiday Inn gives a volkssport rate for rooms excluding race weekends. This course will lead through shaded, residential areas of Topeka as well as the downtown area. It will be mostly on city sidewalks or paved streets on fairly flat terrain.

Wichita - Two 10km Walks (YR072 & YR983) 12km Walk (YR511) 27km Bike (YR512) 30km Bike (YR086) **Jan 1-Dec 31**
A Award available
Sponsoring Club: AVA-211, Wichita Skywalkers
POC: John Wickham, 316-788-6406. 1101 Briarwood Rd, Derby, KS 67037-3701.

Start Point: Family Inn, 316-267-9281. 221 E Kellogg. Intersection of Kellogg (US 54) and Broadway in downtown Wichita. From I-135 exit 5B/6A, west on Kellogg Ave (US54) exit at Central Business District exit (CBD), west 1 block to Broadway. South 1/2 block to start. From the east, I-35 to Exit 50, west on Kellogg Ave, exit at CBD exit, west 1 block to Broadway, south 1/2 block to start. From the west, East on US 54, exit at CBD exit, east 2 blocks to start.

Event Info: Daily, dawn to dusk. All trails are rated 1, suitable for strollers & wheelchairs. Pets must be leashed. **WALKS:** YR072 is along the Arkansas River on a walking path & includes historic & scenic sites & city parks. **YR511** is on footpaths in Sedgwick County Park in NW Wichita. Adjacent to the park is one of the midwest's finest zoos, Sedgwick County Zoo. **YR983** goes along the Arkansas River on a walking path & includes historic sites, city parks & sculptures made from tree trunks by local artist Gino Salerno. Latter part of the course goes through Old Town, a revitalized multi-block district filled with antique shops, eateries, stores, clubs, a farm & art market, etc. **BIKES:** Bikers must sign the waiver and should wear helmets. **YR86** is along the Arkansas River on a bike path and includes historic and scenic sites and city parks. **YR512** is on bikepaths in Sedgwick County Park, adjacent to the zoo.

KENTUCKY

Brandenburg - 11km Walk (YR580) **Mar 1-Dec 31**
A Award available
Sponsoring Club: AVA-694, Derby City Walkers, Inc.
POC: Robert Miller, 502-459-4929. 3578A Fincastle Rd, Louisville, KY 40213

Start Point: Otter Creek Park Lodge, 502-583-3577. 850 Otter Creek Road. Located 30 minutes from downtown Louisville near Muldraugh and Fort Knox. Take Gene Snyder Freeway west, turn left at 31 west. Go 12 miles to Hwy 1638 and turn right. Turn right at Otter Creek Park entrance (approximately 2 miles from 31W). Follow signs in Park to the Lodge (2 miles from entrance). Lodging accommodations, campgrounds, picnic areas and a restaurant are available.

Event Info: Daily 7-5. Trail is rated 3 and is not suitable for strollers or wheelchairs. Pets must be leashed and are not allowed in the Lodge. A park entrance fee is possible. Restroom & restraunt are available at the start/finish. Trail restrooms are seasonal. Suggest you carry water. This very scenic trail meanders through densely forested areas with spectacular over looks of the Ohio River.

Covington - 10km Walk (YR078) Two 11km Walks (YR624 & YR787) **Jan 1-Dec 31**
YR787 has an A Award available B Awards available for other events
Sponsoring Club: AVA-548, Northern Kentucky Trotters
POC: Geni Fryman, 606-331-7776. 8 Thompson Rd, Ft Mitchell, KY 41017

Start Point: Perkin's Restaurant, 503 Third St. From I-75 N or S to Covington/5th Street exit (#192). Go East on 5th to first light. Turn left on Philadelphia & go to 3rd street. Turn right & Perkin's Restaurant will be on your left.

Event Info: Daily, dawn to dusk. Closed Christmas & after 3pm on Thanksgiving. Pets are allowed on all events if leashed.   YR078 (Historic Covington) is rated 1+. This is a historic walk along city sidewalks with one gradual hill & stairs. Enjoy riverfront views and historic buildings.   **YR624** (Devou Park) is rated 2+. It takes you past overlooks with spectacular views of Cincinnati & the Ohio River Valley. It also goes past an archaeological museum. It is very hilly & combines sidewalks & paved roads. You must drive to the start in the park. YR787 (Two State Walk) is rated 1+. Trails are not suitable for strollers or wheelchairs. All events allow pets but they must be leashed. This is a two-state walk that follows the scenic riverside area with views of the Cincinnati skyline. Crosses three bridges & explores Cincinnati's riverside parks.

Frankfort - 10km Walk (YR1228) **Jan 2-Dec 31**
Credit Only Event
Sponsoring Club: AVA-853, Central Kentucky Volksmarchers
POC: Carole Schoo, 606-873-2028, 495 Scarborough Drive, Versailles, KY 40383

Start Point: YMCA, 402 Broadway. From Lexington & Versaqilles: US60 into downtown Frankfort. Make a right turn onto Broadway (very steep hill). YMCA is on the right. From Louisville: Get off

KENTUCKY, cont. ——————————————————————

I-64E at Frankfort/Lawrenceburg exit. Take US 127 into Frankfort. Get off downtown and the Holiday Inn will be at the exit. You can park in the garage across from the Holiday Inn on your right (Clinton St). You can take Clinton St to the next block where you can make a right turn and take a second right onto Broadway. There is parking in front of the YMCA.

Event Info: Mon-Fri, 6am-9pm; Sat 8-3; Sun 1-5. Closed holidays. Trail is rated 3 and is not suitable for strollers or wheelchairs. Pets are allowed. Call POC in advance if you wish to walk early on Sunday morning. There are few places to stop for restrooms and/or water on Sunday mornings. Take your own water. Pets are not allowed inside the capital building. This walk goes through the downtown area, across two bridges, through historic residential areas, circles the capital building, the governor's mansion and passes the floral clock. It also goes through the Frankfort cemetary where Daniel Boone is buried. Bring your camera.

Louisville - 10km Walk (YR083) 11km Walk (YR087) **Jan 2-Dec 31**
YR083 is a Credit Only Event   YR087 has an A Award available
Sponsoring Club: AVA-694, Derby City Walkers, Inc.
POC: YR083: Herb Zimmerman, 502-456-6126(eves) 502-574-3365(days). 1363 Tyler Park Dr, Louisville, KY 40204-1539. YR087: Pat O'Connor, 502-896-4127. 119 McArthur Dr #3, Louisville, KY 40207

Start Point: Downtown YMCA, 502-587-6700. 555 South 2nd St. Southbound I-71 take Third St and River Road exit and go south on 3rd St to York St and turn left. At the next light turn left onto 2nd St. Drive north two blocks to YMCA on the right. Southbound on I-65 take 3rd St exit and follow above directions. Northbound on I-65, take Muhammad Ali Blvd exit and go west to 3rd St. Turn left onto 3rd and follow above directions to YMCA. Eastbound on I-64, take the 9th St downtown exit to Roy Wilkins Blvd. Continue straight south to Chestnut St and turn left. Go east eight blocks to Second St. Turn left and YMCA will be on your right. Parking meters and lot are available nearby.

Event Info: Mon-Sat 7-5; Sun 9-5. Closed holidays. Call YMCA in advance if in doubt. **YR083** is rated 2+ and is not suitable for strollers or wheelchairs. Pets must be leashed. You register for this event at the YMCA and then drive 6 miles to Iroquois Park for the walk. Direction maps are supplied at the registration area. Trail restrooms are seasonal. This trail meanders through an urban park on varying terrain and park roads. One hillside trail takes walkers to several over looks of the city. **YR087** is rated 1 and is suitable for strollers and wheelchairs. Pets must be leashed. This trail meanders through the downtown area on city streets. Downtown landmarks, turn-of-the-century homes and a walk way along the river front are on the route.

Versailles - 10km Walk (YR1227) **Jan 1-Dec 31**
Credit Only Event
Sponsoring Club: AVA-853, Central Kentucky Volksmarchers
POC: Carole Schoo, 606-873-2028. 495 Scarborough Drive, Versailles, KY 40383

Start Point: Farmhouse Antiques & Gifts, 175 N Main St. From Frankfort: 60W to Versailles (approx 12 miles). Enter town on Frankfort St. At the watertower turn right onto Main St to start. From Lexington: Take 60W to Versailles (approx 12 miles). Turn right when you come to Main St. There is parking at the side of the building on Green St.

Event Info: Mon-Sat 10-5; Sun 1-5. Closed holidays. Trail is rated 2 and is not suitable for strollers or wheelchairs. Pets are allowed. Most of this walk is on sidewalks or a paved path in the park. There is some roadside walking and steep hills. It goes through residential/historical areas.

LOUISIANA

Baton Rouge - 10km Walk (YR539) **Jan 2-Dec 31**
Credit Only Event
Sponsoring Club: AVA-651, Red Stick Walkers
POC: Peggy Fleniken, 504-275-6189. 11221 Tams Drive, Baton Rouge LA 70815

Start Point: Baton Rouge Area Convention & Visitors Bureau, 1st Floor, Louisiana State Capitol Bldg, 900 North Third Street; 1-800-LA ROUGE. From I-10, exit onto I-110 (northbound). Proceed to the North Street exit (1D) on the left. Caution: stay in the left lane to exit. Proceed to Fourth St (4th traffic light) and turn right. Go to Spanish Town Rd and turn left. Go to Third St and turn right. Go to State Capitol Rd.

Event Info: Daily, 8-4:30. Closed Easter, Thanksgiving & Christmas. Trail is rated 1, but is not recommended for strollers or wheelchairs. An alternate route is available. Pets are allowed but must be leashed. This is the State Capitol of Louisiana with lots of free parking. Hotel, RV accommodations, sightseeing & restaurant info available thru the Baton Rouge Area Convention & Visitors Bureau at 1-800-LA-ROUGE. This trail takes you by the old State Capitol which was replaced by our present skyscraper built by "The Kingfish", Governor Huey P. Long, in 1932. You'll pass the LA Naval War Memorial, a vintage airplane, the USS Kidd (A WWII Destroyer) Catfish Town and the Belle of Baton Rouge Riverboat Casino on the Mississippi River. You'll walk several blocks under the umbrella of oak trees, along a brick walkway landscaped with many azaleas in the median of North Blvd. You will see many older homes built in our original Beauregard and Spanish towns. There are historic markers along the entire trail.

New Orleans - 10km Walk (YR076) **Jan 1-Dec 31**
A Award available
Sponsoring Club: AVA-473, Crescent City Volkssport Club
POC: Heinz Kloth, 504-455-6413. 3005 Kent Ave, Metairie, LA 70006

Start Point: Fritzel's Bar, 504-561-0432. 733 Bourbon St. From the East on I-10, exit right at Superdome/Claiborne Ave. Stay on Claiborne Ave to Canal St and take a right on Canal. Go down Canal to Bourbon and take a left to start. From the East on I-10 exit right at French Quarter/Orleans Ave/Vieux Carre exit. Turn left on Orleans Ave for one block to Claiborne. Take a right and go to Canal St. Take a left and go to Bourbon.

Event Info: Daily, 11 till dusk. Trail is rated 1 and is suitable for strollers & wheelchairs. Pets must be leashed. Walk goes through the historic French Quarter.

MAINE

Auburn - 10km Walk (YR1266) **Apr 1-Nov 30**
A Award available
Sponsoring Club: AVA-193, Southern Maine Volkssport Assn
POC: John Tibbetts, 207-774-8306. 1544 Congress St, Portland, ME 04102

Start Point: Shop 'n Save Supermarket, 95 Spring St. From the North or South take exit 12 of the Maine Turnpike (I-495); turn left onto Rt 4 and drive 4.8 miles to the traffic light at Court St. Turn right on Court St and take a right at either Railroad St or Spring St.

Event Info: Daily, dawn to dusk. Closed Easter and Thanksgiving. Trail is rated 1; suitable for strollers or wheelchairs. Pets are allowed. This route goes along city sidewalks in the cities of Auburn and Lewiston, home of Bates College, and riverside manufacturers.

Augusta - 10km Walk (YR1179) **Apr 1-Nov 30**
A Award available
Sponsoring Club: AVA-193, Southern Maine Volkssport Association
POC: John Tibbetts, 207-774-8306. 1544 Congress St, Portland, ME 04102

Start Point: Best Western Senator Inn. 284 Western Ave (at I-95). From I-95 use exit 30 northbound; exit 30A southbound. Keep right onto Rte 202 East towards Augusta.

Event Info: Daily, dawn to dusk. Must be finished by dusk. Trail is rated 3. Strollers & wheelchairs should use discretion. Pets are allowed but must be leashed. Trail has several very steep hills. Although paved the entire way, strollers & wheelchairs may have difficulty.

Bath - 11km Walk (YR673) **Apr 1-Nov 30**
A Award available
Sponsoring Club: AVA-193, Southern Maine Volkssport Association
POC: John Tibbetts, 207-774-8306. 1544 Congress St, Portland, ME 04102

Start Point: Holiday Inn, 207-443-9741. 139 Western Ave. Bath is located on US Rt 1 about 30 miles NE of Portland. Leave Rt 1 at the Congress Ave exit. From the South: left off the exit ramp onto Witch Spring Rd, right onto Western Ave. From the North: left off the exit ramp onto Congress Ave, pass over Rt 1, left on Witch Spring Rd. Right on Western Ave.

Event Info: Daily, dawn to dusk. Trail is rated 1, suitable for strollers & wheelchairs. Pets must be leashed. This trail takes you through the beautiful "City of Ships" , and along its waterfront past the Bath Iron Works.

Freeport - 10km Walk (YR672) **Apr 1-Oct 31**
A Award available
Sponsoring Club: AVA-193, Southern Maine Volkssport Association
POC: John Tibbetts, 207-774-8306. 1544 Congress St, Portland, ME 04102

Start Point: L.L. Bean Retail Store. 218 Rte 1. Freeport is located on I-95 about 20 miles NE of Portland. Leave I-95 at exit 19 (Desert Rd). From the south: turn right at the top of the exit ramp. From the north, turn left at the top of the exit ramp. At the traffic lights, bear left onto US Rt 1. Follow Rt 1 into Freeport and the start.

Event Info: Daily, dawn to dusk. Trail is rated 1+ but is not suitable for strollers or wheelchairs. Pets must be leashed. Walk takes you along streets and sidewalks of a manufacturing and residential town that is home to retail giant L.L. Bean.

Greenville - 10km Walk (YR788) **May 15-Oct 15**
B Awards available
Sponsoring Club: AVA-800, Wandering Maine-iacs
POC: David Muzzy, 207-854-5424. 455 Duck Pond Rd, Westbrook, ME 04092

Start Point: Indian Hill Motel, 207-695-2623. South Main St. (RT 15). One kilometer south of Greenville on Rt 15.

Event Info: Daily, 7 a.m. to dusk. Must be off the trail by dark. Trail is rated 2, not suitable for wheelchairs and strollers may have difficulty. Pets must be leashed. No smoking in fields or wooded areas. This trail takes you through the town of Greenville and adjoining woods & fields. There is an exceptional panoramic view of Moosehead Lake. Considerable wildlife may be seen on this walk.

Portland - 11km Walk (YR029) **Jan 1-Dec 31**
A Award available
Sponsoring Club: AVA-193, Southern Maine Volkssport Association
POC: John Tibbetts, 207-774-8306 (eves). 1544 Congress St., Portland ME 04102

Start Point: Ramada Inn, 207-774-5611. 1230 Congress St. Just west of the intersection of I-295 & Congress St. From I-95 northbound, use exit 6A and then take the Congress St exit. Take the first left to reverse direction and continue under I-295 to the Ramada. Heading south on I-95, use exit 7 and follow the signs to I-295. Take Congress St exit and then left to reverse directions as above. Traveling south on I-295, take the Congress St (west) exit.

Event Info: Daily, dawn to dusk. Rated 1+, suitable for strollers & wheelchairs. Leashed pets with clean up. This trail takes you through Portland's historic waterfront, old Port District & Western Promenade areas.

Rockland - 10km Walk (YR1214) **Mar 21-Nov 29**
A Award available
Sponsoring Club: AVA-508, Wicked Good Wanderers
POC: Chris Hennings, 207-236-3583. PO Box 298, Rockport, ME 04856-0298

Start Point: Rockland Public Library, 207-594-0333. 80 Union St. From the south follow US Rt 1 to Rockland, turn north on Main St and turn left after State Ferry Terminal following US Rt 1 South (Union St). Turn right on Beech or Limerock Sts. Library is between Beech & Limerock.

Event Info: Mon-Fri, 9-5; Sat 9-noon. Closed Sunday. Trail is rated 1 and is suitable for strollers & wheelchairs. Pets are allowed on a leash. Route goes past Farnsworth Art Museum to Main St. Great harbor views and old Main St and residential areas.

South Portland - Three 11km Walks (YR864) **Apr 1-Jun 30**   (YR865) **Jul 1-Sep 30** (YR866) **Oct 1-Nov 30**
B Awards available
Sponsoring Club: AVA-800, Wandering Maine-iacs
POC: Sylvia Allen, 207-774-8524. 887 Spring St, Westbrook, ME 04092

Start Point: Shop 'n Save, 50 Cottage Rd. From the south: Take Exit 7 from the Maine Turnpike (I-95). Follow the divided highway to U.S. Route 1. Turn left on Rt. 1 to Broadway; bear right on Broadway and continue to Cottage Rd; turn left and Shop 'n Save is on your right. From the north: coming south on the Maine Turnpike, take Exit 7 and follow the directions above. Coming south on I-95, continue into Portland on I-295. Use Exit 6A and follow Route 77 to South Portland. After crossing the bridge, traffic bears right. Turn left at the first set of lights - onto Market Street - and then continue straight ahead crossing Ocean and entering Hinckley until you see the Shop 'n Save. Because of extensive construction on the new bridge, you may have to make inquiries locally if you are unable to follow these directions.

Event Info: Daily, 7-dusk. Closed Easter & Thanksgiving. Trails are rated 1+. Strollers may have difficulty. An alternate route is available to avoid stairs & beach. Pets must be leashed and are not allowed on the beach from May 1-Sept 30. People with pets can use the alternate route during these times. The walk route is generally along sidewalks & pathways but there will be some stairs & a stretch of sandy beach. A 2km walk to the Portland Harbor Light is an optional "add-on" to these events.

MARYLAND ━━━━━━━━━━━━━━━━━━━━━━━━━━

Annapolis - 11km Walk (YR264) **Jan 2-Dec 31**
B Awards available
Sponsoring Club: AVA-595, Annapolis Amblers
POC: Bob/Mary Graham, 410-757-2155. 13 Ashcroft Court, Arnold, MD 21012

Start Point: Regina's Continental Delicatessen & Restaurant, 410-268-2662. 26 Annapolis St. Take I-95 to Baltimore. Exit at I-895, through the tunnel to exit 14 and then exit 14A (Route 3). Follow Route 3 to I-97, Annapolis. I-97 merges into US 50/301. Exit US 50/301 at MD 70 South, Rowe

Blvd. From the west, this is identified as exit 24. Turn left at first traffic light onto Melvin Ave, 2 blocks to Annapolis St, turn right, one block to start on left.

Event Info: Sun 8-2; Mon 7-4; Tue, Thur & Fri 7-5; Sat 8-4; Wed 7-9. Call ahead if in doubt about hours. Closed New Year's, Easter, Memorial Day, July 4th, Labor Day, Thanksgiving and Christmas. Rated 2, suitable for large wheeled strollers & wheelchairs. Some brick sidewalks are rather rough. Dogs are not encouraged due to USNA restrictions. The event goes through a historic area & waterfront of Annapolis, plus the Naval Academy. Pets are not allowed on the Academy grounds.

Annapolis - 10km Walk (YR1176) **Jan 1-Dec 31**
B Awards available
Sponsoring Club: AVA-595, Annapolis Amblers
POC: Jean or George Bankey, 410-255-6350. 1177 Ridge Dr., Pasadena, MD 21122

Start Point: Mcdonald's, Bay Ridge Rd (Forest Dr.) From the north (Baltimore & northern Anne Arundel Cty) take I97 south to exit 22 (Rt 665/Aris Allen Blvd). Follow 665 to end and merge with Forest Dr. Follow Forest Dr approx 2 miles. Continue past Exxon Station at Hillsmere Dr (there is a sign at the station saying "Quiet Waters Park - Next Right". The start is 1/2 block past the Exxon Station. From the south & west follow Rt 50 to exit 22 (665) and continue as above.

Event Info: Daily, 7-dusk. Closed Tuesdays, Christmas & Thanksgiving. Trail is rated 1+ and is suitable for strollers & wheelchairs. Pets must be leashed. Route is along roads and paved paths. There is a wooded park with views of South & West Rivers.

Baltimore - 10km Walk (YR362) **Jan 2-Dec 31**
Credit Only Event
Sponsoring Club: AVA-418, Baltimore Walking Club
POC: Mary Kowalski, 410-282-4953. 8163 Gray Haven Rd, Baltimore MD 21222

Start Point: Baltimore City Life Museum, 410-396-3523. 800 E. Lombard St. Take 95 to exit 53 onto 395 toward the Inner Harbor. Turn right onto Conway St to end at Light St. Turn left on Light, stay in right lane following around Harbor Place and onto Pratt St. After passing Harbor Place, get into left lane and turn left onto President St (Rt 83). Go 2 blocks and turn right on Baltimore St. Take the first right (Front St) to entrance to Museum. From Rt 83: Go to end as it becomes President St. Turn left onto Baltimore St. Take the first right onto Front St to the entrance of Museum.

Event Info: Daily, 10-5. Closed major holidays. Trail is rated 1+, suitable for strollers & wheelchairs with curbs & steps. Pets must be leashed & are not allowed in the museum. Includes historic Fells Point and the busy Inner Harbor.

Baltimore - Four 10km Walks (YR1155) **Jan 2-Mar 31** (YR1156) **Apr 1-Jun 30** (YR1157) **Jul 1-Sep 30** (YR1160) **Oct 1-Dec 31**
Credit Only Events
Sponsoring Club: AVA-418, Baltimore Walking Club
POC: Marie/Frank Kupres, 410-592-3171. 12 Ridgecliff Court, Kingsville, MD 21087

Start Point: The Hopkins Delly, 410-366-6603. 110 West 39th St. Take the Baltimore Beltway, Rt 695 to exit 25, Charles St. Proceed 8 miles on Charles St to 39th St. Turn right to Delly.

Event Info: Daily, 8-8. Closed some holidays. Call for verification. All trails are rated 1, suitable for strollers & wheelchairs with considerations for curbs. Pets must be leashed. Summer/Fall/Winter/Spring---All different trails. All will go through the prestigious communities & around landmarks that are so much a part of Baltimore.

Brandywine - 10km Walk (YR885)   27km Bike (YR886) **Apr 12-Sep 30**
Walk has A Award available   Bike is a Credit Only Event
Sponsoring Club: AVA-021, Washington DC Area Volksmarching Club
POC: Steve Arnett, 301-449-6325/6427. 7229 Easy St., Temple Hills, MD 20748

Start Point: Cedarville Grocery, 301-888-1273. 11800 Cedarville Rd. From the Capital Beltway (I-95) take exit 7A, Maryland Rt 5 South. Drive 12 miles. Turn left onto Cedarville Rd. Drive approx 4.1 miles. Just after crossing the railroad tracks, the start will be on the left at the corner of Ashbox Rd.

Event Info: Mon-Sat 8-8; Sun 8-1. Open 1/2 day (am) on Memorial Day, July 4th & Labor Day. Closed Christmas. Call if in doubt. Walk is rated 2, not suitable for wheelchairs or strollers. Pets are allowed. Bike is rated 2. Bikers must sign waiver. Helmets are highly recommended. The walk trail is mostly natural surfaces and will be more difficult after heavy rains. The bike is mostly asphalt (2/3) and some natural surface (1/3). There are a few significant hills. The trail will also be more difficult after heavy rains.

Cambridge - 10km Walk (YR1046) **Jan 2-Dec 30**
A Award available
Sponsoring Club: AVA-190, Freestate Happy Wanderers
POC: Bob Caldwell, 301-937-6124. 11810 Macon St, Beltsville, MD 20705

Start Point: Dorchester County Family YMCA, 410-221-0505. 201 Talbot Avenue. Cross Choptank River Bridge via Rt 50 (south). Turn right at 1st traffic light onto Maryland Ave. Continue on to 3rd traffic light. Turn right onto Spring St. At next light (large church on corner), turn right onto High St. Continue to Water St (just before Harbor Park). Turn left on Water. Water St becomes Hambrooks Ave after a small jog left at Choptank Ave. Continue on Hambrooks after a small jog right at Belvedere Ave. Turn left on Talbot Ave, three blocks after Belvedere. NOTE: the street sign is hard to see - watch for museum sign on corner of Talbot. The YMCA is on the right in the 2nd block after turning off Hambrooks. Ask the desk clerk for the "Walk Box".

Event Info: Mon-Sat 9am-6pm; Sun 1-6. Closed New Years Eve & Day, Easter, Memorial Day, July 4, Labor Day, Thanksgiving & Christmas. Trail is rated 1+, suitable for strollers and wheelchairs. Pets must be leashed. This is a level course mostly along sidewalks & some residential side streets. Nearly half the trail has a view of the Choptank River.

Cockeysville - 11km Walk (YR183) 25km Bike (YR996) **Apr 1-Nov 2**
Credit Only Events
Sponsoring Club: AVA-418,Baltimore Walking Club
POC: Edna Ford, 410-828-0834. 32 Southwark Bridge Way, Lutherville, MD 21093

Start Point: Hampton Inn, 410-527-1500. 11200 York Road. Via Rt 83, take exit 20A, Shawan Rd-East. Proceed to York Rd. Turn right on York to the 1st light at Ashland Rd. Inn is on the right.

Event Info: Daily, dawn to dusk. Both trails are rated 1. The walk is suitable for strollers & wheelchairs, with consideration for trail surface. Pets must be leashed. This is an easy walk on a converted railbed. Surface is finely crushed stone. The bike is also on a converted railbed. Bikers must sign waiver & we recommend you wear helmets. Inclement weather will affect trails. Both allow for easy enjoyment of nature.

College Park - 11km Walk (YR1045) 25km Bike (YR1044) **Jan 1-Dec 31**
B Awards available
Sponsoring Club: AVA-481, Great Greenbelt Volksmarchers
POC: Salva J. Holloman, 301-937-3549. 4617 Lincoln Ave, Beltsville, MD 20705

Start Point: College Park Airport Operations Building. From I-95 exit 23, Kenilworth Ave, South (Rt 201) then right on Calvert Rd/Paint Branch Pkwy. Go right on Cprl Frank Scott Dr - 3 blocks to start.

Event Info: Daily, dawn to dusk. The walk is rated 1+, suitable for strollers & wheelchairs. Pets are allowed but must be leashed. This event is on a paved surface trail with several inclines. The bike is rated 1+ and has all paved path. Bikers must sign a waiver. Please wear helmets.

Columbia - Two 10km Walk (YR216 & YR1042) **Jan 1-Dec 31**
A Awards available
Sponsoring Club: AVA-264, Columbia Volksmarch Club
POC: Jim Moore, 410-381-1837. 7328 Kindler Rd, Columbia, MD 21046

Start Point: Roy Rogers Restaurant, 410-995-6153. Owen Brown Village Center, 7244 Cradlerock Way. From I95 take exit 38 (Rt 32) West towards Columbia. Take 1st exit right on Brokenland Parkway. Turn right at 2nd light (1/2 mile) onto Cradlerock Way. Enter Village Center on left (1/4 mile) between Mobile Station and roy Rogers.

Event Info: Mon-Sat 6:30am-10pm; Sun 7am-9pm. Closed Thanksgiving & Christmas. Trails are rated 1+, suitable for strollers but not wheelchairs. Pets are allowed. Restroom & water available at start. Trails are mainly on asphalt paths & sidewalks.

Columbia - 10km Walk (YR740) 25km Bike (YR370) **Jan 1-Dec 31**
Walk has A Award available   Bike is a Credit Only Event
Sponsoring Club: AVA-264, Columbia Volksmarch Club
POC: Jim Moore, 410-381-1837. 7328 Kindler Rd, Columbia, MD 21046

Start Point: McDonalds Restaurant/Harpers Choice Village Center, 410-730-5571. 5485 Harpers Farm Road. From I-95 take exit 38 (Rt 32) West towards Columbia and Clarksville. Take 3rd exit right onto Cedar Lane. Stay on Cedar Lane to end at intersection with Harpers Farm Rd and turn left. Start is immediately on the right after turning off Cedar Lane.

Event Info: Mon-Sat 6am-11pm; Sun 7am-10pm. Closed Thanksgiving & Christmas. Walk is rated 1+ and is suitable for strollers but not wheelchairs. Pets are allowed. It is mainly on asphalt paths & sidewalks with one short segment on the side of highway with local traffice. The bike is rated 2. Bikers must sign waiver and should wear helmets. This route is along residential streets and country roads with some hills. Traffic may be heavy in some areas on weekday commuting hours.

Easton - 10km Walk (YR822) **Jan 2-Dec 31**
B Awards available
Sponsoring Club: AVA-595, Annapolis Amblers
POC: Gene/Roberta Ganske, 410-544-2243. 1234 Timber Turn, Arnold, MD 21012

Start Point: The Chaffinch House, 410-822-5074. 132 S. Harrison St. From US 50 in the Easton area, exit onto MD 322. Exit 322 at MD 33 (Bay St). At the end of Bay St, turn right onto Washington St. Turn left on Brooklets Ave. Go one block and start is on the far corner.

Event Info: Daily, 8-dusk. Trail is rated 2, suitable for strollers and wheelchairs. Pets must be leashed. Parking is limited to two hours in vicinity of start. Park in public parking lot just west of Washington St, one short block after you have passed the courthouse. Walk from there to the start. This event is on the streets of historic downtown area & residential Easton.

Frederick - 10km Walk (YR1279) **Jan 2-Dec 31**
Credit Only Event
Sponsoring Club: AVA-476, Piedmont Pacers
POC: Steve Duex, Sr., 410-848-4469. 916 Wampler Rd, Westminster, MD 21158

Start Point: Visitor's Center, 800-999-3613. 19 East Church St. From the East/West via I-70, take exit 54, Market St/MD 355. At the end of the ramp turn left and follow Market St north towards downtown Frederick. From the south, take I-270 to US Rt 15 North and follow the instructions below. From the North/Rt 15, take Rosemont Ave (exit 7) toward downtown Frederick and follow Information Signs to the Visitors Center. Park in garage adjacent to Center.

Event Info: Daily, 9-4:30. Must be finished by 4:30. Closed New Years, Easter, Thanksgiving & Christmas. Trail is rated 1+ and is suitable for strollers but not wheelchairs. Pets must be leashed. The trail is along the streets of historic Frederick to Mt Olivet Cemetary, the burial place of Francis Scott Key and other local historic figures.

Gaithersburg - Two 10km Walks (YR889 & YR890) **Jan 2-Dec 31**
B Awards available
Sponsoring Club: AVA-419, Seneca Valley Sugarloafers Volksmarch Club, Inc.
POC: Ed Branges, 301-340-9418. 1830 Greenplace Terr, Rockville MD 20850-2942

Start Point: Upper Montgomery County YMCA, 301-948-9622. 10011 Stedwick Rd. From South: I-495 to I-270 north to exit 11 (Rt 124E). *Continue on 124 East (Montgomery Village Ave) 1.90 miles past Lake Whetstone on right to Stedwick Rd. Left on Stedwick. Right on Mills Choice to YMCA parking lot on right. From North: I-270 south to exit 11A, Rt 124 east. Proceed from * above.

Event Info: Mon-Sat 6:30-dusk; Sun 10-dusk. Closed New Year's, ML King Day, Easter, Thanksgiving & Christmas. Trails are rated 1+. Suitable for strollers & wheelchairs. Pets must be leashed. Both trails are on paved bike paths & sidewalks leading through residential & recreational areas of Montgomery Village.

Gaithersburg - Two 10km Walks (YR339 & YR735) **Jan 1-Dec 31**
B Awards available
Sponsoring Club: AVA-419, Seneca Valley Sugarloafers Volksmarch Club, Inc.
POC: Ed Branges, 301-340-9418. 1830 Greenplace Terr, Rockville, MD 20850-2942

Start Point: Gourmet Grog Deli Store, 301-869-8100. 614 Quince Orchard Plaza From the south: I-270 to exit 10 (Rt 117). Left at 2nd light using inside turn lane. Right into Quince Orchard Plaza. From the north: I-270 to exit 11B (Quince Orchard Rd/Rt 124 West). Stay in right lane. Continue past 2nd light & turn right into Quince Orchard Plaza after passing Friendly's Restaurant. After registering, find directions to walk start point in box and drive to park to begin walk.

Event Info: Deli Open Mon-Sat 10-10; Sun 11-8. Closed Christmas & Thanksgiving. Seneca Creek State Park is open 8am to sunset Apr-Sep; 10-sunset Oct-Mar. Trails are rated 2 & 2+. Not suitable for strollers or wheelchairs. No pets allowed. **YR339** leads along Seneca Creek and Clopper Lake. It is mostly wooded and mostly on natural surfaces. There are some challenging hills. **YR735** leads around Clopper Lake on mostly woodland paths. Wet conditions may affect trail rating. Hiking boots and walking sticks are advised. Both trails offer scenic beauty and wildlife.

Greenbelt - 10km Walk (YR296) 300mtr Swim (YR1043) **Jan 1-Dec 31**
Credit Only Events
Sponsoring Club: AVA-481, Great Greenbelt Volksmarchers
POC: John Holloman, 301-937-3549. 4617 Lincoln Ave, Beltsville, MD 20705-1524

Start Point: Greenbelt Aquatics & Fitness Center, 301-397-2204. 101 Centerway. Take I-95 (495) to exit 23, Rt 193 east to Southway. Southway to Centerway. Baltimore-Washington Pkwy traffic: Northbound, exit MD193. Remain in far right lane of exit & bear right at end of ramp on Greenbelt Rd. Bear right before next traffic light onto Southway. Continue straight ahead to Greenbelt Center. Southbound: exit MD 193. Remain in far right lane of exit & bear right at end of ramp onto Southway. continue straight ahead to Greenbelt Center.

Event Info: Mon-Fri, 6am-10:30pm; Sat & Sun 8am-10pm. Open all holidays but call ahead for hours. You must pay an entry fee to use the pool. All swimmers must sign a waiver. Bring your own suit, towel & lock for locker. This is an indoor heated pool. The walk is rated 2, not suitable for strollers or wheelchairs. Pets must be leashed. You must make a short drive from the Aquatics & Fitness Center to the park where the event starts. The park is closed at dark. This trail is entirely on natural surfaces with a few brief departures from level. Wear adequate walking shoes. A walking stick is helpful if the trail is wet. There is one minor hill. Remember bug repellant in summer months. Poison Ivy is near much of the trail.

Havre de Grace - 10km Walk (YR131) **Jan 2-Dec 31**
Credit Only Event
Sponsoring Club: AVA-418, Baltimore Walking Club
POC: Richard/Carol Lindsley, 410-679-3594. 1223 Abinjud Dr, Abingdon MD 21009

Start Point: The Spencer Silver Mansion Bed & Breakfast, 200 S. Union St; 410-939-1097. From the North: Take Rt 95 to exit 89, Superior St as you enter Havre de Grace. Stay on Superior St to the end at Juniata St. Turn right to Bourbon St and turn left, continue to Union Ave. The start is on the corner on the right. From the South: Take Rt 95 north to exit 85-Aberdeen. Follow signs to Rt 40. Take Rt 40 East (toward Havre de Grace) for 1.5 miles to Rt 7. Take the right fork onto Rt 7 over the bridge. Rt 7 is Revolution St. Continue to Union St. Turn left to Bourbon St. Start is on the corner on the left.

Event Info: Start box is on front porch. Daily, 10-4. Must be finished by 7. Trail is rated 1, suitable for strollers & wheelchairs. Pets are allowed. This trail is on sidewalks through a historic town on the Susquehanna River. This is the duck decoy capital of the United States & offers the Decoy Museum, a historic lighthouse, & a boardwalk along the river.

Laurel - 10km Walk (YR219) **Jan 1-Dec 31**
A Award available
Sponsoring Club: AVA-190, Freestate Happy Wanderers
POC: Roger Turczyniski, 410-674-5518. 1848 Robin Court, Severn, MD 21144

Start Point: Comfort Suites, 301-206-2600. 14402 Laurel Place. From I-95, take exit 33A, Rt 198 East toward Laurel. At US Rt 1, turn right & continue south on US Rt 1 for about .2 miles. At Mulberry St, turn right (Bennigan's on opposite corner) & follow Mulberry St a short distance to Laurel Place. Turn right on Laurel Place & start will be on the left. Please park near back of lot. Ask the desk clerk for the volksmarch registration materials. The trail is not marked. A map & directions will be provided in the registration materials. Please remember that hotel guests come first.

Event Info: Daily, dawn to dusk. Trail is rated 1+, suitable for strollers but not wheelchairs. Pets must be leashed. This trail is relatively flat & is mostly on sidewalks & streets in the town of Laurel.

Monkton - Two 11km Walks (YR130 & YR1158) 27km Bike (YR1159) **Apr 1-Nov 2**
Credit Only Events
Sponsoring Club: AVA-418, Baltimore Walking Club
POC: William Ermatinger, 410-357-8611. 7 Owl Branch Lane, Parkton, MD 21120

Start Point: Monkton Bike Rental, 410-771-4058. 1900 Monkton Rd. Take I-83 to exit 27, Rt 137. Go east on 137 for 1/2 mile to Rt 45. Turn right on Rt 45-York Rd for 1/10 a mile to Rt 138, Monkton Rd. Turn left on Monkton Rd for 3 miles to start.

Event Info: Weekdays 10-6; Weekends, 8-6. Hours are subject to change because of weather. **Call to verify hours.** May be closed some holidays. The walks are rated 1, suitable for strollers & wheelchairs. Pets must be leashed. Inclement weather will affect all trails. **YR1158** goes south from

Monkton on converted railbed. **YR130** goes North from Monkton on a converted railbed. **YR1159**, the bike is rated 1. Bike rentals are available. Bikers must sign waiver and helmets are recommended. The bike trail goes North from Monkton on converted railbed. The surface of all events is finely crushed stone.

Rockville - Two 10km Walks (YR887 & YR888) **Jan 2-Dec 31**
B Awards available
Sponsoring Club: AVA-419, Seneca Valley Sugarloafers Volksmarch Club, Inc.
POC: Ed Branges, 301-340-9418. 1830 Greenplace Terrace, Rockville, MD 20850

Start Point: Norbeck Deli Beer & Wine, 301-460-1400. 5514 Norbeck Rd. I-495 to I-270 to exit 6A (W Montgomery Ave). Follow West Montgomery Ave 1.7 miles (follow signs for Veirs Mill Rd/Wheaton) to First St. Turn left onto First St. Continue about 1.5 miles to Bauer Dr. Turn right on Bauer Dr. Turn right into shopping center parkinglot.

Event Info: Deli Hours, Daily, 10-10 except Thur 10-9; Sun 10-7. Closed New Year's, Thanksgiving & Christmas. Both trails are rated 1+. Suitable for strollers & wheelchairs. Pets must be leashed. Leash laws are strictly enforced in Rockville. Both trails follow paved hiker/biker paths in Rock Creek Park along scenic Rock Creek. Nicely shaded paths. YR887 also visits Lake Needwood. YR888 visits Parklawn Memorial Park (pets are not allowed here so use optional trail instructions found in registration box).

Savage - 10km Walk (YR575) **Jan 2-Dec 31**
A Award available
Sponsoring Club: AVA-190, Freestate Happy Wanderers
POC: Sandy Lynch, 301-725-0918. 8548 Pineway Court, Laurel, MD 20723

Start Point: Antique Center II @ Savage Mill, 301-470-4373. 8600 Foundry St. From I-95, take exit 38A, Rt 32 East toward Ft. Meade. Follow for 1 mile to US Rt 1 South exit. At end of exit, turn right & follow Rt 1 for a short distance to 1st traffic signal - Howard St (Exxon station on corner). Turn right onto Howard. Follow Howard which becomes Baltimore St to dead end at end of town. Turn left onto Fair St & follow to West Parking Lot of Historic Savage Mill. Park in upper portion of lot & walk down to New Weave Building at opposite end of lot. Use the left entrance of the bldg to enter the Antique Center II. Ask the salesperson at the cash register for the volksmarch registration materials. The trail is partially marked with wooden AVA markers but a map and directions are needed and will be provided. Please remember that customers of the Antique Center come first.

Event Info: Daily, 9:30-3. Finish by 5. Bldg closes at 5:30. Closed New Years, Easter, Thanksgiving & Christmas. Trail is rated 2+, not suitable for strollers or wheelchairs. Pets are allowed. About half of this trail follows the Patuxent River along unpaved natural surface pathways & contains several moderate hills. The remainder of the trail is in residential areas & is relatively flat.

Severna Park - 12/16km Walk (YR746) 12km Walk (YR884) 26km Bike (YR738) 37km Bike (YR883) **Jan 2-Dec 31**
B Awards available
Sponsoring Club: AVA-616, Chesapeake Bay Country Wanderers
POC: Pam Donnick, 410-360-7913. 387 Cork Rd, Glen Burnie, MD 21060

Start Point: Community Center at Wood's, 410-647-5843. 623 Baltimore-Annapolis Blvd. From the north, go south from I-695 on Rt 10 (exit 2) for about 8 miles to Rt 2 (Governor Ritchie Hwy). Turn left onto Rt 2 and then right at the 7th traffic light onto Cypress Creek Rd (about 3.6 miles). From Cypress Creek Rd, go 0.2 miles to Summit Rd. Turn right. The Community Center is the beige colored building on the left. From the south, go north from Rt 50 on Rt 2 (Governor Ritchie Hwy) for about 5.1 miles. At the 5th traffic light (do not count the fire house lights) turn left onto Cypress Creek Road and follow directions above.

Event Info: Mon-Sat, 8-5. Sun, 1-5. Must be off trails by 5. Closed New Year's, Easter, Memorial Day, 4th of July, Labor Day, Thanksgiving & Christmas. May close for special occasions. Call if in doubt. YR746 is rated 1, suitable for strollers & wheelchairs. YR884 is rated 1+ and is suitable for strollers but not wheelchairs. Pets must be leashed. Both trails are on a macadem trail bed and neighborhood streets. Both bikes are rated 1+. They also follow a macadem trail bed and neighborhood streets. Bikers must sign waiver and should wear helmets.

Thurmont - 10km Walk (YR1280) **Jan 1-Dec 31**
Credit Only Event
Sponsoring Club: AVA-476, Piedmont Pacers
POC: Joe Wolfe, 301-271-3106. 13607 Winesap Circle, Thurmont, MD 21788

Start Point: Busy Bee Bakery, Mountain Gate Plaza, 140 Frederick Rd. From the south, exit US Rt 15 at green "Thurmont - MD 806" sign. Turn right at stop sign and left at traffic light onto Frederick Rd. Make immediate right into Exxon station and Mountain Gate Plaza. Start is on the right end. From the north, exit US Rt 15 at MD806. Turn left at stop sign and proceed as above.

Event Info: Daily, dawn to dusk. Trail is rated 1+. Strollers and wheelchairs will have difficulty. Route is on sidewalks and paved shoulders.

Westminster - 10km Walk (YR046)   27km Bike (YR723) **Jan 2-Dec 31**
Credit Only Events
Sponsoring Club: AVA-476, Piedmont Pacers
POC: Helen Lewis, 410-848-2480. 14 Spyglass Court, Westminster, MD 21158

Start Point: The Westminster Inn, 410-876-2893. 5 South Center St. From MD140/Center St Intersection turn towards downtown Westminster (away from Cranberry Mall) on Center St. At next stop light (Main St) go straight 1/2 block. Turn left onto South St. Inn is on the right. Park at the rear.

Event Info: Daily, 7-three hours before dusk. Finish by dusk. Closed New Years, Memorial Day, Thanksgiving & Christmas. For other major holiday, please call ahead. Walk is rated 1+, suitable for strollers but wheelchairs would have great difficulty. Pets must be leashed. It is on city sidewalks & streets. There are several instances where the route is slightly uphill. Bike is rated 2+. Bikers must sign waiver & wear helmets. The bike is on city streets & country roads and is not very difficult. 3/4 of one mile is on a gravel road.

Wheaton - 10/12km Walk (YR1167) **Jan 2-Dec 31**
Credit Only Event
Sponsoring Club: AVA-246, Walter Reed Wandervogel
POC: Dan Hessmann, 301-649-3910, 10941 Rocky Mount Way, Silver Spring, MD 20902

Start Point: Strosnider's Hardware Store, Kemp Mill Shopping Center, 301-593-5353. 1386 Lamberton Dr. From I-495, the Washington Beltway, exit on Georgia Av/MD-97 north, toward Wheaton. Go 2.5 miles passing 7 traffic lights. At the 8th light, Arcola Ave, turn right & go 1.5 miles passign 2 lights. At the 3rd light, Lamberton Ave, turn right into shopping center.

Alternate Start Point: Wheaton Metro Station, Georgia Ave & Reedie Dr. Take the Red Line on Washington metrorail to Wheaton Station. For walk details from Wheaton Station send a SASE to POC listed above.

Event Info: Mon-Fri 8am-8pm; Sat 8-6; Sun 9-3. Closed Easter, Memorial Day, July 4th, Labor Day, Thanksgiving & Christmas. Trail is rated 1+, suitable for strollers & wheelchairs. Pets are allowed. Each person will need a $1.10 fare card for the 10km option. It can be purchased at the Forest Glen Station.

Wheaton - 10km Walk (YR144) 10km Walk (YR233) **Jan 1-Dec 31**
A Award available
Sponsoring Club: AVA-190, Freestate Happy Wanderers
POC: Ann Hawthorne, 301-345-8583. 9439 Rhode Island Ave, College Park, MD 20740

Start Point: McDonald's. 12313 Georgia Ave (at Randolph Rd). From the Capitol Beltway (I-495) take exit 31A and follow Georgia Ave/Rt97, north toward Wheaton for 3.2 miles. McDonald's is on the corner of Georgia Ave & Randolph Road.

Event Info: Daily, 8-dusk. Closed Christmas. **YR144** is rated 2 but is not suitable for strollers or wheelchairs. Pets are not allowed. This event is mostly within Wheaton Regional Park & features natural surface & hardtop pathways, a wide variety of gardens, a greenhouse & a lake setting. **YR233** is rated 2+ and is not suitable for strollers or wheelchairs. Pets must be leashed. Bring your own water for this trail. It is on primarily natural surfaces with some steep hills.

MASSACHUSETTS ━━━━━━━━━━━━━━━━━━━━━

Bedford - 10/13km Walk (YR928) **Jan 1-Dec 31**   10/13km Ski (YR927) **Jan 1-Mar 31**
10/13km Roller Blade/Skate (YR294) **Apr 15-Sept 30**
Credit Only Events
Sponsoring Club: AVA-269, Walk 'n Mass Volkssport Club
POC: Charlie Smith, 508-263-5093. 1 Mohawk Dr, Acton, MA 01720

Start Point: Pro-Motion Shop, 617-275-1113. 111 South St. From Rt 128 take exit 31B (Rts 4/225) west to Bedford. At approximately 1.5 miles, turn left on Loomis St. Follow Loomis to end at South Rd. Start is across the street.

Event Info: Jan-Apr & Oct-Dec: Mon, Wed, Thur, Fri & Sat, 10-2; Tues & Sun, noon-2. Apr-Oct: 9-3 daily. All trails are rated 1. **YR928** is suitable for strollers & wheelchairs. Pets must be leashed. **YR294** is the skate event. Roller blade rentals & lessons are available. **YR927** is a ski event. It may NOT BE walked for credit except on the last weekend if there has been NO chance to ski the event. Call for verification of hours and snow conditions. . Rental skis & lessons are available. No strollers or wheelchairs. Pets must be leashed. All events follow the Minute Man Recreation Trail which is flat & paved. Alternate country routes for the walk & ski are not suitable for strollers or wheelchairs and you should not ski it alone. Restroom facilities are not available on the country route. REMEMBER: Only one event credit for each of these events, even if you do both distances.

++Boston - 10km Walk (YR1090-Back Bay & Beacon Hill) 11km Walk (YR730-Freedom Trail)
Apr 1-Dec 12
A Award available
Sponsoring Club: AVA-269, Walk'n Mass Volkssport Club
POC: Don Meltzer, 508-443-8513. 341 Old Lancaster Rd, Sudbury, MA 01776

Start Point: Boston National Historical Park Visitor Center, 15 State St. across from the Old State House. From I-93S take exit 25 (Haymarket Sq/Gov't Ctr). Parking garage is at the bottom of the ramp. Driving to start, left at 1st light (Merrimac St which becomes Congress). Right at State St (4th light). From I-93N take exit 22 (Atlantic/Northern Ave). Right onto Atlantic & left on State. Public Transportation: Rapid Transit System-Orange "T" line to State St. Commuter rail to either North or South Station. Then Orange "T" Line to State St.

Event Info: Memorial to Labor Days: 8am-6pm. Labor Day to Memorial Day, 8am-5pm. Both trails are rated 1, suitable for strollers & wheelchairs. Pets must be leashed. **YR730** is on downtown city streets & walkways; exploring a plethora of historic sites, monuments, museums & landmarks. **YR1090** is on city sidewlaks & park pathways through the posh Back Bay & aristocratic Beacon Hill sections of Boston.

Chicopee - 10km Walk (YR926) Jan 1-Dec 31
A Award available
Sponsoring Club: AVA-784, Connecticut Valley Volkssport Club
POC: Donna Rabitaille, 413-594-3161. PO Box 251, Glastonbury, CT 06033-0251

Start Point: Store 24, 413-592-6910. 201 Exchange St. **From I-90** east or west, take Chicopee exit 5. After toll, bear right. Right at light on Rt 33, go down hill & around left curve. (You see Rt 141 E signs). Cross wire bridge in right lane. Bear right at the end of the bridge. Go straight thru intersection to end of street. You will pass Chicopee Fire and Police stations. Left on Grove St one block to Front St. Go right on Front 1.4 miles to junction of 116 (City Hall is on your left). Go thru intersection to first left (1/2 block), Cabet St which is one way so be in right lane as you turn into Plaza parking lot right away. Store 24 is in the Plaza. **From I-91North** to I-391, take 1st exit #2 (Chicopee/Elms College). Right on Exchange St, three blocks to Perkins St. Left on Perkins right into Plaza parking lot. Disregard DO NOT ENTER sign in Perkins St as it is for the rest of the street after the Plaza. **From I-91 South,** to 391 right after the CT River Bridge. Loop under and get on I-391 north. Be in right lane. Follow I-91 north directions from here.

Event Info: Daily, dawn to dusk. Trail is rated 1, suitable for strollers & wheelchairs. Pets must be leashed.

Concord - 11km Walk (YR223) Apr 1-Dec 14
A Award available
Sponsoring Club: AVA-269, Walk'n Mass Volkssport Club
POC: Jeanette Dose', 508-663-6756. 7 Shedd Rd, Billerica, MA 01862

Start Point: Best Western Motel, 508-369-6100. Rt 2 and Elm St. From Rt 128/95, take Rt 2 west toward Concord. Pass Emerson Hospital on left. Turn right at the second set of lights after the hospital. Start is in front of you. From Rt 495 take Rt 2 East. After Concord Rotary, take a left at 1st set of lights. Start is in front of you.

Event Info: Daily, dawn to dusk. Trail is rated 1+. Suitable for strollers & wheelchairs. Pets must be leashed. This is a historical route that inlcudes North Bridge & multiple sites of the Revolutionary War beginning. Walk during daylight hours only.

Danvers - 10km Walk (YR245) Jan 1-Dec 31
A Award available
Sponsoring Club: AVA-573, Two Town Walking Club
POC: Joe Piffat, 508-762-0494. 56 Ledgewood Dr, Danvers, MA 01923

Start Point: Super 8 Motel, 508-774-6500, 225 Newbury St (Rt 1 North). From the north take I-95 South to exit 48 & go north on US Rt 1 for 1/2 mile. Start is on the right. From the south take US Rt 1 north from Boston and points south or from I-95 N and Rt 128.

Event Info: Daily, dawn to dusk. Start box is under the desk at the side door. Trail is rated 1+ suitable for strollers & wheelchairs. Pets must be leashed. The trail goes by many homes & monuments dating from the time of witchcraft hysteria (1690s) and when town was an early center for the shoe industry (19th century).

Ipswich - 10km Walk (YR631) Apr 1-Dec 1
B Awards available
Sponsoring Club: AVA-573, Two Town Walking Club
POC: Peg Boudreau, 508-468-4765. 6 Eddel Ave, Wenham, MA 01984

Start Point: Bruni Farms, Inc, 508-356-2332. Rt 133, Essex Rd. From I-95 take exit 54 onto Rt 133 east toward Rowley. When Rt 133 joins Rt 1A, follow Rt's 133/1A through Ipswich center and stay on Rt 133 turning left as 1A continues straight. Look for start/finish 1/4 mile on left.

Event Info: Daily, dawn to dusk. Trail is rated 1+, suitable for strollers & wheelchairs. Pets must be leashed. This trail goes by many 17th & 18th century historic homes and over the oldest stone bridge in North America.

Lexington - 27km Bike (YR295) **Apr 15-Nov 2**
Credit Only Event
Sponsoring Club: AVA-269, Walk 'n Mass Volkssport Club
POC: Betty Foley, 508-443-4857. 807 Boston Post Rd, Sudbury MA 01776

Start Point: Bikeway Cycle Center, 617-861-1199. 3 Bow St. From Rt 128/95, take Rt 2A·east toward Lexington for 3 miles. Turn right onto Rt 4/225 and go one mile. Bear left onto Massachusetts Ave. Keep to left lane. Turn left onto Bow St. Cycle shop is on the right. Parking in rear.

Event Info: Mon-Fri, 10-6; Sat, 10-4; Sun, 12-3. Trail is rated 1. Helmets are mandatory and participants must sign a waiver. Carrying water is recommended. Bike rentals are available. This is a completely flat trail on a newly constructed bike trail which parallels Paul Revere's famous ride on April 19, 1775.

Nahant - Two 10km Walks (YR1086 & YR1087) **Apr 15-Dec 2**
A Award available
Sponsoring Club: AVA-573, Two Town Walking Club
POC: Richard Rossi, 508-887-5901. 91 Washington St, Topsfield, MA 01983

Start Point: Nahant Liquor & Variety, 617-581-1060. 2A Wilson Rd. Take I-95 north or south to Rt 1. Go south on Rt 1 to Rt 129 in Lynnfield. Take Rt 129 east, cross Rt 1A to Shore Dr. Go left to Rotary & Nahant - s/f at the end of Causeway left.

Event Info: Daily, dawn to dusk. Call 617-581-1060 if in doubt about hours or days of operation. Both trails are rated 1+ and are suitable for strollers & wheelchairs. Pets must be leashed. YR1086 passes by many unique homes & has many panoramic ocean views. YR1087 goes along an ocean causeway & beach from Nahant to Lynn & Swampscott & back. Panoramic ocean views.

Newburyport - 10km Walk (YR1265) **Apr 1-Dec 1**
A Award available
Sponsoring Club: AVA-573, Two Town Walking Club
POC: Benedict Andreozzi, 508-465-8603. 201 Storey Ave, Newburyport, MA 01950

Start Point: Maudslay State Park, 508-465-7223. Curzon Mill Rd. From Rt 95 in Newburyport, take exit 57 onto Rt 113 (Story St). Go west towards West Newbury. Pass Phillips St (right) then Phillips (right) again, Artichoke (right) and take the next right onto Hoyls Lanes. After 1/2 mile turn right onto Mill Rd and park on the right.

Event Info: Daily, 8-dusk. Trail is rated 1+ and is suitable for strollers & wheelchairs during dry times. Pets must be leashed. This trail consists of two 5km loops on the park trails. You will pass over several bridges with views of the Merrimack River and gardens in the Estate section.

Salem - 10km Walk (YR060) **Jan 1-Dec 31**
A Award available
Sponsoring Club: AVA-573, Two Town Walking Club
POC: Joan Chandler, 508-927-8785. 350 Old Essex Rd, Beverly, MA 01915

Start Point: Brothers Deli & Restaurant, 283 Derby St. From I-95 take exit 45. Take Rt 128 North towards Beverly/Gloucester. Take exit 26 and follow US National Park signs until you get on Rt 1A. Take right on Derby St. Deli is on left.

Event Info: Daily, dawn to dusk. Trail is rated 1 and is suitable for strollers & wheelchairs. Pets must be leashed. This is a very bewitching walk in historic (1630 era) Salem. It has ocean views & a wide selection of architecture.

Sandwich - Two 10km Walks (YR608 & YR1095) **May 23-Sept 30**
YR608 has an A Award available   YR1095 has B Awards available
Sponsoring Club: AVA-410, Empire State Capital Volkssporters
POC: Dan Schryver, 518-765-4630. 5667 Depot Rd., Voorheesville, NY 12186. PO Box 6995, Albany, NY 12206

Start Point: Dan'l Webster Inn, 149 Main St; 508-888-3622. From Rt 25 or 28, cross over Bourne Bridge, around Rotary 3/4 way to 6A exit. Drive on 6A to 3rd set of lights, turn right on Jarves St. At end turn right onto Main St. Start is on your right a short way down. From Rt 3, cross Sagamore Bridge which exits onto Rt 6. Take exit 2/Rt 130, turn left at end of ramp. Follow for 2 miles & turn right at fork in road onto Main St. Inn is on the left.

Event Info: Daily, dawn to dusk. Both trails are rated 1+, suitable for strollers & wheelchairs. Pets must be leashed. **YR608** is a journey through Cape Cod's oldest town. Pass several museums, gardens & across a boardwalk over a salt flat. **YR1095** circles the Sandwich Marina & takes you along the Cape Cod Canal for 3 miles.

South Hamilton - 26km Bike (YR334) **Apr 1-Dec 1**
Credit Only Event
Sponsoring Club: AVA-573, Two Town Walking Club
POC: Diana Campbell, 508-468-3164. 22 Grant Ave, South Hamilton, MA 01982

Start Point: Bay Road Bike Shop, 52 Railroad Avenue; 508-468-1301. From I-95 north take exit 45 on to Rt 128 north towards Gloucester. On Rt 128 take exit 20A, Rt 1A north towards Hamilton. Pass Wenham Lake on left through Wenham. After Mobil Station take first left (Railroad Ave). Bike shop is on your left across from Post Office.

Event Info: Daily, 10-6. Closed Sunday to 1pm. Call bike shop to make sure it is open. Rated 1+. The course is on paved roads in Hamilton & Ipswich. Passes by many horse & animal farms.

Springfield - 10km Walk (YR1335) **Jan 1-Dec 31**
A Award available
Sponsoring Club: AVA-784, Connecticut Valley Volkssport Club
POC: Donna Robitaille, 413-594-3161. PO Box 251, Glastonbury, CT 06033

Start Point: Store 24, 413-732-3150. 808 Main St. From the south: I-91 north to exit 4, Broad St. Take right onto Broad St then left onto Main St and continue five or six blocks to start on the left. From the north: I-91 south to exit 5, Broad St. Take left on Broad to Main then left onto Main to start. From the east: I-90 (Mass Pike) to exit 6 (Rt 291) to I-91 S and follow above directions from the North. From the west: I-90 (Mass Pike) to exit 5 (West Springfield) to I-91 S and follow above directions from the North.

Event Info: Daily, dawn to dusk. Trail is rated 1+ and is suitable for strollers and wheelchairs. Pets are allowed. Route follows city streets & sidewalks.

Sudbury - 10km Walk (YR836) **Apr 15-Nov 31**
A Award available
Sponsoring Club: AVA-269, Walk'n Mass Volkssport Club
POC: Dave Bagley, 508-443-8253. 21 Stubtoe Lane, Sudbury, MA 01776

Start Point: Coach House Inn, 508-443-2223. 738 Boston Post Rd (Rt 20). From Rt 128/95 take exit 26-Rt 20 West- for 10 miles. The Inn is on the right. From Rt 495 take Rt 20 East through Marlborough into Sudbury for 8 miles. Inn is on the left.

Event Info: Daily, dawn to dusk. Trail is rated 1+ and is suitable for strollers & wheelchairs. Pets must be leashed. Route follows rural country roads to the Wayside Inn Historical Area made famous by Longfellow and is the oldest continuously operating Inn in the US.

Williamstown - 10km Walk (YR867) **Apr 1-Nov 30**
A Award available
Sponsoring Club: AVA-410, Empire State Capital Volkssporters
POC: Beryl Wolf, 518-383-2880. 605-B Clifton Park Center Rd, Clifton Park, NY 12065. Lois Heyer, 518-477-6236. 12 Boncroft Dr, East Greenbush, NY 12061

Start Point: The Williams Inn, 413-458-9371. Junction of Rtes 2 & 7. 30 miles from Massachusetts Turnpike Exit B-3 to Rt 22N.

Event Info: Volkssporters receive a 10% discount on rooms & meals. Daily, 8-dusk. Rated 1+, suitable for strollers & wheelchairs with help. Pets must be leashed. The trail follows paths through the streets & sidewalks in the picturesque village of Williamstown & through the campus of Williams College.

MICHIGAN ━━━━━━━━━━━━━━━━━━━━━━━━

Berrien Center - 10km Walk (YR1338) **Apr 1-Nov 14**
A Award available
Sponsoring Club: AVA-0855, Healthy Berrien Volksmarch Club
POC: Pat Underwood or park staff, 616-471-2617. 9228 Huckleberry Rd, Berrien Center, MI 49102

Start Point: Love Creek County Park, Nature Center, 616-471-2617. 9228 Huckleberry Rd. Take MI Rt 31 to Dean's Hill Rd to Huckleberry Rd.

Event Info: Daily, 9-5. Closed Mondays. Trail is rated 2 and is not suitable for strollers or wheelchairs. Pets are not allowed. Route goes over rolling hills through heavily wooded area.

Holland - 10km Walk (YR1275) **Apr 1-Nov 30**
A Award available
Sponsoring Club: AVA-461, Historic Pathwalkers
POC: Jean Woltjer, 616-392-2844. 185 Glendale Ave, Holland, MI 49423

Start Point: The Mole Hole, 616-396-7467. 15 West 8th St. From the North: Take US31 south to 8th St and turn right. Go to the 1st light and turn left into town. Start will be on the right. From the South and East: I-196 to exit 52 (16th St/Adams St). Go west 4 miles to River Ave. Turn right and go 7 blocks to 9th St. Turn right and go 1 block to Central Ave. Turn left and go 1 block to 8th St and turn left. Start is on the right.

Event Info: Mon-Sat, 10-6. Closed Sundays & major holidays. Trail is rated 1, suitable for strollers and wheelchairs but not all corners have cuts. Pets are allowed. This course starts in Historic downtown Holland and goes through neighborhoods, the campus of Hope College and along the river trail with a view of the authentic windmill imported from the Netherlands.

Ionia - 10/13km Walk (YR536) **Jan 1-Dec 31**
A Award available
Sponsoring Club: AVA-461, Historic Pathwalkers
POC: John W. Pierce, 616-527-2413. 2215 Marquette Rd, Ionia, MI 48846

Start Point: Dan's Bicycle & Lock Shop, 616-527-0471. 116 S. Depot. Ionia is located halfway between Lansing & Grand Rapids, 7 miles N of I-96 (exit 67) or at the junction of M-21 & M-66. To reach Dan's Bicycle & Lock Shop, go two blocks east of M-66 on Main St (downtown business district) to Depot St. Turn south to last building on the east side.

Event Info: Mon-Fri, 9-6; Sat, 9-3. Hours are subject to change. Call to verify. Closed Sundays & major holidays. Trail is rated 2. Suitable for strollers & wheelchairs though not all corners are handicap accessible. Pets are allowed. Trail is through historic Ionia, including National Register Historic Districts.

Lansing - 10km Walk (YR953) **Apr 1-Nov 30**
A Award available
Sponsoring Club: AVA-461, Historic Pathwalkers
POC: John Pierce, 616-527-2413. 2215 Marquette Rd, Ionia, MI 48846-9513

Start Point: Michigania, 517-484-1137. 113 S Washington Square. From I-496, exit 6 (Walnut & Pine Streets. Take Walnut north (one-way) to Allegan St (south side of capitol) go east on Allegan (one-way) to Washington Square. Go north on Washington Square to start 1/2 block down on the east side.

Event Info: Mon-Fri, 9:30-6; Sat, 10-4. Closed Sundays & major holidays. Hours are subject to change. Call first to verify. Trail is rated 1. Suitable for strollers & wheelchairs although not all curbs have cuts. Pets must be leashed and are not allowed in the bldgs. The course goes by historic Capitol & governmental bldgs; city neighborhoods & 3 miles of river trail.

Mackinaw City - Two 10km Walks (YR959 & YR960) 13km Walk (YR961) 26km Bike (YR962) **May 24-Sep 1**
B Awards available
Sponsoring Club: AVA-824, Mackinaw Walkers Volkssport Club
POC: Jim Muma, 618-234-8706. 1706 Pine, Belleville, IL 62226-4256

Start Point: Tee Pee Campground, 616-436-5391. US-23, one mile from Mackinac Bridge. From I-75, use exit 337, turn right on M-108 then right on US-23 or from the north, use exit 338 to US-23. Campground is about one mile. On Saturday and Sunday (Aug 30 and 31) ONLY, register at Shepler's Dock in Mackinaw City.

Event Info: Daily, 9-4 and finish by 7 p.m. All trails are nearly flat, rated 1 and suitable for strollers or wheelchairs. Pets are allowed but must be leashed. Pets are not allowed in public buildings. Restrooms and water are available along the trails, except only at the Visitor Center and British Landing on Mackinac Island. Bikers must sign a waiver. Tee Pee Campground offers a 10% discount to volksmarch campers. Shepler's Ferry offers a reduced fee to volksmarchers going to the island. Events are at Mackinaw City, Mackinac Island and St. Ignace.

Niles - 10km Walk (YR1339) **Jan 1-Dec 31**
A Award available
Sponsoring Club: AVA-855, Healthy Berrien Volksmarch Club
POC: Jay Dean or park staff, 616-683-8280. 3038 Adams Rd, Niles, MI 49120

Start Point: Madeline Bertrand County Park, 616-683-8280. 3038 Adams Rd. Take MI Rt 31 to Rt 12 to Third St to Adams.

Event Info: Daily, dawn to dusk. Trail is rated 2 and is not suitable for strollers or wheelchairs. Pets must be leashed. Route follows St Joseph River and goes through wooded areas in two states (Michigan & Indiana).

━━━━━━━━━━━━━━

South Haven - 10km Walk (YR561) **Apr 1-Nov 30**
A Award available
Sponsoring Club: AVA-461, Historic Pathwalkers
POC: Daryle & Joan Fountain, 616-527-4854. 2303 Marquette Rd, Ionia, MI 48846

Start Point: The Blueberry Store, 616-637-6322. 525 Phoenix St. Additional start cards & maps available across street at Arkins Gift Shop for early participants. Exit I-196 at exit 20 (Phoenix Road). Turn left (west) on Phoenix to Blueberry Store.

Event Info: Daily, 10-5. Early participants can get startcards at Arkins Gift Shop as noted above. Call The Blueberry Store to confirm hours and days open. Trail is rated 2, suitable for strollers & wheelchairs but all corners do not have cuts. Pets are allowed but must be leashed and cleaned up after. Route is entirely on city streets. South Haven is a cozy resort town on Lake Michigan. The trail takes you through lovely parks, quaint shops, museums, lighthouse, pier & beach. Bring your swimsuit.

St. Joseph - 10km Walk (YR1340) **Jan 1-Dec 31**
A Award available
Sponsoring Club: AVA-855, Healthy Berrien Volksmarch Club
POC: Brian Bailey or seasonal park staff, 616-982-0533. Lake St.

Start Point: Silver Beach County Park, 616-982-0533. Lake St. Take Business 94 to Park St to Lake Michigan (Silver Beach).

Alternate Start Point: Lions Park Beach. Registration: Park Inn International, 1-800-228-5885. 4290 Red Arrow Highway, Stevensville, MI 49127. Call Park International for directions.

Event Info: Park office is staffed in summer from 9-5. Register at Park Inn International during other seasons. Trail is rated 2 and is suitable for strollers and wheelchairs. Pets must be leashed. Route follows Lake Michigan and passes through the historic homes district. It is all paved.

MINNESOTA ━━━━━━━━━━━━━━━━━━━━━━━

Albert Lea - 10km Walk (YR119) **May 23-Sep 1**
B Awards available
Sponsoring Club: AVA-601, Minnesota State Parks
POC: Jerry Katzenmeyer, 507-373-5084. Myre Big Island State Park, Rt 3, Box 33, Albert Lea, MN 56007

Start Point: Park Office, Myre Big Island State Park, 507-373-5084. (May be self-registration) Rt 3, Box 33. The park is located three miles SE of Albert Lea on County Hwy 38. I-90 and I-35 intersect just north of Albert Lea. Both Interstates have signs directing visitors to the park. Exit 11 on I-35 is the most convenient approach to the park.

Event Info: Daily 8am-1pm. Finish by 5. Park Office may not have staff available to stamp IVV books until ater 10:30 am. Please plan your schedule accordingly. Trail is rated 2 and contains moderate and gently rolling hills. It is not suitable for strollers or wheelchairs. Pets must be leashed. Route is on all natural trails through mixed open and wooded areas and along a lake.

Apple Valley - 10km Walk (YR104) **Jan 1-Dec 31**
A Award available
Sponsoring Club: AVA-MN, Minnesota Volkssport Assn.
POC: Darwin Lay, 612-432-7318/612-456-6633. 14081 Glazier Ave, Apple Valley, MN 55124

MINNESOTA, cont.

Start Point: Americinn Motel, 612-431-3800. 15000 Glazier Ave. 10 miles south of Mall f America in Bloomington on #77 (Cedar Ave) to 147th and Cedar. East one block to Glazier and turn right to Motel.

Event Info: Daily, dawn to dusk. Trail is rated 1 and is suitable for strollers and wheelchairs. Pets must be leashed. Walk before 4:00 and plan to walk in and enjoy Minnesota largest zoo. Entrance fee required for zoo. Route is mostly on a bike/hike paved trail. A couple of intersections could be busy.

Argyle - 10km Walk (YR123) **May 23-Sept 1**
B Awards available
Sponsoring Club: AVA-601, MN State Parks
POC: Mary Broten, Old Mill State Park, 218-437-8174. Rt 1, Box 42, Argyle, MN 56713

Start Point: Old Mill State Park Office, 218-437-8174. The park is located in northwestern Minnesota between the towns of Argyle and Newfolden. From Argyle, go 12 miles east on CR 4, then head north on CR 4 for one mile to CR 39. From Newfoldn, go 10 miles west on CR 4.

Event Info: Park is open 8am-10pm. Walkers may start from 9am on but must finish by 5pm. Trail is rated 2 and is suitable for strollers or wheelchairs. Pets must be leashed. Water is available at the park office. The route includes shaded, wooded trails interspersed with open tall grass and blooming prairie areas. A few gentle, rolling hills. Historic mill site is on the route.

Austin - 10km Walk, (YR1260) **Apr 1-Nov 31**
Credit Only Event
Sponsoring Club: AVA-114, Twin Cities Volksmarchers
POC: Bonita Johnson, 612-789-4416. 1618 Madison St, NE, Minneapolis, MN 55413

Start Point: Austin Auto Truck Plaza, 1509 10th Place NE. Exit 179 off I-90 in Austin.

Event Info: Daily, dawn to dusk. Trail is rated 1+ suitable for strollers or wheelchairs with some difficulty. Pets must be leashed. The majority of this trail is in the Hormel Nature Center.

Bloomington - Two 10km Walks, (YR594 & YR807) **Jan 1-Dec 31**
B Awards available
Sponsoring Club: AVA-793, Meandering Minnesotans
POC: Milt Luoma, 612-890-7560. 303 Concorde Place, Burnsville, MN 55337

Start Point: Super America, E 90th & Old Cedar Ave. Take MN Hwy 77 to Old Shakopee Rd. Go west on Old Shakopee Rd to Old Cedar Ave. Go north on Old Cedar Ave to E 86th St.

Event Info: Daily, dawn to dusk. Trails are rated 1 and are suitable for strollers and wheelchairs. Pets must be leashed. YR807 is near the Mall of America and through residential neighborhoods. YR594 is entirely within the Mall of America.

Detroit Lakes - 10km Walk (YR1098) **Apr 1-Nov 15**
Credit Only Event
Sponsoring Club: AVA-114, Twin Cities Volksmarchers
POC: Bonita Johnson, 612-789-4416. 1618 Madison St NE, Minneapolis, MN 55413

Start Point: Americinn Motel, 777 Highway 10 East. Located on south side of Highway 10, 1.4 miles east of Downtown on 10E.

Event Info: Daily, 7-dusk. Trail is rated 1, suitable for strollers & wheelchairs. Pets must be leashed. Walk by beautiful Lake Detroit & see the City of Detroit Lakes.

MINNESOTA, cont.

Duluth - Two 10km Walks (YR618 & YR808) **Jan 1-Dec 31**
B Awards available
Sponsoring Club: AVA-793, Meandering Minnesotans
POC: Milt Luoma, 612-890-7560. 303 Concorde Place, Burnsville, MN 55337

Start Point: St. Luke's Hospital, 915 East First St. Take I-35 to Lake Ave. Lake Ave west two blocks to Superior St. North to London Rd. Left to First St. Left to St. Luke's

Event Info: Daily, 8am-9pm. Trails are rated 1 and are suitable for strollers or wheelchairs. Pets must be leashed. YR618 is along Duluth's Lake Walk on the shores of Lake Superior. YR808 is along Duluth's downtown city streets.

Grand Rapids - 10km Walk (YR1064) **Apr 1-Sept 30**
A Award available
Sponsoring Club: AVA-697, Central Minnesota Volkssports
POC: Karla Gengler, 320-251-5285. 1715 9th Ave SE, St Cloud, MN 56304.

Start Point: Sawmill Inn, 2301 South Pokegama Ave. Located on the southern edge of Grand Rapids on Hwy 169.

Event Info: Daily, dawn to dusk. Trail is rated 1, suitable for strollers & wheelchairs. Pets must be leashed. This is a pleasant walk starting near the birthplace of Judy Garland & going through & around the village. The Forest History Center is nearby.

Hastings - 10km Walk (YR934) **May 23-Sep 1**
B Awards available
Sponsoring Club: AVA-601, Minnesota State Parks
POC: Calvin Kontola/Gene Groebner, 612-436-5391. Afton State Park, 6959 Peller Ave South, Hastings, MN 55033

Start Point: Interpretive Center, Afton State Park, 612-436-5391. 6959 Peller Ave South. Located 9 miles east of St. Paul on I-94 to County Rd 15; 7 miles south on Cty 15, then 3 miles east on Cty Rd 20. Register at the park office or at a self-registration near the office.

Event Info: Daily start 9am-11am and finish by 5pm. Trail is rated 4 and is not suitable for strollers or wheelchairs. Pets must be leashed. Route is very hilly along the St Croix Valley. Travels through maple-basswood valleys along the St Croix River and through restored prairie areas.

Hutchinson - 10km Walk (YR546) **Jan 1-Dec 31** 25km Bike (YR1258) **Apr 1-Sept 30**
B Awards available
Sponsoring Club: AVA-837, Crow River Crawlers
POC: Murray Swenson, 320-587-6815. 408 Alan Street SW, Hutchinson, MN 55350

Start Point: Citgo Quik Mart, Main St & 4th Ave. Located at intersection of Hwy 7 & Hwy 15.

Event Info: Daily, dawn to dusk. Walk trail is rated 1+. Strollers & wheelchairs may experience some difficulty. Pets must be leashed. Follows city sidewalks, loose gravel & park trails along the Crow River. The bike is also rated 1+. It follows some city streets, a gravel state trail and a former railroad bed. Biker should wear helmets and must sign the waiver.

Lake Bronson - 11km Walk (YR121) **May 23-Sep 1**
B Awards available
Sponsoring Club: AVA-601, Minnesota State Parks
POC: Garry Barvels, 218-754-2200. Box 9, Lake Bronson, MN 56734

Start Point: Park Office, Lake Bronson State Park, 218-754-2200. The park is located one mile east of the town of Lake Bronson on Country Rd #28.

Event Info: Daily 8am-10pm. Walkers must finish by 5pm. Trail is rated 2 and is not suitable for strollers or wheelchairs. Pets must be leashed. Route is fairly flat on all natural trails through open prairie and wooded areas and along a lake. Excellent opportunity to see deer and moose. Combine this event with Old Mill State Park & Zippel Bay State Park as well as a walk or two in Canada. The Winnipeg Club has many events this season. Cal 204-888-5307 for more information.

Lake City - 11kmWalk (YR188) **May 3-Oct 19 (Weekends & Holidays only)**
B Awards available
Sponsoring Club: AVA-601, Minnesota State Parks
POC: Harry Roberts, 612-345-3401or Al Holmes, 612-345-3401. Frontenac State Park, 29223 Co 28 Blvd, Lake City, MN 55041

Start Point: Park Office/Contact Station, 612-345-3401. Frontenac State Park, 29223 Co 28 Blvd. Park is located 7.5 miles NW of Lake City on TH. 61. Turn right on Goodhue County Rd 2 in small community of Frontenac. Proceed one mile to park entrance.

Event Info: Weekends & Holidays 8am-10pm. Weekday walks can be arranged by appointment. Trail is rated 4 and is not suitable for strollers or wheelchairs. Pets must be leashed. Water is available at the start and at one water station along the route. The trail ranges from level fields and bluff tops to rolling hills and moderate slopes. Elderly and physically challenged people should consult with manager before attempting trail. Surface is mostly sod with some hardpack areas. Trail begins with 1/2 mile uphill segment; about half the trail covers rugged terrain. The second half is quite flat.

Mankato - Two 10km Walks (YR192 & YR769) **Apr 1-Dec 31**
B Awards available
Sponsoring Club: AVA-161, Riverbend Striders
POC: Audrey/Earl von Holt, 507-625-5375. 1709 Linda Ln, N. Mankato MN 56003

Start Point: Holiday Inn Downtown, 101 Main St. From Hwy 169 take the downtown exit onto the bridge. Exit right onto Main St and the Holiday Inn is on your left.

Event Info: Holiday Inn offers a Volkssport Discount on rooms. Daily, dawn to dusk. **YR192** is rated 2, suitable for strollers & wheelchairs with some difficulty in areas. Pets must be leashed. this trail is mostly sidewalks. It is in town through residential, business & park areas with some natural trails. **YR769** is rated 3. Strollers & wheelchairs would have to bypass stairs to get to the trail. Pets are not allowed on this trail. This is an in-town walk along the river through residential areas & parks. Mostly flat, however it has one flight of stairs & some grassy & natural trails.

McGregor - 10km Walk (YR122) **Jun 1-Sep 6**
B Awards available
Sponsoring Club: Minnesota State Parks
POC: Tom Remus, 218-426-3271. Savanna Portage State Park, HCR 3, Box 591, McGregor, MN 55460

Start Point: Park Hqs, Savanna Portage State Park, 218-426-3271. HCR 3, Box 591. The park is located 7 miles north of McGregor on State Hwy 65, then 10 miles NE on SCAH 14.

Event Info: Park is open daily 8am-10pm. Walkers may start from 9-1 and must finish by 5. Trail is rated 3+ and is not suitable for strollers or wheelchairs. Pets must be leashed. This route will include a portion of the historic Savanna Portage, used by the voyageurs for two centuries. It is a wilderness trail with abundant wildflowers, songbirds and wildlife, pine and hardwood forests. May be wet in low areas. Water available at start/finish only. Brind a canteen for supplemental water.

MINNESOTA, cont.

Minneapolis - Two 10km Walks (YR525 & YR526) **Jan 1-Dec 31** 25km Bike (YR528) **Apr 1-Oct 31**
YR525 is a Credit Only Event. YR526 has an A Award available   Bike has B Awards available
Sponsoring Club: AVA-114, Twin Cities Volksmarchers
POC: Darlene Peterson, 612-722-2261. 4020 45th Ave South, Minneapolis, MN 55406

Start Point: Super America Station, 4320 East Lake St.

Event Info: Daily, dawn to dusk. **YR526** is rated 1 and is suitable for strollers or wheelchairs. Pets must be leashed. See the east bank of the Mississippi and the Univeristy of Minnesota. **YR525** is rated 2, no strollers or wheelchairs. Pets must be leashed. See the Mississippe River, Minnehaha Falls and beautiful park areas. **YR528** is rated 2, no wheelchairs, strollers or pets. It follows paved trails along the Mississippi River. Bikers must sign a waiver and helmets are recommended.

Minneapolis - 10km Walk (YR791) 12km Walk (YR792) **Jan 1-Dec 31**
YR791 has an A Award available   YR792 has B Awards available
Sponsoring Club: AVA-114, Twin Cities Volksmarchers
POC: Bonita Johnson, 612-789-4416. 1618 Madison St NE, Minneapolis, MN 55413

Start Point: Regal Minneapolis Hotel, 612-332-0371. 1313 Nicollet Mall.   Located in downtown Minneapolis.

Event Info: Daily, dawn to dusk. Pets are allowed on both events if leashed. **YR791** is rated 1+, suitable for strollers & wheelchairs. This is the "Stone Bridge Walk". You will cross the Mississippi on the historic Stone Bridge & see early Minneapolis District (restored). **YR792** is rated 1 and is suitable for strollers or wheelchairs. You will walk around beautiful lakes and parks in Minneapolis, the City of Lakes.

Monticello - 10km Walk (YR187) **Apr 19-Oct 19**
B Awards available
Sponsoring Club: AVA-601, Minnesota State Parks
POC: Mark Crawford, 612-878-2325. Lake Maria State Park, 11411 Clanceta Ave NW, Monticello, MN 55362

Start Point: Lake Maria State Park. 612-878-2325. Rt 1, Box 128. Park is located about 35 miles west of the Twin Cities, just south of I-94. Park can be reached from the north via County State Aid Highway 8 and Wright County 111 and from the south via County State Aid Highway 39 & Wright County 111. Watch for brown state park signs.

Event Into: Park hours 8am-10pm. Walkers may start from 8am-1pm. Must finish by 5pm. Trail is rated 3 and is not suitable for strollers or wheelchairs. Pets must be leashed. The trail winds through gently rolling wooded areas with a mixture of sun and shade. Trail surface is a combination of hardpack and grass. Water is available at the start/finish. It is recommended that you bring supplemental water.

Moorehead - 10km Walk (YR762) **Apr 1-Nov 15**
A Award available
Sponsoring Club: AVA-032, Red River Volkssport Association
POC: Don/Glenna Scoby, 701-235-3389. 3302 North 2nd St #22, Fargo ND 58102

Registration: Super 8 Downtown, 301 Third Avenue North, Fargo, North Dakota. Located near the Red River, north of the Civic Center. Drive across river to Moorehead, MN to start this walk. You may also register for YR191 which starts from the Super 8. Get two states with one stop.

Start Point: Follow the directions on the trailmap to cross the Red River Bridge to the Heritage Hjemkomst Center Parking Lot where the trail starts.

Event Info: Daily, 6-dusk. You must be off the trail by dark. Trail is rated 1, suitable for strollers & wheelchairs. Pets must be leashed. The Super 8 offers special rates for volkssporters. Mention when registering. The trail consists of city sidewalks past many beautiful historic homes and city park trails following the north flowing Red River. During flooding season an alternate route is available. Most of the trail is shaded.

Sauk Rapids - 10km Walk (YR1259) **Apr 1-Sept 30**
A Award available
Sponsoring Club: AVA-697, Central Minnesota Volkssports
POC: Melanie Ditrich, 320-253-6595. 501 N 1st St, Sartell, MN 56377

Start Point: Little Dukes Gas & Convenience Store, 3 North Benton Dr. From I-94 going north, take Hwy 15 exit to St. Cloud. Stay on Hwy 15 north to Benton Dr. Take Benton Dr south to Downtown Sauk Rapids. Start is located next to Burger King. OR From hwy 10 going north, exit Benton Dr just north of St. Cloud. Take Benton Dr to start.

Event Info: Daily, 7 am to dusk. Trail is rated 1+, suitable for strollers but not wheelchairs. Pets must be leashed and you must clean up after them. There is one steep hill. Route goes along the Mississippi River and thru three parks and residentail areas. There are no sidewalks in some areas.

Silver Bay - 10/18km Walk (YR402) **May 23-Sep 1**
B Awards availalble
Sponsoring Club: AVA-601, Minnesota State Parks
POC: Gary Hoeft, 218-226-3539. 474 Hwy 61 East, Silver Bay, MN 55614

Start Point: Trailhead at Tettegouche State Park. The park is located 4.5 miles east of Silver Bay on US Hwy 61. Watch for brown park signs.

Event Info: Park is open daily 8am-10pm. You may start from 8-1 and must finish by 5. Trail is rated 5 and is not suitable for strollers or wheelchairs. Pets are allowed on a leash. This trail runs past several overlooks and visits the Tettegouche Camp, which allows hikers to experience a turn-of-the-century recreation club and breathtaking scenery, including overlooks of Lake Superior and Conservancy Pines. The terrain is rugged but it is worth the trip. There are two different routes available. Only one event credit even if completing both routes but you may walk both routes for a total of 18kms.

Spring Grove - 10km Walk (YR309) **May 1-Sept 30**
B Awards available
Sponsoring Club: AVA-122, Syttende Mai Komiteen Folkemarsj Stiftelse
POC: Maribeth Anderson, 507-498-5669. PO Box 391, Spring Grove MN 55974-0391

Start Point: Ballard House, 507-498-5434. 163 W. Main (Hwy44).

Event Info: Daily. Start 10-2, finish by 5. Trail is rated 1, suitable for strollers, wheelchairs or wagons. Pets must be leashed. This is a town trail, mostly sidewalks with one grassy park area.

St. Cloud - 25km Bike, (YR771) **Apr 1-Sept 30**
B Awards available
Sponsoring Club: AVA-697, Central Minnesota Volkssports
POC: Susan Nielsen, 320-255-1933. 1320 10th Avenue South, St. Cloud, MN 56301

Start Point: U Pik-Kwik Convenience Store & Texaco Station, 1100 4th Ave South. From I-94 exit at St Cloud/St Augusta, Cty Hwy 75 and proceed toward St. Cloud. At the 1st traffic light, turn right onto Clearwater Rd. At 11th Street South, turn right and proceed about 5 blocks to the start.

Event Info: Daily, 7 to dusk. Trail is rated 1+. No strollers, wheelchairs or pets. During the summers and on weekends during the school year, parking is allowed inthe Halenbeck Hall parking lot on the

MINNESOTA, cont. ━━━━━━━━━━

SCSU Campus which is adjacent to the start. Weekdays during the school year, one must park on an adjacent street. This route proceeds through a "rural" residential area, past the rose gardens and along the Mississippi River on the Beaver Islands Trail. Bikers must sign a waiver and helmets are recommended.

St Cloud - Four 10km Walks (YR308) **Jan 1-Mar 31** (YR1062) **Apr 1-Jun 30** (YR1063) **Jul 1-Sep 30** (YR1065) **Oct 1-Dec 31**
B Awards are available
Sponsoring Club: AVA-697, Central Minnesota Volkssports
POC: Chuch & Lois Head, 320-252-7348. 2810 Island View Ct, St. Cloud, MN 56301

Start Point: Best Western Kelly Inn, 1 Sunwood Plaza, Hwy 23 & South 4th Ave. From Hwy 23, (Division St) turn North on 4th Ave South, to the Inn on the right.

Event Info: Daily, dawn to dusk. These are the same trails, sanctioned as Seasonal Events. They are rated 1+, suitable for strollers & wheelchairs if they use the alternate route directions. Pets must be leashed. This trail is along and over the Mississippi River, featuring Munsinger Park & the Virginia Clemens Rose Gardens (renowned for wrought iron structures). It also includes historic residential & downtown areas as well as the St. Cloud State University campus.

St Paul - Two 10km Walks (YR1003 & YR1004) **Jan 1-Dec 31**
YR1003 is a Credit Only Event. YR1004 has an A Award available
Sponsoring Club: AVA-114, Twin Cities Volksmarchers
POC: Margery Shellack, 612-698-8507. 1447 Berkeley, St Paul, MN 55105

Start Point: Super America Station, 612-222-7216. 925 Grand Ave. One block south of Summit Ave at Grand & Milton Ave.

Event Info: Daily, dawn to dusk for both events. **YR1003** is rated 1+ & is the "Historical Summit Ave Walk". See beautiful homes of early St Paul inhabitants. **YR1004** is rated 2. This is a "State Capitol Walk". See the City of St Paul & interesting architecture. Both of these events are suitable for strollers & wheelchairs. Pets are allowed on both trails but must be leashed.

St Paul (North) - 25/38/63km Bike (YR527) **Apr 1-Oct 31**
Credit Only Event
Sponsoring Club: AVA-114, Twin Cities Volksmarchers
POC: Darlene Peterson, 612-722-2261. 4020 45th Ave South, Minneapolis, MN 55406

Start Point: Hardee's, 612-777-5602. 2600 Centennial Drive.

Event Info: Daily, dawn to dusk. No strollers, wheelchairs or pets. Trail is rated 2 and follows a converted railroad bed. It is mostly flat with some hills. Bikers must sign a waiver & helmets are recommended. Only one event credit even if doing all trails.

St Peter - 10km Walk (YR194) **Apr 1-Dec 31**
B Awards available
Sponsoring Club: AVA-161, Riverbend Striders
POC: Audrey/Earl von Holt, 507-625-5375. 1709 Linda Ln, N. Mankato MN 56003

Start Point: Americinn Motel, 700 N. Minnesota Ave. 12 miles north of Mankato on Hwy 169 (which is named Minnesota Ave within city limits).

Event Info: If staying at the Americinn Motel, be sure to ask for the Volksmarchers Discount. Daily, dawn to dusk. Trail is rated 3, suitable for strollers & wheelchairs with some difficulty.
Pets must be leashed. This is a town walk through residential & park areas featuring the Gustavus Adolphus College Campus. It has one significant hill and is mostly on sidewalks or streets.

Stillwater - 10km Walk (YR100) **Apr 1-Dec 31**
A Award available
Sponsoring Club: AVA-MN, Minnesota Volkssport Assn.
POC: Don & Lucy Anderson, 612-439-3997. 6111 Paris Ave. N., Apt 5A, Stillwater, MN 55082

Start Point: Fina Oasis Market, 103 North Main St. (Located in downtown Stillwater at the intersection of N Main & Myrtle). Stillwater is accessible from Hwy 36 West or East and Hwy 95 from the North.

Event Info: Daily, dawn to dusk. Trail is rated 2 and is suitable for strollers but not wheelchairs. Pets allowed if leashed. Trail is on city sidewalks and streets featuring scenic and historic sections of Stillwater. There are some hills.

Two Harbors - 10km Walk (YR933) **May 23-Sept 1**
B Awards availalbe
Sponsoring Club: AVA-601, Minnesota State Parks
POC: Rich Hoskins, Split Rock Lighthouse State Park, 218-226-6377. Box 2010A Hwy 61E, Two Harbors, MN 55616

Start Point: Park Office, Split Rock Lighthouse State Park, 218-226-6377. Box 2010A, Hwy 61 East. The park is located 20 miles NE ot Two Harbors on Hwy 61. Watch for brown state park signs.

Event Info: Park is open daily 8am-10pm. Walkers may start from 8-1 and must finish by 5pm. Trail is rated 3 and is not suitable for strollers or wheelchairs. Pets must be leashed. The trail is hilly but well maintained; hard packed and wide with no excessively steep grades. Partial to full shade on the entire route. Historic sites include Split Rock Lighthouse, Corundum Mine Site, Site of the Little Two Harbors Fishing Village. It follows the lakeshore and includes overlooks of Lake Superior. Seasonal walks are also available of Gooseberry Falls and Tettegouche State Parks. Water is available at start/finish only.

Two Harbors - 10km Walk (YR932) **May 23-Sep 1**
B Awards available
Sponsoring Club: AVA-601, Minnesota State Parks
POC: Paul Sundberg, 218-834-3855. Gooseberry Falls State Park, 1300 Hwy 61 East, Two Harbors, MN 55616

Start Point: Lakeview Picnic Shelter, Gooseberry Falls State Park, 218-834-3855. 1300 Hwy 61 East. The park is located 13 miles NE of Two Harbors on US Hwy 61. Watch for the brown state park signs.

Event Info: Park is open daily 8am-10pm. Walkers may start from 8-1 and must finish by 5pm. Trail is rated 3+ and is not suitable for strollers or wheelchairs. Pets must be leashed. The trail starts along Lake Superior's shoreline and follows the west side of Gooseberry River with its view of the river valley and numerous falls. The Interpretive Center is the checkpoint. Seasonal walks are also at Tettegouche and Split Rock Lighthouse State Parks.

Williams - 10km Walk (YR931) **May 23-Sep 1**
B Awards available
Sponsoring Club: AVA-601, Minnesota State Parks
POC: Park Manager, 218-783-6252. Zippel Bay State Park, HC 2, Box 25, Williams, MN 56686

Start Point: Zippel Bay State Park, Park Office, 218-783-6252. HC 2, Box 25. From the town of Williams, (State Hwy 11), take County Rd 2 north for 5 miles then east on County Rd 8 for 6 miles.

Event Info: Park is open daily 8am-10pm. You may start from 9-11 and must finish by 5. Trail is rated 3 and is not suitable for strollers or wheelchairs. Pets must be leashed. This trail winds through Aspen, Jack Pine and Balsam forest. Hike through lowlands with Alder, Willow and tall grasses. Visit the free-flowing well (water is suitable for drinking) at the nearby beach area.

MISSISSIPPI

Bay St Louis - 10km Walk (YR332) **Jan 1-Dec 31**
Credit Only Event
Sponsoring Club: AVA-310, Magnolia State Volkssport Club
POC: Vernon Shockley, 601-467-5962. 1068 St. Joseph St, Waveland, MS 39576

Start Point: Bay St Louis Police Department, 601-467-9221. 310 Old Spanish Trail. From I-10 from the west, take exit 2 or 13. Then go south to Hwy 90 & go east. From the east, take exit 34A (Gulfport) south to Hwy 90. Then go west 15 miles to Bay St. Louis. Turn south at the Mississippi Power Company (Dunbar St which becomes St Francis then Old Spanish Trail) and go .8 miles to the police department bldg on the left.

Event Info: Daily, dawn to dusk. Trail is rated 1, suitable for strollers & wheelchairs. Pets must be leashed. This trail travels through old historic Bay St Louis. There are lots of historic homes & shops. Ideal event for photo buffs.

Biloxi - 10km Walk (YR126) **Jan 2-Dec 31**
A Award available
Sponsoring Club: AVA-310, Magnolia State Volkssport Club
POC: Kathleen Garlotte, 601-497-4835. 3533 Ling Dr, Gautier, MS 39553

Start Point: Biloxi Visitor's Center, 710 Beach Blvd; 601-374-3105. From I-10 exit #46 south to Hwy 90. Go east on 90E. Start is located on the left at the corner of Main &6 Hwy 90.

Event Info: Mon-Fri, 8-5; Sat 9-4; Sun noon-4. In the winter, closed on Sunday. The Visitor's Center is subject to close. Call to check on times and to verify that they are open before coming. Trail is rated 1, suitable for strollers & wheelchairs. Pets must be kept leashed. This trail winds along the beach & through the historic area of Biloxi.

Jackson - 10km Walk (YR1184) **Mar 1-Sep 30**
Sponsoring Club: AVA-310, Magnolia State Volkssport Club
POC: Kate Hearn, 601-366-0707. PO Box 5305, Jackson, MS 39296

Start Point: Mississippi Agriculture Museum, 601-354-6113. 1150 Lakeland Dr. From I-55 north or south, take exit 98B (Lakeland Dr). Go east to first traffic light (Cool Papa Bell Dr) & turn left. Entering parking area, go to extreme far left, cross wooden pedestrian bridge to Jim Buck Ross Bldg which is the start.

Event Info: Mon-Sat 9-5; Sun 1-5. Closed Sundays, Labor Day to Memorial Day. Trail is rated 2+ and is not suitable for strollers or wheelchairs. Pets are not allowed. $.50 pedestrian fee to enter State Park. Follow level roads through LeFleur's Bluff State Park with some wooden pathways and steps, residential neighborhoods & Belhaven College.

Ocean Springs - 10km Walk (YR053) **Jan 1-Dec 31**
A Award available
Sponsoring Club: AVA-310, Magnolia State Volkssport Club
POC: Neal Gambler 601-872-3059. 3226 Nottingham Rd, Ocean Springs, MS 39564

Start Point: Master Grill Restaurant, 601-875-5888. Corner of Hanley Rd. & Hwy 90 East. From I-10 take exit 50 & go south to Hwy 90 & then east 1.8 to Master Grill corner of Hanley Rd & Hwy 90. Parking available at shopping center across the street.

Event Info: Daily, dawn to dusk. Walk is rated 2 & is not suitable for strollers or wheelchairs. Pets must be leashed. Checkpoint is open daily 8-5. Use of bug spray is recommended during the summer months. The trail winds through the Gulf National Seashore Park & along the beachs of the Gulf Coast.

MISSOURI

Carthage - 10km Walk (YR1002) **Jan 1-Dec 31**
Credit Only Event
Sponsoring Club: AVA-765, Dogwood Trailblazers
POC: Carolyn Wolfe, 417-451-6016. 13465 Kodiak Rd, Neosho, MO 64850

Start Point: Mr. Q's Convenient Store, 417-358-2946. 1308 West Oak. Located on US Alt 71 - 5 miles north of junction with I-44. From US Alt 71 take exit for US 71/MO 96. Travel east into Carthage on Central Ave. Turn right on Baker Blvd (2nd street). Continue south 2 blocks & Mister Q's Citgo is on the right.

Event Info: Daily, 6am-dusk. Trail is rated 1+, suitable for strollers and wheelchairs if they can manage curbs and uneven sidewalks. It follows urban sidewalks and quiet neighborhood streets with well-kept Victorian, Italiante and American Federal style homes.

Columbia - 10km Walk (YR1049) **Jan 1-Dec 31**
B Awards available
Sponsoring Club: AVA-781, Columbia Parks and Recreation, Tiger Striders
POC: Karen Ramey, 314-874-7636. PO Box N, Columbia, MO 65205

Start Point: Hardees, Columbia Store #3, 200 S Providence Rd. From I-70 take Providence Road exit. Go south on Providence Rd, one block south of the Broadway intersection. Hardees is on the left (east) corner of Providence and Locust St. From I-63 take the Stadium Blvd (740) exit. Go west to Providence Rd intersection. Turn right (north) on Providence Rd and go to Locust St intersection.

Event Info: Daily, 6:30am to dusk. Trail is rated 1+ and is suitable for strollers or wheelchairs. Pets are allowed. This event includes a nature trail, old residential neighborhoods, downtown Columbia and all three college campuses.

Ellisville - 10km Walk (YR551) 12km Walk (YR014) **Jan 2-Dec 31**
B Awards available
Sponsoring Club: AVA-221, Die Ballwin Wanderfreunde
POC: Francis & Bamby Craig, 314-227-5909. 859 Hollyridge Dr, Ballwin, MO 63011

Start Point: Video counter, Dierbergs Supermarket Clayton/Clarkson Ctr., at Clayton & Clarkson Roads. West St. Louis County. From the east take I-64 west through St. Louis. Exit at Clarkson, turn left; go on Clarkson about 3.9 miles to Clayton Rd. Start is on the right. From the west take I-64 (Hwy 40) eastbound; exit at Clarkson; turn right and follow directions above. From the north or south, take I-270 to I-64. Take I-64 westbound; exit at Clarkson Rd.

Event Info: Daily, 7:30-dusk. Closed Easter, Thanksgiving, Christmas & New Years. Routes are rated 2 but are on paved trails and roads with a few moderate hills. Not suitable for strollers or wheelchairs. Pets must be leashed and are not allowed in buildings. Do not walk during electrical storms. Snow and ice are not removed from the trails in the winter. Both routes go through several wooded parks connected through attractive subdivisions.

Fenton - 10km Walk (YR1088) **Jan 2-Dec 31**
B Awards available
Sponsoring Club: AVA-466, Missouri Marching Mules
POC: Flo Painter, 314-291-5268/314-353-0560. 3157 Smiley Rd, Brigeton, MO 63044

Start Point: Fenton Community Center, 314-343-0067. 625 New Smizer Mill Road. From I-44 take exit 272, Rt 141 South approximately 3 miles to Fenton City Hall/Community Center.

Event Info: Mon-Sat, 8-5; Sun 12-5. Closed New Years, Easter, Thanksgiving, Christmas & Sundays in the summer. Trail is rated 1, suitable for strollers & wheelchairs. The trail will be closed during flooding of the Meramec River. Route passes through the George Winter Park, Felton City Park, Meramec Greenway Trail and historic Fenton.

MISSOURI, cont. ————————————————

Hannibal - 10km Walk (YR980) **Jan 1-Dec 31**
A Award available
Sponsoring Club: AVA-842, The Mark Twain Walking Club
POC: Hannibal Visitors Bureau, 573-221-2477. 505 North Third, Hannibal, MO 63401

Start Point: Hannibal Visitors Bureau, 573-221-2477. 505 North Third. From the east, take Hwy 72 into Hannibal. Visitors Bureau is at the left at the foot of the Mark Twain Bridge. From the north, take Hwy 61 into Hannibal, turn left or east onto Hwy 36; then turn right onto Third St. From the west, take Hwy 36 into Hannibal. Turn right on Third St (Hwy 79). From the south, take Hwy 61 into Hannibal. Turn right (east) onto Hwy 36 and turn right on Third St.

Event Info: Mon-Fri 8-5; Sat-Sun 9-4. Closed Christmas, Thanksgiving & New Year's. Trail is not suitable for strollers & wheelchairs. It is rated 3 and although it is mostly paved, it includes a number of difficult hills and a staircase. Pets are allowed.

Hermann - 10km Walk (YR281) **Mar 1-Dec 31**
Unknown whether awards are available
Sponsoring Club: AVA-018, Hermann Volkssport Association
POC: Tom Cabot, 573-486-2747. RR 1, Box 60A, Hermann, MO 65041

Start Point: Die Hermann Werks, 214 East 1st St. Hwy 19 South from I-70. After crossing the Missouri River, go left on First Street 1 1/2 blocks. Store has two golden eagles on windows on right side of street after "First Bank".

Event Info: Mon-Sat, 9:30-5; Sun, 11-4. Closed Easter, Thanksgiving & Christmas. Rated 1. Suitable for strollers & wheelchairs. Pets must be leashed. Be sure to bring your camera. The route is somewhat level through the historic district with checkpoints at wineries. This course is 5km and must be done twice for the 10km credit. Reversal of the second lap is recommended.

Independence - 10km Walk (YR032) **Jan 2-Dec 31**
A Award available
Sponsoring Club: AVA-MO, Missouri Volkssport Association
POC: Bobbi Pommer, 816-524-3067 (eves). 211 N Main, Lee's Summit, MO 64063

Start Point: Truman Home Ticket Center, 816-254-7199. 219 N Main St. East or west on I-70 to Noland Road; go north on Noland Rd to Truman Rd; go west on Truman Rd to Main St. Ticket Center is on the southeast corner of Truman Rd and Main St in the Truman Home Ticket Office.

Event Info: Daily, 8:30-3. Ticket Center closes promptly at 5. Closed Thanksgiving, Christmas and New Years. Trail is rated 1+ and is suitable for strollers & wheelchairs with a little difficulty. Pets must be leashed & are not allowed in buildings. Bring your own water for the trail. Water is only available at the start point and the checkpoint. Please let touring groups and people sign in first at the start point. Route is on city streets and sidewalks with a couple of low-grade hills.

Jefferson City - 10km Walk (YR454) **Jan 1-Dec 31**
A Award available
Sponsoring Club: AVA-MO, Missouri Volkssport Association
POC: Alene Plackemeier, 314-949-2512. 610 Friedens Rd, St Charles, MO 63303

Start Point: Coastal Mart, 1940 W Main. From I-70 turn south on Hwy 54 or Hwy 63 to Jefferson City. After crossing the Missouri River, exit at Main St heading west (right) to start.

Event Info: Daily, dawn to dusk. Trail is rated 2+, suitable for strollers & wheelchairs. Pets must be leashed and are not allowed inside the start point. The trail takes you by the Capitol Building, the Supreme Court Bulding and the Governor's Residence.

Joplin - 10km Walk (YR535) **Jan 1-Dec 31**
A Award availalbe
Sponsoring Club: AVA-765, Dogwood Trailblazers
POC: Carolyn Wolfe, 417-451-6016. 13465 Kodiak Rd, Neosho, MO 64850

Start Point: Hall's Food Mart, 703 West 7th. From I-44 turn north at the US 43 (Main St) exit. Follow Main St north to 7th St and turn left (west). From US 71 take the Joplin exit onto Business 72. Continue straight to US 43 and turn left (south). US 43 becomes Main St. Follow this to First St.

Event Info: Daily, 7am-9pm. Trail is rated 1+, suitable for strollers and wheelchairs if they can manage curbs and uneven sidewalks. Pets are allowed on a leash and are not allowed in the start. Route goes through town on sidewalks or paved roads.

Kansas City - 10km Walk (YR304) **Jan 2-Dec 31**
A Award available
Sponsoring Club: AVA-644, Pace Setters Volkssport Club
POC: Peter/JoAnn Moroz, 816-246-0187. 530 NW Murray Rd, Lee's Summit, MO 64081

Start Point: Longview Lake, Longview Recreation Center Registration Counter. 3801 SW Longview Rd. Take I-470 to View High Drive Exit, go South on View High Dr to stop sign at View High & Third St. Go right (west) on Third to first entrance on left, then turn right into recreation center parking lot. Center is multi-story red brick building.

Event Info: Mon-Fri, 6am-8pm; Sat, 8am-6pm; Sun 10am-6pm. Closed all major holidays. Trails are rated 1, suitable for strollers & wheelchairs. You will be driving from the rec center to the walk start location on the other side of the lake. Pets must be leashed. Route follow an asphalt trail.

Kansas City - 11/13km Walk (YR1089) **Apr 7-Oct 26**
Credit Only Event
Sponsoring Club: AVA-739, Clay-Platte Trackers of KC
POC: Ed McLees, 816-436-5588. 1508 NE 98th St, Kansas City, MO 64155

Start Point: Trinity Lutheran Hospital, 3030 Baltimore Ave. I-35 to Broadway exit. Take Broadway south to 31st St. Go left on 31st to Baltimore. Left on Baltimore. Park in Hospital Visitor's Parking garage.

Event Info: Daily, 7am to dusk. Trail is rated 2+. It is suitable for strollers and wheelchairs. Pets are allowed. Ask volunteers at the reception desk in the main lobby for the box. This is a city trail through downtown Kansas City past historic sites. Historic points of interest information is available.

Kirkwood - 10km Walk (YR1238) **Jan 1-Dec 31**
A Award Available
Sponsoring Club: AVA-221, Die Ballwin Wanderfreunde
POC: Patricia Roerig, 314-487-7312. 1015 H Adworth Dr, St. Louis, MO 63125

Start Point: Bagel Street Cafe, 314-821-6677. 427 S Kirkwood Rd. Cafe is located near the clock tower in Woodbine Center. From I-44 go north on Lindbergh (Hwy 61,67). From I-64 (Hwy 40) go south on Lindbergh (Hwy 61,67). Lindbergh becomes Kirkwood Rd in the City of Kirkwood. The Cafe is about 3 1/2 blocks from the Amtrak Train Depot.

Event Info: Mon-Fri, 6:30am-7pm; Sat & Sun, 7:30-3:30. Closed Thanksgiving & Christmas. Other Holidays they are open weekend hours. Trail is rated 1 and is suitable for strollers or wheelchairs. Pets must be leashed. Please pay by check only. Route follows tree shaded sidewalks through historic residential and small business area. It will pass several eateries and interesting shops.

Lemay - Four 11km Walks (YR919) **Jan 2-Mar 31** (YR918) **Apr 1-Jun 30** (YR917) **Jul 1-Sep 30** (YR916) **Oct 1-Dec 31**
A Award available
Sponsoring Club: AVA-466, Missouri Marching Mules
POC: Shirley Thompson, 314-352-7118. 7910 Delmont, St Louis, MO 63123

Start Point: Hardee's, 314-892-1950. 2866 Telegraph Rd. From I-255, take exit #2, Telegraph Road, Route 231. Go north approximately 1/2 mile. Start will be on your right.

Event Info: Daily, dawn to dusk. Closed New Years, Easter, Thanksgiving and Christmas. All events are on the same trail which is rated 1+, suitable for strollers and wheelchairs. Pets are allowed. Route passes through Sylvan Springs Park, Jefferson Barracks Historical Park and Jefferson Barracks National Cemetery.

Liberty - 10km Walk (YR609) **Jan 1-Dec 31**
A Award available
Sponsoring Club: AVA-739, Clay-Platte Trackers of Kansas City
POC: Barbara Bueher, 816-630-3367. 1000 Magnolia West, Excelsior Springs, MO 64024

Start Point: Cody's Quick Stop, 405 East Mill St. Take I-35N from Kansas City to Liberty (about 20 minutes from downtown). Exit on Hwy 152 East. Continue to the town square. Turn right on Main St. Continue one block to Mill St. Turn left to Start/Finish approximately 2 blocks.

Event Info: Daily, 7am to dusk. Trail is rated 2+ and is not suitable for strollers or wheelchairs. Pets must be leashed. Walk through old downtown Liberty, the Campus of William Jewell College and area neighborhoods. There are a number of hills and stairs on the route.

Mound City - 10km Walk (YR958) **Jan 1-Dec 31**
A Award available
Sponsoring Club: AVA-719, Missouri Riverbluff Ramblers
POC: Helen Caton, 816-232-3344 or fax 816-232-1427. 315 S 6th St, St. Joseph, MO 64501

Start Point: George's Total Convenient Store, 711 State (Hwy 59 South). Halfway between Kansas City and Omaha. Turn east off exit 84 on I-29. Drive east to State St (Hwy 59 South). Turn south and go two blocks to start.

Event Info: Daily, dawn to dusk. Trail is rated 2+. Not suitable for strollers or wheelchairs. Pets must be leashed. Please checks only -- no cash. Trail is through park, residential and business areas. A map/brochure is given out that highlights prominent structures on the trail made from native red stones.

Republic/Springfield - 10km Walk (YR1001) **Jan 1-Dec 31**
A Award available
Sponsoring Club: AVA-765, Dogwood Trailblazers
POC: Carolyn Wolfe, 417-451-6016. 13465 Kodiak Rd, Neosho, MO 64850

Registration:: Total Station/Store, 417-882-9144. Junction of Hwy MM & US 60. Three miles east of Republic and 10 miles southwest of Springfield. From I-44 take exit 70 (MO Hwy MM) south 3.8 miles to US 60.

Start Point: Drive to Wilson's Creek National Battlefield for the walk location.

Event Info: Start/finish is open daily, 24 hrs. Walk point is open daily, 8-5 and is closed Thanksgiving and Christmas. Trail is rated 1+, suitable for strollers and wheelchairs. Pets must be leashed. The National Park Service may charge a park entrance fee for the Battlefield tour. Route consists of rolling hills on a paved path.

St Charles - 10km Walk (YR399) **Jan 1-Dec 31**
B Awards available
Sponsoring Club: AVA-682, S.M.T.M. Volkssport Society

POC: Nell Bruce, 314-831-8175. 1300 New Florissant Rd North, Florissant, MO 63033-2122
Start Point: St. Joseph Health Center Information desk in main lobby. 300 First Capitol Dr. From I-70 exit 5th St North to First Capitol; right to Health Center (on left) between 2nd and 4th.

Event Info: Daily, dawn to dusk. Trail is rated 1+. Suitable for strollers and wheelchairs. Pets are allowed if leashed and if clean-up is provided. Trail is on the Katy Trail, a rails-to-trails with a crushed limestone surface.

St Charles - 10km Walk (YR1109) **Jan 1-Dec 31**
A Award available
Sponsoring Club: AVA-304, Missouri Woodland Walkers
POC: Alene Plackemeier, 314-949-2512. 610 Friedens Road, St. Charles, MO 63303-3814

Start Point: Quik Trip, 229 North Kings Highway. From I-70 east or west exit at St Charles First Capitol (exit 228). Proceed north on First Capitol to Kings Highway; left on Kings Highway to Quik Trip (approximately 3 blocks on the left).

Event Info: Daily, dawn to dusk. Trail is rated 1+ and is suitable for strollers or wheelchairs but there are some small hills. Pets are allowed on a leash but not in buildings. Please wait for clerk to be free of customers before asking for walk info. The trail goes through St. Charles and includes the historic district and shops as well as many of the old landmark churches and buildings.

St Joseph - 10km Walk (YR034) **Jan 2-Dec 30**
A Award available
Sponsoring Club: AVA-719, Missouri Riverbluff Ramblers
POC: Helen Caton, 816-232-3344 or fax 816-232-1427. 315 S 6th St, St. Joseph, MO 64501

Start Point: St. Joseph Museum, 816-232-8471. 1100 Charles St. 45 minutes north of Kansas City. Take I-29 to US 36 west; exit US 36 to I-229 north; exit I-229 at Edmond Street Central Business District; continue east on Edmond for eight blocks to 11th Street; turn right onto 11th St for one block to Charles St. Parking available around museum block.

Event Info: Mon-Sat, 9-5; Sun, 1-5. Closed Thanksgiving, Dec 24, 25 & 31 and New Year's Day. The trail is rated 3 and may not be suitable for strollers or wheelchairs. Pets must be leashed. Trail goes through historic St. Joseph downtown, by the Pony Express National Memorial and the Jesse James Home. You will have a panoramic view of the Missouri River.

St Louis - 10km Walk (YR455) **Jan 1-Dec 31**
Credit Only Event
Sponsoring Club: AVA-355, St. Louis-Stuttgart Sister City
POC: Betty Hoffman, 314-867-6897. 1535 St Ives Drive, St. Louis, MO 63136

Start Point: Best Western Inn at the Park, 314-367-7500. 4630 Lindell Blvd. From I-64/Hwy 40 east or west, take Kings Highway exit north to Lindell; right (east) on Lindell 1.5 blocks to Hotel on right.

Event Info: Daily, dawn to dusk. Trail is rated 1, suitable for strollers & wheelchairs. Pets are allowed. Walk thru the history of the turn of the century homes, pubs and restaurants representing a variety of ethnic cuisine. Old-world ambiance reminiscent of the cities of Europe.

St Louis - 10km Walk (YR030) **Jan 1-Dec 31**
A Award available
Sponsoring Club: AVA-355, St. Louis-Stuttgart Sister City
POC: Betty Hoffman, 314-867-6897. 1535 St. Ives Drive, St. Louis, MO 63136

Start Point: Hampton Inn, 314-241-3200. 2211 Market St. From I-55/I-70 north or south, take Memorial Dr to Market St., 1.5 miles west on Market to the hotel. Start is on south/left side of street. From Hwy 40/I-64, West, exit 21st St to Market. Go left on Market to Hotel on the right. From Hwy 40/I-64 East, exit Jefferson. Go left on Jefferson to Market. Go right on Market to Hotel on the left.

Event Info: Daily, dawn to dusk. Trail is rated 1, suitable for strollers and wheelchairs. Pets are allowed. This trail winds thru the heart of downtown St. Louis with its historic churches, domed stadium, Laclede's Landing, gambling boats, Gateway Arch, Mississippi River, Baseball stadium and commercial shopping areas.

St Louis - 10km Walk (YR941) **Jan 1-Dec 31**
Credit Only Event
Sponsoring Club: AVA-355, St. Louis-Stuttgart Sister City
POC: Ralph/Joyce Bass, 314-524-1234. 420 La Motte Lane, St. Louis, MO 63135

Start Point: McDonald's Restaurant, 314-521-2272. 10873 W Florissant Ave. From I-270, east or west, exit West Florissant South. Continue on West Florissant to Festival Shopping Center on right (approx 2 blocks)

Event Info: Daily, dawn to dusk. Trail is rated 1 and is suitable for strollers and wheelchairs. Pets are allowed. Route goes thru the gentle hilly terrain of a suburg of St. Louis called Ferguson with tree-lined streets of "Century Homes".

St Peters - Two 10km Walks (YR210 & YR247) **Jan 1-Dec 31**
B Awards available
Sponsoring Club: AVA-682, S.M.T.M. Volkssport Society
POC: Flo Painter, 314-291-5268. 1300 New Florissant Rd North, Florissant MO 63033-2122

Start Point: Dierbergs Supermarket (video counter). 290 Mid Rivers Mall Dr. From I-70 (exit 222) Mid Rivers Mall Dr. Go south three short blocks to start on the left.

Event Info: Daily, dawn to dusk. Closed New Years, Christmas, Easter & Thanksgiving. Trails are rated 1+, suitable for stroller and wheelchairs. Pets must be leashed with clean-up provided. Routes are on sidewalks and paved bike paths. Mostly flat with mild grades.

MONTANA

Bannack - 10km Walk (YR776) **May 24-Sept 1**
B Awards available
Sponsoring Club: AVA-519, Madison County Volkssport Club
POC: Elaine Mason, 406-683-6615. Box 264, Virginia City, MT 59755

Start Point: Bannack State Park Visitor Center, 406-834-3413. 25 miles west of Dillon off I-15, exit 59.

Event Info: Daily, 10-6. $3.00 per car entry fee. Trail is rated 3+ and is not suitable for strollers or wheelchairs. Elevation starts at 5,700 ft & will gain approximately 500 ft. Carry your own water. No food is available at Bannack. Pets must be leashed.

Great Falls - 10km Walk (YR1272) **Jan 1-Dec 31**
B Awards available
Sponsoring Club: AVA-203, Big Sky Wanderers
POC: Serene Vance, 406-452-6946. 631 Carol Dr, Great Falls, MT 59405 or Henry Butler, 406-452-0222. 3109 5th St NE, Great Falls, MT 59404

Start Point: Perkins Restaurant/Mid-Town Motel, 406-453-2411. 526 2nd Ave North. From I-15 take 10th Ave South exit. Go to 6th St South and turn left (north). Go 12 blocks and Perkins is on the corner of 6th St North and 2nd Ave North. From Hwy 87/225 (From the North) go to 2nd Ave North turn right and go 9 blocks to Perkins. From Hwy 87 (From the South) Hwy 200/89, take 10th Ave South to 6th St South and turn right (north) and proceed 12 blocks to Perkins. Please do not leave cars parked in Perkins' parking lot as space is limited. Ample parking across the street and in the city parking lot.

Event Info: Daily except closed Christmas. Trail is rated 1+ and may be possible for strollers but not wheelchairs. Pets must be leashed. Mid-Town Motel gives volkssporters a 10% discount.

Helena - 11km Walk (YR556) **May 1-Sept 30**
Credit Only Event
Sponsoring Club: AVA-170, Helena Hikers
POC: Roy Hockett, 406-443-7010. 69 Homestead Estates, Box 2248, Clancy, MT 59634

Start Point: Jorgenson's Restaurant, 1714 11th Ave. From I-15 north or southbound, take exit 192, 12 West Capitol Area. Proceed west on Prospect Ave to Lamborn St & turn left to start.

Event Info: Daily, 6:30am-10pm. Closed Memorial Day, July 4th and Labor Day. Trail is rated 2+, suitable for strollers but difficult for wheelchairs. Pets must be leashed. The route is on paved streets & includes the original Governor's Mansion, Last Chance Gulch, a restored miner's village, the state capitol, Montana Historical Society & many other historical landmarks.

Virginia City - 10km Walk (YR105) **May 1-Sep 30**
B Awards available
Sponsoring Club: AVA-519, Madison County Volkssport Club
POC: Jayne Welton, 406-843-5512. PO Box 72, Virginia City, MT 59755

Start Point: Stonehouse Inn Bed & Breakfast, 406-843-5504. 306 East Idaho. Self start box is located on the front porch. From I-15 turn at Dillon. Take 41 to Twin Bridges, then 287. From I-90 turn off east of Butte at Whitehall. Take 55, then 41 to Twin Bridges, then 287: From Bozeman, take 84 to Norris, then 287 turning right at Ennis to Virginia City: From West Yellowstone, take 27, turning left out of Ennis. The start is one street south of the main street.

Event Info: Daily, dawn to dusk. Trail is rated 3 due to elevation of 6,000 ft. It is not suitable for strollers or wheelchairs. Carry your own water on the trail. Pets must be leashed. Restrooms are available in the city park.

NEBRASKA

Beatrice - 10km Walk (YR278) **Jan 1-Dec 31**
A Award available
Sponsoring Club: AVA-492, Homestead Striders
POC: Jean Miller, 402-228-1783. 1918 Lincoln Blvd, Beatrice NE 68310

Start Point: Gas' N Shop, 402-223-2522. 1116 N 6th St. From North on Hwy 77, continue to the start on your left. From the south on Hwy 77, continue to the start on your right. From the west on Hwy 136, go east on 136 (Court St) to Hwy 77 (Sixth St). Turn left on 6th & proceed to start on your right. From the east on Hwy 136, continue west on 136 to Hwy 77. Turn right & proceed to start on your right.

Event Info: Daily, dawn to dusk. Trail is rated 1, suitable for strollers & wheelchairs with some difficulty from curbs. Pets must be leashed. This trail is through the residential areas of Beatrice.

Fremont - 10km Walk (YR244) **Jan 1-Dec 31**
B Awards available
Sponsoring Club: AVA-510, Fremont Volkssport Club
POC: Mary M. Benderson or Doris Rector, 402-721-7996. 635 E 20th St, Fremont, NE 68025-3072

Start Point: Holiday Lodge, 1220 East 23rd St. From east or west on Hwy 30 to 23rd & bell St. From north or south on Hwy 77 to Hwy 30 which is 23rd St to Bell St.

Event Info: Daily, dawn to dusk. Trail is rated 1, suitable for strollers & wheelchairs. It is a very flat trail. Pets must be leashed. Walk goes through a shady residential area, past Midland College, the May Museum & two parks. All paved paths & sidewalks.

Fremont - 10km Walk (YR513) **May 1-Oct 31**
B Awards available
Sponsoring Club: AVA-510, Fremont Volkssport Club
POC: Mary Benderson, 402-721-1943 or Doris Rector, 402-721-7996. 635 E 20th, Fremont NE 68025

Start Point: Touch & Go, 740 N Davenport Ave. From the east or west on Hwy 30, go to Broad St which is Hwy 77 to Military Ave. Turn west, cross the railroad tracks onto Davenport Ave. Turn north to start. From the north or south, go to Military & turn west, cross tracks to Davenport Ave & turn north.

Event Info: Daily, 6:30am-9pm. Walk only during daylight hours. Trail is rated 1, very flat & suitable for strollers & wheelchairs. Pets must be leashed. This trail is through a State Park past many lakes & wooded areas & several beaches. All paved paths & sidewalk. Pack a picnic lunch!

Grand Island - 10km Walk (YR966) **Jan 1-Dec 31**
A Award available
Sponsoring Club: AVA-822, Mid-Nebraska Trail Seekers
POC: Lois Stienike, 308-385-5308. PO Box 1302, Grand Island, NE 68802

Start Point: Holiday Stationstore, 308-381-7815. 1420 South Locust St. FromI-80 use exit 312, north on Hwy 281 to Stolley Park Rd. Turn right on Stolley Park Rd to South Locust St, then left on South Locust to the start.

Event Info: Daily, dawn to dusk. Trail is rated 1, suitable for strollers & wheelchairs. Pets must be leashed. Water & restrooms are available at the start/finish year round but during the summertime only at the City Park. Trail is through residential areas, city park, past the city zoo & beautiful churches.

Kearney - 10km Walk (YR761) **Jan 1-Dec 31**
A Award available
Sponsoring Club: AVA-818, Kearney Volkssport Club/Buffalo Trailblazers
POC: Art Hansen, 308-237-5435. Rt 3, Box 14E, Kearney, NE 68847

Start Point: C-Store No 1, 3912 17th Avenue. Off I-80 North on 2nd Ave to 39th. West on 39th St to 17th Ave.

Event Info: Daily, dawn to dusk. Trail is rated 2, suitable for strollers & wheelchairs with some difficulty. Trail has some hills. Pets must be leashed. A mix of sidewalks, paved roads and country trails through residential and developed rural areas.

Lincoln - Two 10km Walks (YR017 & YR704) 25/29km Bike (YR306) **Jan 1-Dec 31**
YR017 has B Awards available   YR704 has an A Award   YR306 is a Credit Only Event
Sponsoring Club: AVA-102, Lincoln Volkssport Club, Inc.
POC: Rose Quackenbush, 402-464-6972. 1519 N. 58th St, Lincoln NE 68505-1706

Start Point: (YRE 017 & YRE306) Russ's IGA , 68th & 'O' St. (Sign-up only) YRE 704 starts at 33rd & 'J'. From I-80 West, ext 396 to 'O' St. Turn left on 'O' St to 66th. Turn left on 66th to the first intersection. Turn right and park in the shopping center lot. From I-80 East, exit 409 to Hwy 6. Turn left on Hwy 6 to 84th St. Turn left on 84th to 'O'. Turn right on 'O' to 68th. Turn right on 68th to the first intersection and park in the shopping center lot.

Event Info: Daily, 7am-dusk. Walks are rated 1, suitable for strollers & wheelchairs with some difficulty with curbs. Pets must be leashed. Be sure you get the right map. YR017 is on a hike/bike trail and a residential area & East Campus of the University. YR704 is the Historical Walk. It goes thru the business area & Univeristy area, Hay Market & Capitol & residential area. The bike is on the MoPac Hike/Bike Trail and the Limestone Trail. You must sign a waiver to bike. A helmet is recommended. Be sure you get the bike map. Payment by check payable to Lincoln Volkssport Club.

Nebraska City - 10km Walk (YR554) **Jan 1-Dec 31**
A Award available
Sponsoring Club: AVA-102, Lincoln Volkssport Club, Inc.
POC: Rose Quackenbush, 402-464-6972. 1519 North 58th St, Lincoln NE 68505-1706

Start Point: Apple Inn Motel, 506 South 11th St. Parking only behind Embers Steak House across the street. From West on Hwy 2, exit on Business Hwy 2. Straight ahead (east) for 3 miles to start. From North on Hwy 75: Turn left (east) to Business Hwy 75 for 4 miles to start. South on Hwy 75: Intersection of Hwy 75 & 2. Go straight ahead (north) one mile to South 11th St. North or South on I-29: Take Nebraska City Exit #10. Turn west (toward river) on Hwy 2 for 5 miles to 1st stop light. Turn right (north) on South 11th St one mile to start.

Event Info: Daily, 7-dusk. Trail is rated 1, suitable for strollers & wheelchairs. Pets must be leashed. Payment must be by check payable to Lincoln Volkssport Club. Trail goes through historic business & residential areas. Arbor Lodge Historical Park & apple orchard & Lieb Convention Center. Trail may not be cleared of snow through the orchard and the bike/hike trail.

North Platte - 10km Walk (YR775) **May 24-Sept 1**
A Award available
Sponsoring Club: AVA-856, Wild West Walkers
POC: Sandra Owen, 308-534-8149. 922 North Emory, North Platte, NE 69101

Start Point: Lincoln County Historical Museum, 2403 North Buffalo. From I-80 take exit 177 north into North Platte. At "A" St, leave Dewey via lanes that curve left onto a two-way road (Jeffers St). Go north on Jeffers (over the viaduct) to Rodeo Rd (aka Hwy 30). Go left (west) on Rodeo Rd to Buffalo Bill Ave. Go north (right) on Buffalo Bill Ave. The start is on the right side (one mile).

Event Info: Daily, 9-8. Trail is rated 1. 1/2 mile each way has no sidewalk and you must walk on a two lane paved road. It is suitable for strollers or wheelchairs if the above mentioned 1/2 mile doesn't bother you. Pets must be leashed. Route is fairly flat except for the viaduct that goes over the railroad tracks. These may cause difficulty for wheelchair users.

North Platte - 10km Walk (YR770) **Jan 1-Dec 31**
A Award available
Sponsoring Club: AVA-856, Wild West Walkers
POC: Sandra Owen, 308-534-8149. 922 North Emory, North Platte, NE 69101

Start Point: North Platte Recreation Center, 1300 McDonald Rd. From I-80 take exit 177 north into North Platte. Turn left (west) on Francis. Go to McDonald and turn left (south). Rec Center is on the northeast corner of McDonald & Leota. Parking is available at both east & south sides of Rec Center building.

Event Info: Mon-Fri 6am-8:30pm; Sat 8am-8:30pm; Sun 1-8:30. Closed New Year's Day, Easter, last week of Aug, Thanksgiving & Christmas. Trail is rated 1 and is suitable for strollers and wheelchairs.

Pets must be leashed. This is an easy walk thru North Platte's newer residential area. There are a couple of places where the sidewalks are not poured yet so you will need to walk on a wide, paved road.

Omaha - Two 10km Walks (YR093 & YR622) **Jan 2-Dec 31**
B Awards available
Sponsoring Club: AVA-016, Nebraska Wander Freunde
POC: Ed Beran, 402-556-1621. 4525 Oak St, Omaha NE 68106

Start Point: Nebraska Game & Parks/Visitor Center, 1212 Deer Park Blvd across from zoo. I-80, exit 13th St. Follow signs.

Event Info: Mon-Fri, 8-5 except Mar 1-Oct 31 when hours are 9-5 daily. Closed New Year's, MLK Day, Veterans Day, Thanksgiving & Christmas. Trails are rated 1+. YR093 is suitable for strollers or wheelchairs with difficulty. YR622 is not suitable for strollers or wheelchairs. Pets must be leashed. Both routes follow city streets.

Sidney - 10km Walk (YR383) **Jan 1-Dec 31**
B Awards available
Sponsoring Club: AVA-564, Panhandle Walkers
POC: Bev Sonntag, 308-254-7000(w) 308-254-6130(h) 1024 Sixth Ave, Sidney, NE 69162-1144

Start Point: Cheyenne County Community Ctr, Registration Desk, 627 Toledo; 308-254-7000. Turn east from 11th Ave onto Toledo & turn right into parking lot. Coming from Fort Sidney Rd, turn west onto Toledo at the Lodgepole Valley 4-H Youth Camp. Continue past the city swimming pool & turn left into Center parking lot. Use the south entrance.

Event Info: Mon-Fri dawn to dusk; Sat, 8-8; Sun, noon-6. During June, July & August, the Center will be closed on Sunday and will be open from 10-4 on Saturday. Closed on major holidays and all three days of a three-day weekend. Call ahead to make sure. Trail is rated 2, suitable for strollers & wheelchairs with some difficulty. Pets must be leashed. There is an alternate route available for bad weather. Start point is the same but the route would be the indoor walking track at the Cheyenne County Community Center. A daily use fee must be paid to use this track. Trail is on city sidewalks & paved streets with some gradual inclines. The route will include historical Fort Sidney & downtown landmarks.

York - 10km Walk (YR302) **Mar 1-Dec 31**
A Award available
Sponsoring Club: AVA-666, Wellness Wanderers
POC: Arnold Richert, 402-362-4997. 1423 Florida Ave, York, NE 68467

Start Point: Bosselman's Pump & Pantry #16, 109 Lincoln Ave. On I-80 exit 353 and to north approximately 3 miles. From Hwy 34 exit south on Hwy 81 & continue south for approximately 2 1/2 miles.

Event Info: Daily 6am -11pm (including holidays). Trail is rated 1, suitable for strollers & wheelchairs. Pets must be leashed. Route goes through residential areas & parks.

NEVADA

Carson City - 10km Walk (YR936) **Jan 1-Dec 31**
Credit Only Event
Sponsoring Club: AVA-683, Sierra Nevada Striders
POC: Linda Nary, 702-882-3346. 605 Highland, Carson City, NV 89703

Start Point: Downtowner Motor Inn, 702-882-1333. 801 North Carson St. (Hwy 395). Take I-80 to Reno. Exit Hwy 395 south to Carson City (27 miles). From South Lake Tahoe, travel east on Hwy 50 to Hwy 395 then north (left) to start point on corner of 395 (Carson St) & East Washington St.

Event Info: Inn offers a 10% discount to all AVA walkers on room rates. Daily, dawn to dusk. Trail is rated 1, suitable for strollers & wheelchairs. Pets must be leashed with clean-up. Follow the historic "Kit Carson Trail" and listen to the Old Talking Houses. You will pass the beautiful old Capitol Complex of this charming city from the past.

Incline Village - 10km Walk (YR190) 10/12km Walk (YR189) **Apr 1-Dec 31**
Credit Only Events
Sponsoring Club: AVA-683, Sierra Nevada Striders
POC: Barbara Currie, 702-831-4356. PO Box 4344, Incline Village, NV 89450

Start Point: Fleet Feet, 702-831-0668. 930 Tahoe Blvd (Raley's Center). From Hwy 50 in the Sacramento area, travel east to Hwy 28, turn left & follow this until you reach Incline Village. Turn right onto Village & right into second driveway (Raley's Center). From I-80 travel east from Sacramento to exit 267, Truckee. Hwy 267 to Hwy 28, turn left & follow to Incline Village. Left on Village & right into 2nd driveway.

Event Info: Mon-Sat 10-6; Sun noon-5. July 4-Sept 5: Mon-Sat, 9-6; Sun 11-5. Closed Thanksgiving & Christmas. **YR190** is rated 3 due to hills & altitude. Strollers will have difficulty with hills. No wheelchairs. Route is on hilly roads and dirt shoulders. Walkers will be rewarded with spectacular view of Lake Tahoe and the surrounding mountains. Please carry water. **YR189** is rated 1+, suitable for strollers. A handicapped route is provided. This is a fairly level route that follows residential streets thru neighborhoods of beautiful homes and views of Lake Tahoe can be seen from the recreational trail. Pets are allowed on both routes if leashed and if clean up is provided. Snow and/or ice cancels both events.

Las Vegas - 11km Walk (YR208) 12km Walk (YR474) **Jan 1-Dec 31**
YR208 has an A Award available   YR474 has B Awards available
Sponsoring Club: AVA-296, Las Vegas High Rollers & Strollers
POC: Dick Lisk, 702-438-0145. 4869 Harris Ave, Las Vegas, NV 89110-2442

Start Point: Best Western Mardi Gras Inn, 800-634-6501. 3500 Paradise Rd. Exit I-15 at Flamingo East. Cross Las Vegas Blvd to Paradise Rd. Turn North to the start. Ask the clerks at the registration desk for the volksmarch box.

Event Info: Daily, dawn to dusk. Trails are rated 1, suitable for strollers & wheelchairs. The hotel offers a VIP rate of $39.00 per night for a suite. This includes double occupancy. **YR474** is on busy city streets. Use caution & use traffic lights. Pets must be leashed. Part of the trail goes through UNVL Campus with its various gardens and passes by Liberace Museum which gives a discount to volksmarchers. **YR208** is also on busy city streets. It goes by most of the major casinos. No pets are allowed on this trail. No picture taking in casinos. Recommend evening walking as the "Strip" is lit up with the glamour of the Casinos.

Reno - 10km Walk (YR935) 25/35km Bike (YR697) **Jan 1 - Dec 31**
A Awards available
Sponsoring Club: AVA-683, Sierra Nevada Striders
POC: Judy Gordon, 702-331-5561. 2105 Carville Dr, #H, Reno, NV 89512

Start Point: National Automobile Museum, 702-333-9300. 10 Lake St South. From Hwy 395 north or south, exit I-80 west; exit Wells Ave. Turn left onto Wells. From I-80 east or west, exit Wells Ave. Eastbound will turn right onto Wells, westbound will turn left onto Wells. Turn right onto Mill St & right at Museum Dr. Parking lot is on your left.

Event Info: Mon-Sat, 9:30-5:30. Sun 10-4. Closed Thanksgiving & Christmas. **YR935** is rated 2 and is suitable for strollers but not advisable for wheelchairs because of hills. Pets are allowed if leashed and if clean up is provided. This route goes thru the casino district, lovely UNR Campus, Rancho San Rafael Park, the Reno Riverwalk and residential neighborhoods. There are a couple of gradual hills, three staircases on the campus and a dirt trail in the park. **YR697** is rated 1. It is a beautiful bike ride down the Truckee River. It is on a paved bike trail for 25km. The 35km has a short distance on streets. Snow and/or ice cancels both events.

NEW HAMPSHIRE ━━━━━━━━━━━━━━━━

Concord - 10km Walk (YR292) **Apr 1-Nov 30**
A Award available
Sponsoring Club: AVA-247, Seacoast Striders
POC: Al Moulton, 603-778-0267. 111 Union Rd, Stratham, NH 03885-2245

Start Point: Holiday Inn, 172 North Main; 603-224-9534. From I-93, exit 14. If coming from the south, turn left at the end of the ramp. If coming from the north, turn right at the end of the ramp. Turn right onto North Main St and the Inn is immediately on the right. From the east, take Rt 4 to Rt 9 and turn right onto North main St.

Event Info: Daily, dawn to dusk. Trail is rated 1+, suitable for wheelchairs and strollers. Pets are allowed. Volkssporters can receive a discount on tour of Kimball-Jenkins Estate & New Hampshire History Museum. Show walk card. This event is through New Hampshire's historic capital city, home of the Concord Coach that opened the West, the 14th US President and teacher in space, Christa McAuliffe. Many architectural styles are present.

Durham - 25km Bike (YR930) **Apr 26-Nov 2**
Credit Only Event
Sponsoring Club: AVA-247, Seacoast Striders
POC: Al Moulton, 603-778-0267. 111 Union Rd, Stratham, NH 03885-2245

Start Point: Burger King, 603-868-1332. 1 Mill Road. From Rt 4, take Rt 155A. If coming from the west, turn right at end of ramp. If coming from the east, turn left at the end of the ramp. Continue to downtown Durham past two sets of flashing yellow lights. Take the first right after the bus stop, Mill Rd. Turn left into parking lot and Burger King will be the store on the far left.

Event Info: Daily, 8:30 to 1/2 hr before dusk. Trail is rated 3+ because of hills. The trail will take you through the college town of Durham and other nearby country towns. Bikers must sign waiver and should wear a helmet.

Nashua - 10km Walk (YR929) **Apr 30-Nov 30**
A Award available
Sponsoring Club: AVA-247, Seacoast Striders
POC: Al Moulton, 603-778-0267. 111 Union Rd, Stratham, NH 03885-2245

Start Point: Comfort Inn, 10 St Laurent Rd, 603-883-7700. From the north: Rt 3 exit 7E across Rt 3 overpass. Turn left at lights, first left to hotel. From the south: Rt 3 exit 7E, straight through lights, first left to Hotel. From the east: Rt 111A into Nashua, cross Main st, straight on W Hollis onto Rt 3. Follow direction from south. From West: Rt 101A across Rt 3 overpass, left at lights, first left to hotel. The Comfort Inn offers a discount to walkers.

Event Info: Daily, dawn to dusk. Trail is rated 1, suitable for strollers & wheelchairs. Pets must be leashed. Event is along residential streets, through a city park & through Nashua Historic District. Route is generally flat. Except for a short distance on unpaved park road, it runs alongside paved roads & on city sidewalks.

Portsmouth - 10km Walk (YR132) **Apr 1-Nov 30**
A Award available
Sponsoring Club: AVA-247, Seacoast Striders
POC: Al Moulton, 603-778-0267. 111 Union Road, Stratham, NH 03885

Start Point: Howard Johnson's Hotel, Interstate Rte 1 Traffic Cir; 603-436-7600. Located at the Portsmouth Traffic Circle, crossroads of Northern New England, at the intersections of I-95 (exit 5), routes 1, 4, 16 & the Spaulding Turnpike.

Event Info: Daily, dawn to dusk. Trail is rated 1+, suitable for strollers & wheelchairs. This route highlights the new & old of Portsmouth. From Portsmouth's original settlement (1623), its history is depicted at the Strawberry Banke Museum & many other locations throughout the city including the John Paul Jones House, the Portsmouth Navy Yard & the submarine Albacore. The trail is generally flat on city (brick) sidewalks.

NEW JERSEY ━━━━━━━━━━━━━━━━━

Belmar - 10km Walk (YR737) **Jan 1-Dec 31**
A Award available
Sponsoring Club: AVA-623, Fort Monmouth Road Warriors
POC: Ed Tognola, 908-747-5572 (eves). 121 Dorchester Way, Shrewsbury NJ 07702

Start Point: Mayfair Hotel, 908-681-2620. 1001 Ocean Ave. Take I-195 East until it ends. Stay in left lane, ramp onto Hwy 35 (north) for one mile. Turn right onto 10th Ave and follow to its end at Ocean Ave. Hotel is on the right hand side. North/South: Take the Garden State Pkwy until exit 98. Travel east until Ocean Ave. Go north on Ocean.

Event Info: Daily, dawn to dusk. Rated 1, suitable for strollers & wheelchairs. Pets are not allowed during the bathing season on Boardwalk. The route follows paved sidewalks & has a long boardwalk stretch.

Cape May - 10km Walk (YR1107) **Jan 1-Dec 31**
Credit Only Event
Sponsoring Club: AVA-623, Fort Monmouth Road Warriors
POC: Jeff Parrish, 908-544-0625. 14 Wedgewood Circle, Eatontown, NJ 07724

Start Point: Queen's Hotel, 609-884-8702. 601 Columbia Ave. Take the Garden State Parkway (GSP) south to its end where it becomes Hwy 109. Continue south on Hwy 109 which becomes Lafayette St. Turn left onto Ocean Ave & go 3 blocks to Columbia Avenue. Turn left onto Columbia. Queen's Hotel is on the left-hand corner.

Event Info: Daily, 8:30 to dusk. Closed New Year's & Christmas. Trail is rated 1, suitable for strollers & wheelchairs but some curbs are not cut. No pets allowed curing bathing season. Volkssporters will receive lower rates at the hotel. This event is mostly on paved sidewalks, ocean boardwalk, etc.

Ft Monmouth - 10km Walk (YR1174) **Jan 1-Dec 31**
Credit Only Event
Sponsoring Club: AVA-623, Fort Monmouth Road Warriors
POC: John P. Bellantoni, 908-747-3721 (eves). 35 Little Silver Pkwy, Little Silver, NJ 07739-1118

Start Point: Physical Fitness Center, Bldg 114, 908-532-3275. Avenue of Memories/Nicodemus Ave. Take Garden State Pkwy to exit 105. Go east on Hwy 36 to first intersection (Hope Rd). Go north on Hope Rd until reaching Tinton Ave. Turn right onto Tinton Ave. Travel east on Tinton until its end at Hwy 35 and Post's West Gate (Brickwork). Travel through West Gate straight until start point on the right hand side by small traffic circle.

Event Info: Mon-Fri, 6am-9pm; Sat , Sun 7 Holidays, 9am-4pm. Closed New Year's & Christmas. Trail is rated 1, flat, easy on mostly paved sidewalks. It is suitable for strollers & wheelchairs but ground in the Arboretum may get soft in the rain and is slightly uneven dirt. Pets are allowed.

Hamilton Square - 10km Walk (YR1199) 25km Bike (YR1200) **Jan 1-Dec 31**
Credit Only Events
Sponsoring Club: AVA-333, Garden State Wanderers
POC: Vasily Serpikov, 609-587-5251. 19 Misty Pine Lane, Hamilton, NJ 08690

Start Point: Black Forest Acres, 609-586-6187. 1100 Rte 33. Take the NJ Turnpike to exit 7A. Take I-195 west to US Rt 130 North (New Brunswick). Rt 130 north to Co Rt 526 (traffic light). Turn left. Bear left at next traffic light (Rt 526 & Rt 33). Stay on Rt 33 to Paxson Ave (sixth traffic light). Turn right and right again into parking lot for start/finish.

Event Info: Mon-Fri, 9:30-7:30; Sat 9:30-6; Sun 12-4. ·Early start box available. Closed Christmas, New Year's, Easter, memorial Day, 4th of July, Labor Day & Thanksgiving. Trail is rated 2 and is not suitable for strollers or wheelchairs. Pets must be leashed. Route is mostly on paved surfaces with some dirt paths and trails through Hamilton Square with its restored houses. The trail leads through Sayen Gardens, site of the annual Azalea Festival, Veterans Park and surrounding neighborhoods. The bike is rated 2. Please observe and follow safety rules of biking. Bikers must sign a waiver and should wear a helmet. The bike trail is on city streets and country roads, through local parks with some rolling hills.

Point Pleasant Beach - 10km Walk (YR1175) **Jan 1-Dec 31**
Credit Only Event
Sponsoring Club: AVA-623, Fort Monmouth Road Warriors
POC: Jeff Parrish, 908-544-0625. 14 Wedgewood Circle, Eatontown, NJ 07724

Start Point: 7-11 (#23436) Convenience Store, 908-295-3045. Broadway Avenue just off of State Hwy 35. North & South: Take the Garden State Pkwy to exit 91. From the West: take I-195 east till terminus. Follow signs to Hwy 34 and Point Pleasant Beach. From Hwy #35 (South), take the turn onto Broadway, just before the bridge.

Event Info: Daily, dawn to dusk. Trail is rated 1, suitable for strollers & wheelchairs but Boardwalk is crowded in season. No pets allowed. The trail is flat, mostly on paved sidewalks with one stretch of ocean-front boardwalk.

++Princeton - 11km Walk (YR736) **Jan 1-Dec 31**
A Award available
Sponsoring Club: AVA-776, Delaware Valley Volkssporters
POC: David Scull, 609-275-1721(E) 609-897-4953 (D). 22 Bridgewater Dr, Princeton Junction NJ 08550

Start Point: Best Western Palmer Inn, 3499 Rt 1 South (next to Pep Boys). Located on Southbound Rt 1, 2.8 miles north of Jct I-295 & I-95 with Rt 1 (exit 67). Reverse jughandle U-turn at Meadow Rd. Access I-295 from south at Delaware Memorial Bridge and from North at I-95. Register here and drive 4.2 miles to start.

Event Info: Daily, dawn to dusk. Rated 1. Suitable for strollers and wheelchairs with some difficulty with stairs & gravel along route. Pets must be leashed. Actual start point is a 4.2 mile drive from the Palmer Inn. Volkssporters can receive a 10% discount on lodging at the Palmer Inn. Route will include Princeton University and exclusive residential areas. There are many historic bldgs & sculptures along the trail. Bring a camera.

Spring Lake - 10km Walk (YR1173) **Jan 1-Dec 31**
A Award available
Sponsoring Club: AVA-623, Fort Monmouth Road Warriors
POC: Jeff Parrish, 908-544-0625. 14 Wedgewood Circle, Eatontown, NJ 07724

Start Point: Warren Hotel, 908-449-8800. 901 Ocean Ave. North & South: Take Garden State Pkwy until exit 98. From West: Take I-195 easst until its terminus. Stay in righthand lane. Curve right with the ramp onto State Hwy 35 (south). Drive onto Rt 524, east to the coast. Turn right and drive eleven blocks to Mercer Ave.

Event Info: Daily, 8am-9pm. Hotel reduces hours in off-season. During Oct-May, call ahead to verify 908-449-9353 (Banquet Office). Closed New Year's, Christmas, Thanksgiving, etc. Trail is rated 1, suitable for strollers & wheelchairs. Pets are not allowed. Route is along the Boardwalk, sidewalks and residential areas.

NEW MEXICO

Alamogordo - 10km Walk (YR067) **Jan 1-Dec 31**
Credit Only Event
Sponsoring Club: AVA-014, Holloman Sun Runners
POC: Robert Turner, 800-545-4021 days/505-434-0405 eves. 3405 Fayne Ln, Alamogordo NM 88310

Start Point: J & J Mini Market, 1400 E 9th St. From US 54, 70, & 82, turn east on 9th St. Proceed to the corner of 9th & Washington.

Event Info: Daily, dawn-three hours before dark. Trail is rated 1, suitable for strollers & wheelchairs. Pets must be leashed at all times. Route is all on paved streets through the city of Alamogordo.

Albuquerque - 10km Walk (YR547) **Jan 1-Dec 31**
A Award available
Sponsoring Club: AVA-826, Santa Fe Trail Blazers
POC: Don Hueszel, 505-293-7968. 14356 Camino Del Rey NE, Albuquerque, NM 87123

Start Point: New Mexico Museum of Natural History, 505-841-2800. 1801 Mountain Rd NW. From I-40 take exit 157A south on Rio Grande Blvd 0.5 miles. Left on Mountain Rd, 0.3 miles, left on 18th St, one block & left into Museum Parking Lot. The start point is in the Subway Sandwich Shop on the 2nd floor of the Museum. Do not pay the museum entrance fee but go directly to the Subway Shop.

Event Info: Daily, 9-5. Call 505-841-2800 to verify hours and days open. Trail is rated 1 and is suitable for strollers & wheelchairs. Pets are allowed. Call or write the POC for one brochure that lists all 10 northern New Mexico Year Round Events. Route is on the "Old Town Albuquerque Tour Excursion". See the Kings Road from Mexico City to Santa Fe, Rte 66 from Chicago to Los Angeles, and the Pan American Highway from Mexico to Canada.

Cloudcroft - 10km Walk (YR315) **Jan 1-Dec 31**
Credit Only Event
Sponsoring Club: AVA-014, Holloman Sun Runners
POC: Robert Turner, 800-545-4021 (days) 505-434-0405 (eves). 3405 Fayne Ln, Alamogordo NM 88310

Start Point: The Aspen Motel & Restaurant, 505-682-2526. Hwy 82. Take US Hwy 82 from the east or west to Cloudcroft. The start point is located on the south side of US Hwy 82 near the eastern edge of Cloudcroft.

Event Info: Daily, 8-three hours before dark. Rated 2, with altitude above 9,000 ft. We recommend that you stop frequently to avoid over-exertion. Participants with heart or blood pressure conditions should take special precautions. Pets must be leashed. Trail is suitable for strollers and wheelchairs if they bypass parts of it. Call for snow conditions in winter. Route is mostly on city streets with some unpaved sections.

Los Alamos - Two 10km Walks (YR1105 & YR1301) **Jan 1-Dec 31**
A Awards available
Sponsoring Club: AVA-826, Santa Fe Trail Blazers
POC: Heather Darby, 505-662-9962. 2500 Trinity Dr, Los Alamos, NM 87544

Start Point: Los Alamos Police Department, 505-662-9962. 2500 Trinity Dr. From I-25 take exit 282. Go north on St Francis (US 84) 19.3 miles. Turn left on NM 502 for 16.5 miles. Bear left on Trinity for 1 mile, right on Oppenheimer and immediately right into Police Department parking lot.

Event Info: Daily dawn to dusk. **YR1105** is rated 2 due to elevation. It is suitable for strollers and wheelchairs and pets are allowed on a leash. It is on the "Los Alamos Manhattan Project Trek". You will be where the US developed the Atomic Bomb and you will have spectacular views of the mesa and canyons on the road to and from the city. **YR1301** is rated 3 and is not suitable for strollers or wheelchairs. Pets are allowed. After registering, you will drive to the North Mesa Picnic Grounds to start. Go left on Oppenheimer 1/2 block, right on Trinity for 1 mile, right on Diamond Dr for 3.1 miles to the North Mesa Picnic Grounds on your left.

Las Cruces - 11km Walk (YR010) **Jan 1-Dec 31**
Credit Only Event
Sponsoring Club: AVA-108, Sun Country Striders, Ltd.
POC: Jacob E. Clevenger, 505-523-1741; E-mail PAE77@AOL.com. PO Box 6787, Las Cruces, NM 88006-6787

Start Point: Las Cruces Hilton, 505-552-4300. 705 S Telshor Blvd. Take Exit 3 off I-25, turn onto Lohman Ave, turn right onto Telshor and turn left at the traffic light into parking lot.

Event Info: Daily, dawn to dusk. Trail is rated 1+, suitable for strollers and wheelchairs.
Pets must be leashed. Route goes through upscale neighborhoods, a shopping mall and past New Mexico State University.

Las Cruces - 10km Walk (YR385) **Jan 1-Dec 31**
Credit Only Event
Sponsoring Club: AVA-108, Sun Country Striders
POC: Jacob E. Clevenger, 505-523-1741. E-mail: PAE77@AOL.com. PO Box 6787, Las Cruces, NM 88006-6787

Start Point: Best Western, Mesilla Valley Inn, 505-524-8603. 903 Avenida de Mesilla. Take exit 140 off I-10, turn onto Avenida de Mesilla.

Event Info: Daily, dawn to dusk. Trail is rated 1 and is suitable for strollers & wheelchairs. Pets must be leashed. Route is on paved streets, gravel roads and canal banks. It is near historic Old Mesilla and rural surroundings.

Las Vegas - 10km Walk (YR1106) **Jan 1-Dec 31**
A Award available
Sponsoring Club: AVA-826, Santa Fe Trail Blazers
POC: Paul & Bertha Herrera, 505-425-9508. PO Box 2691, Las Vegas, NM 87701

Start Point: Las Vegas Police Department, 505-425-7504. 318 Moreno St. From I-25 take exit 343 and go NE on Grand for 0.6 miles. Follow brown "Historic Old Town" signs. Bear left onto New Mexico Ave for 1.2 miles. Go right on National for 0.2 miles, right on W Plaza and immediately right into Police Department parking lot.

Event Info: Daily, dawn to dusk. Trail is rated 1+ due to elevation. It is suitable for strollers and wheelchairs. Pets must be leashed. The "Las Vegas New Mexico History Hike" exposes you to Gen, Kearney announcing the Mexican Acquisition in 1846; the Railroad ending here in 1879; the city riveling Albuquerque and Denver in size in 1882; and Col. Teddy Roosevelt recruiting his Rough Riders from this city in 1898.

Organ - 10km Walk (YR102) **Jan 1-Dec 31**
Credit Only Event
Sponsoring Club: AVA-108, Sun Country Striders, Ltd.
POC: Jacob E. Clevenger, 505-523-1741. E-mail: PAE77@AOL.com. PO Box 6787, Las Cruces, NM 88006-6787

Start Point: Space Murals Museum and Gift Shop, 15450 US Hwy 70 East; 505-382-0977. Take Exit 6A off I-25 onto US Hwy 70 E for 11 miles and turn right into the parking lot next to a large water tank painted with space murals.

Event Info: Mon-Sat, 9-7; Sun, 10-6. Closed Christmas and New Years. Trail is rated 3+. No strollers or wheelchairs. Pets are allowed. Take water with you. This is a trail walk in a wilderness area. It has fantastic scenery of the mountains, an abandoned settlement and a huge rock quarry.

Pena Blanca - 10km Walk (YR1298) **Jan 1-Dec 31**
A Award available
Sponsoring Club: AVA-826, Santa Fe Trail Blazers
*POC:*Ferrell Woodard, 505-465-0032 (h), 505-867-1400 (w). PO Box 1480, Pena Blanca, NM 87041

Start Point: Allsop's Convenience Store, 505-465-2352. Cochiti Lake Highway. From I-25 take exit 264 west on NM16 for 6.5 miles, right at green "Cochiti Dam Spillway" sign 6.7 miles over dam, past the visitor center, left to the Main Rd, to the first right at the bottom of the hill. Park in Allsop's parking lot. Ask the clerk for the volksmarch registration box.

Event Info: Daily, 6am-9pm. Walk in daylight hours only. Trail is rated 2. It is not suitable for strollers or wheelchairs. Pets are allowed. One brochure lists all ten northern New Mexico YRE's. The elevated views of the 5th largest dam in the world, the Jemez range to the west, and the Sangre de Cristo Peaks in the east are spectacular while participating in the "Cochiti Lake Recreation Area Amble".

++Santa Fe - Two 10km Walks (YR155 & YR1103) **Jan 1-Dec 31**
A Awards available
Sponsoring Club: AVA-826, Santa Fe Trail Blazers
POC: Weldon Merritt, 505-466-0278 (h); 505-827-2983 (w). 11 Balde Rd, Santa Fe, NM 87505

Start Point: Le Cafe on the Trail Restaurant, 505-982-7302. 311 Old Santa Fe Trail. From I-25 take exit 282. Go north on St. Francis (US84) 2.8 miles. Right on Cerrillos 0.5 miles, right on Paseo de Prealta 0.5 miles, left on Old Santa Fe Trail 1 1/2 blocks and right into Desert Inn Motel Parking Lot. The registration box is on the counter inside the rear entrance to the restaurant.

Event Info: Daily, dawn to dusk. Restaurant is open 7am-6pm except on Mondays when it closes at 3pm. Closed on holidays. Pets are allowed on both events if leasher. **YR155** is rated 1+ it is suitable for strollers and wheelchairs but it does have 78 stairs. This is the "New Mexico Capital City Adventure". It tours historic 387 year old Santa Fe including the unique Capitol bldg. **YR1103** is rated 1, suitable for strollers and wheelchairs. It is the Canyon Road Art Gallery Stroll. You will tour different downtown streets than on the Capitol City Adventure. However, this route also passes the Capitol Bldg and 55 artists' studios and galleries while walking historic Canyon Rd. One brochure lists all 10 northern New Mexico YREs.

Santa Fe - 10km Walk (YR1299) 11km Skate (YR1300) 25km Bike (YR1104) **Jan 1-Dec 31**
A Awards available on all events
Sponsoring Club: AVA-826, Santa Fe Trail Blazers
POC: Bob & Sharon Patterson, 505-471-5193. 2885 Calle de Pinos Altos, Santa Fe, NM 87505

Start Point: Conoco Quik Stop Convenience Store #8, 505-473-8211. 995 Rodeo Road. From I-25 take exit 282 north on St. Francis Dr (US84) 2 traffic lights. Left on 21A Rd 2.6 miles to Richards Ave (5th light) and straight ahead to the first left turn into the Conoco Service Station. The registration box is on the window shelf on the right side of the entrance door.

Event Info: Daily, dawn to dusk. **YR1299** is rated 2 and is suitable for strollers and wheelchairs. Pets are allowed. It is the "Chamisos Urban Trail Fitness Walk. You will walk on the Chamisos Urban Trail Paved path and stroll through the Monica Lucero & Marc Brandt parks. **YR1300** is rated 1+. After registering for this event, you will drive your car to the Santa Fe Community College for the start. Go right on Rodeo Rd for 1/2 block, right on Richards Ave 1.0 miles. Stop and park on the side of the road in front of the road barrier. Begin your volksskate from the barrier on the 1A1A Rd. The Santa Fe Community College volksskate is isolated from motorized vehicle traffic. It is on a new and unused asphalt road that is barricaded to cars and on a 1 mile loop of the college. **YR1104** is rated 2+. Bring your own bike for the bike event. A multi-speed bike is recommended. While pedaling the "Southwest Santa Fe Volksbike, maximum safety is assured on the 1.1 mile Santa Fe Community College Bike Path; on the 1.7 mile arroyo de los Chamois Urban Trail and on the completely closed 5.4 mile 1A1A Rd.

Silver City - 10km Walk (YR859) **Jan 1-Dec 31**
Credit Only Event
Sponsoring Club: AVA-108, Sun Country Striders, Ltd.
POC: Marye Wagoner, 505-388-4655. PO Box 6787, Las Cruces, NM 88006-6787

Start Point: Copper Manor Motel, 505-538-5392. 710 Silver Heights Blvd. (US Hwy 180E). In Silver City on US Hwy 180, 1/2 mile east of center of town.

Event Info: Daily, dawn to dusk. Trail is rated 2+ due to high altitude. It is suitable for strollers. Pets must be leashed. Route goes around Western New Mexico University, Ditch Park, the downtown area, past a doll museum and the public museum. It is on paved roads and sidewalks with two flights of stairs.

NEW YORK

Albany - 10/12km Walk (YR248) **Jan 1-Dec 31**
A Award available
Sponsoring Club: AVA-410, Empire State Capital Volkssporters
POC: Wayne F. Ubrich, 518-283-4606. 465 N Greenbus Rd, Reasselaer, NY 12144-9441. Or Susan Larson, 518-355-3429. 2910 Old State Rd, Schenectady, NY 12303

Start Point: Albany Urban Park Cultural Center, Visitors Center, 25 Quackenbush Sq; 518-434-5132. From north, east & west, take I-90 to I-787. Go south in I-787 to Clinton Ave exit. Left on Broadway, left on Orange, left into parking lot, following signs to urban Cultural Park Visitors Center. From the south, take NY Thruway to exit 23. I-787 North to downtown exit marked 9N and 20W. Then follow signs for 9N and Clinton Ave. Turn left on Broadway and proceed as above.

Event Info: Daily 10-4. Closed major holidays. Trail is rated 1+, suitable for strollers and wheelchairs with help. Pets must be leashed. Mon-Fri, ignore the "Lot Full" sign at the parking lot and go to the ticket booth. Pay $1.50 parking fee; have ticket stamped in the Visitors Center and the fee will be refunded. The ticket booth is closed on weekends. This trail is through the capital city of New York State passing many historical sites and buildings. Alternate 10 km route available. Only one event credit event if doing both routes.

Binghamton - 10/20km Walk (YR444) **Apr 1-Dec 31**
B Awards available
Sponsoring Club: AVA-790, Fingerlakes Region Volkssports Club
POC: Ellen Uhlig, 607-648-2649. 9 Ellen St, Binghamton, Ny 13901

Start Point: Roberson Center, 607-772-0660. 30 Front St. From I-81/NY17 (same road through city), take exit 4S. Proceed 2 miles on arterial Hwy 363 going through two traffic lights. Cross Chenango River. Turn right at third light onto Front St. Park in the rear and enter through rear entrance.

Event Info: Daily 12-5. The staff is normally in the Center from 10am on and will service walkers. The Center has frequently changed operating hours. Call ahead to confirm times. Trail is rated 1, suitable for strollers and wheelchairs. Only one event credit even if doing both trails. Pets must be leashed. 10 km goes thru the historic West side of Binghamton and passes through Recreation Park where the participant may ride free on an authentic carousel during the summer. Many old homes and tree-lined avenues are viewed. 20 km crosses the Susquehanna River to the South side where a panoramic view of the city is available.

Cooperstown - 10km Walk (YR386) **Apr 27-Dec 28**
A Award available
Sponsoring Club: AVA-410, Empire State Capital Volkssporters
POC: Winifred Balz, 1121 Baker Ave, Schenectady, NY 12309; 518-372-3663. Wayne Ubrich, 518-283-4606. PO Box 6995, Albany NY 12206-6995

Start Point: Clark Gymnasium, Susquehanna Ave. Additional start at: Cooperstown Chamber of Commerce, 31 Chestnut St when the gymnasium is closed. Cooperstown is 70 miles west of Albany. From the west use Thruway exit 30 at Herkimer (Rt 28). From the east use Thruway exit 29 (Rts 10, 20, & 80). Entering the Village on Rt 80, turn right on Chestnut St. Just past the Chamber of Commerce, turn left on Susquehanna. Center is 1 mile on the right. If you are entering from Rt 28, it becomes Chestnut St.

Event Info: Gym is open Mon-Sat 7-7; Sun 10-5. Closed Sundays mid May-Oct. The Chamber is open 10-5. Trail is rated 1+, suitable for strollers & wheelchairs. Pets must be leashed. Please use the auxiliary box at the Chamber of Commerce only when the Gym is closed. Cooperstown, located at the south end of Otsego Lake is home to the Baseball Hall of Fame, Doubleday Field, the Farmers Museum and the Fenimore House.

Cornwall - 11km Walk (YR252) **Jan 1-Dec 31**
Credit Only Event
Sponsoring Club: AVA-505, Volkssport Club of West Point
POC: Donna Gallo, 914-534-7164. 9 Duncan Ave, Cornwall-on-Hudson, NY 12520

Start Point: Cinnamon & Spice Bakery. 291 Main St., 914-534-5209. From the north: I-84 to Newburgh. Rt 9W south to Cornwall exit (Rt 218) to Main St. Start is approximately 3/4 of a mile. From the South: Palisades Parkway north to Bear Mountain Circle. Rt 9W north to Cornwall exit. At the stop sign turn right and proceed on Main St to Cinnamon Spice & Bakery approximately 1/2 mile.

Event Info: Mon-Sat 6-6; Sun 6-3. Trail is rated 2+, suitable for strollers but not wheelchairs due to several steep hills. Pets are allowed if they are leashed. Route goes through business and residential areas, through wooded areas, past the nature museum, and through village parks. Spectacular views of the mountains.

Hamilton - 10km Walk (YR380) **Apr 1-Dec 31**
B Awards available
Sponsoring Club: AVA-790, Fingerlakes Region Volkssport Club
POC: JoAnn Linsley, 315-824-3143. RD 1, Box 140C, Hamilton, NY 13346

Start Point: Colgate Inn, 315-824-2300. Route 12B, Town Center. From the south, take Route 12 north from Binghamton (I-81)/NY 17) to Norwich, then 12 B to Hamilton. From the north, take route 12 B south from Utica (I-90). From the east, take route 23 west from Oneonta (I-88) to Norwich. From the west, take route 41 east from Cortland (I-81) to Hwy 26 north to 23 East to Norwich.

Event Info: Daily 8- dusk. Call the Inn for summer hours of operation. Trail is rated 1. Strollers OK with some steps. Pets must be leashed. Colgate Inn, established in 1840, is the starting point; trail follows village sidewalks past restored homes, the University of Colgate and around a golf course designed by Robert Trent Jones.

Highland Falls - 10km Walk (YR1145) **Jan 1-Dec 31**
Sponsoring Club: AVA-505, Volkssport Club of West Point
POC: Herb Donlan, 914-446-2574. 6 West St, Highland Falls, NY 10928

Start Point: Country Kitchen Cafe, 914-446-1111. 208 Main Street. From the north: I-84 exit at Newburgh. Rt 9W South, exit at Rt 218 into Highland Falls. At fork in road bear left into Main St. Country Kitchen Cafe is in first block on left. From the south: Palisades Parkway north to Bear Mountain Circle. Rt 9W North. exit onto Rt 218 through Highland Falls. Proceed as above.

Event Info: Tue-Fri 7:30-3; Sat 8:30-3; Sun 9-3. Closed Monday. Trail is rated 1, suitable for strollers and wheelchairs. Pets must be leashed. Route goes through business and residential areas. Pass the US Military Academy Museum, Visitor's Center and cadet academic area.

Ithaca - 11km Walk (YR922) **Apr 1-Dec 31**
B Awards available
Sponsoring Club: AVA-790, Fingerlakes Region Volkssport Club
POC: Jim Storelli, 607-257-3421. 9 Sharon Dr, Lansing, NY 14882

Start Point: Cornell University, Plantation's Gift Shop, 607-255-3020. 1 Plantation's Rd. From Rt 13 southbound, take Rt 366 to Judd Falls Rd. From Rt 79 westbound, turn right on Pine Tree Rd which turns into Judd Falls Rd. Note a small jog in Judd Falls Rd at Rt 366. From all other directions, get on Rt 79 eastbound, then onto Rt 366. Turn left on Judd Falls Rd.

Alternate Start Point: Best Western Inn, East Hill Plaza, 607-272-6100. Located at the intersection of Judd Falls Rd and Mitchell St. Follow Judd Falls Rd north to the Plantations.

Event Info: Plantation Gift Shop Hours: Apr, May & Sep-Dec -- Mon-Fri 8-4:30; Sat 10-5; Jun-Aug -- Mon-Fri 8-4:30, Sat/Sun 11-5. Best Western Inn Hours: Daily, 8-6 (Note that from Fall to Spring daylight ends around 5pm). Trail is rated 2, suitable for strollers with some difficulty with stairs. Not suitable for wheelchairs. Pets must be leashed. When beginning from the Best Western during summer months, you may walk later in the evening. Walk on a variety of paved and unpaved surfaces with some stairs, through a variety of natural areas and the Cornell Campus. Noteworthy stops include Collegetown shops, the Johnson Museum of Art and the Cornell Plantations Gift Shop and Herb Garden.

Little Falls - 10km Walk (YR1147) **Apr 1 - Dec 31**
B Awards available
Sponsoring Club: AVA-838, Mohawk Valley Pathfinders
POC: Helene Labrie, 315-866-6908. PO Box 4486, Utica, NY 13504

Start Point: Best Western Motor Inn, 315-823-4954. 20 Albany St. From I-90 take exit 29A. Follow 169 to Little Falls, take a left at intersection of Rt 5, heading west. Take a right onto South Ann St at second traffic light. Take an immediate left into the parking lot of the Best Western Motor Inn.

Event Info: Daily dawn to dusk. Trail is rated 2 and is not suitable for strollers and wheelchairs. The route takes you along the NY State Barge Canal and many peaceful streets of this small city.

Lockport - 10km Walk (YR146) **Apr 1-Nov 30**
A Award available
Sponsoring Club: AVA-589, Niagara Frontier Volkssport Club
POC: Gail Davis, 716-741-2198. PO Box 99, Clarence Center NY 14032

Start Point: Friendly's, 2 Lock Plaza. From I-90, exit 49 (Depew) north on Rt 78 to Lockport (15 miles). Right on W Main St. to Friendly's.

Event Info: Daily 7 a.m. to dusk. Trail is rated 2 and is not suitable for strollers or wheelchairs. Pets allowed on leash. Part of trail is on the towpath of historic 1825 Erie Barge Canal.

Lockport - 10km Walk (YR757) **Apr 1-Nov 30**
A Award available
Sponsoring Club: AVA-788, Niagara Escarpment Volkssport Assn.
POC: Dorothy N. Socie, 716-731-2630. 2181 Violet Circle, Apt. 1, Niagara Falls, NY 14304-2901

Start Point: Best Western Lockport Inn, 716-434-6151. 515 S. Transit Rd. From NY Thruway (I-90) use exit 49, turn left onto Transit Rd and follow north to Best Western Inn. From Niagara Falls follow Rt 31 to Rt 78. Turn right to Best Western.

Event Info: Daily 8 a.m. to dusk. Trail is rated 1, suitable for strollers and wheelchairs. Pets must be leashed. Discounts on Best Western rooms available to volkssporters. Walk follows city streets along Erie Barge Canal through historic area of Lockport. Note: watch traffic carefully when walking along city streets.

New York - 11km Walk(YR1330) 12km Walk (YR1331) **Jan 1-Dec 31**
A Awards available
Sponsoring Club: AVA-419, Seneca Valley Sugarloafers
POC: Ed Branges, 301-340-9418. 1830 Greenplace Terrace, Rockville, MD 20850.

Start Point: Broadway Nut Shop, 212-874-5214. 2246 Broadway. George Washington Bridge to Henry Hudson Pkwy south (becomes West side Dr.) To 79th St. Exit. Proceed east on 79th St. to parking garage on 79th, 80th or 81st Sts. Or take Lincoln Tunnel to north on West Side Dr. Exit at 79th St. and proceed to parking garage as above.

Event Info: Daily, 10 a.m. to 9 p.m. Closed major holidays. Call for holiday hours. Trails are suitable for strollers and wheelchairs. Pets allowed on leash. **YR1331** is rated 2 and goes along Midtown Manhattan sidewalks plus a short distance on paved Central Park paths. **YR1330** is rated 1+ and goes along city sidewalks to and from Central Park. There is a gravel path in Central Park. Note: There are many parking garages available; those listed are just suggestions.

++Niagara Falls - 10km Walk (YR214) 15km Walk (YR862) **Apr 1-Nov 30**
A Awards available
Sponsoring Club: AVA-589, Niagara Frontier Volkssport Club
POC: Marge Brauer, 716-741-2700. 7110 Salt Rd, Clarence Center NY 14032

Start Point: Holiday Inn, 716-285-2521. 114 Buffalo Ave. From I-90, exit to Robert Moses Expressway (Exit 21). Follow signs to State Park and American Falls. Exit at 4th St. towards Convention Center. Left on Buffalo Ave. to Holiday Inn.

Event Info: Daily, dawn to dusk. Trails are rated 1. Suitable for strollers or wheelchairs, but each route has one hill. Pets allowed on leash. **YR214** is along paved walkways, which pass all the attractions of the American side of Niagara Falls. **YR862** passes scenic attractions on both the American and Canadian sides of Niagara Falls. There is a $0.25 fee per person each eay to walk across the Rainbow Bridge into Canada. Note: discounts given at Holiday Inn to volkssporters.

Niagara Falls - Two 10km Walks (YR422 & 1093) **Apr 1-Oct 31**
A Awards available
Sponsoring Club: AVA-788, Niagara Escarpment Volkssport Association
POC: Dorothy N. Socie, 716-731-2630. 2181 Violet Circle #1, Niagara Falls, NY 14304-2901

Start Point: Schoellkopf Geological Museum, Robert Moses Pkwy North; 716-278-1780. Take Robert Moses Pkwy North off Rainbow Blvd. Use first exit off Northbound North Grand Island Bridge off the I-190 and follow Robert Moses Pkwy. Take first exit off Pkwy and follow signs to Schoellkopf Museum.

Event Info: Daily, 10-5. Pets are allowed on both events if leashed. **YR422** is rated 1 and suitable for strollers and wheelchairs. This event goes along mostly city streets and park paths. See Great Lakes Gardens, three falls, Stone Chimney Historic Cemetery and homes. **YR1093** is rated 2+ and is not suitable for strollers or wheelchairs. It goes through historic Village of Lewiston. Walk along Niagara River, see Art Park, and Village of Lewiston Cemetery.

Orchard Park - 10km Walk (YR734) **Apr 1-Nov 30**
A Award available
Sponsoring Club: AVA-589, Niagara Frontier Volkssport Club
POC: Barbara Stafford, 716-626-5890. 8400 Vernon Circle, Williamsville, NY 14221

Start Point: Bihr's Food Shop, 4906 S. Buffalo St. Rt 277. I-90 to exit 56. Left on Mile Strip Rd, 2 miles to South Rt 219. 2.4 miles to Armor Duells Corners Rd. Follow signs to Chestnut Ridge Park & Rt 277 South (7/10 mile). Left on 277 to Bihr's Food Shop (about 100 ft on left). From North & East: I-90 to exit 55. Follow signs for Rt 219 South, 6 miles to Armor Duells Corners Rd (see above directions).

Event Info: Daily, 7 a.m. to dusk. Closed major holidays. Trail is rated 3. Suitable for strollers and wheelchairs, very hilly. Trail is on paved roads with many hills. Pets OK on leash.

Plattsburgh - 10km Walk (YR049) **Apr 5-Oct 26**
Credit Only Event
Sponsoring Club: AVA-084, Adirondack Wanderers
POC: Daniel W. Stockdale, 518-563-4336. 16 Chenango Rd, Plattsburgh, NY 12901

Start Point: Howard Johnson's Motor Lodge, Rt 3 (Upper Cornelia St). Exit 37 off I-87. Right at Exit light. Left at 2nd light into Howard Johnson's.

Event Info: Daily, 7 a.m. to 7 p.m. Trail is on city sidewalks and is rated 1+. Suitable for strollers and wheelchairs. Pets are allowed on leash.

Rhinebeck - 10km Walk (YR1094) **Feb 1-Dec 31**
A Award available
Sponsoring Club: AVA-410, Empire State Capital Volkssporters
POC: Dan Carroll, 914-876-7311. 61 South St, Rhinebeck, NY 12572 or Beryl Wolf, 518-383-2880. 605-B Clifton Park Center Rd, Clifton Park, NY 12065

Start Point: The Delamater House, 44 Montgomery St (Rt 9). NY State Thruway exit 19 (Kingston) to the Rhinecliff/Kingston Bridge (Rte. 199). After crossing bridge, turn right (south) on Rte 9G and right again on Rt. 9 which you will follow into the village of Rhinebeck. The Delamater will be on your right; parking and the office will be in the back.

Event Info: Daily 7-4. Trail is rated 1, suitable for strollers and wheelchairs. Pets on a leash. Beekman Arms/Delamater House give discounts for volkssporters. Phone for details 914-876-7077/914-876-7080. The trail is on sidewalks in the picturesque village of Rhinebeck. You might choose to visit the Aerodrome - Antique Airplanes - Air Shows. Minutes from Hyde Park, home of the FD Roosevelt Museum, Vanderbilt Mansion and the Culinary Institute of America.

Sackets Harbor - 10km Walk (YR938) **Apr 1-Nov 30**
A Award available
Sponsoring Club: AVA-308, North Country Wanderers
POC: Pam Kennedy, 315-646-8000. 256 Clinton St, Watertown, NY 13601

Start Point: Ontario Place Hotel, 315-788-2863. 103 General Smith Dr. Take Exit 45 (Watertown/Arsenal St./Rt 3). Northbound turn left; southbound turn right on NY Rt 3 and continue West approximately eight miles to Sackets Harbor. Take County Rt 75 into Sackets Harbor (the road will split off from Rt. 3). Turn right on Main St. and take the first right to General Smith Dr. The Ontario Place Hotel will be on the left. Ask for the AVA box at the registration counter.

Event Info: Daily dawn to dusk. Trail is rated 1, suitable for strollers and wheelchairs. Pets are allowed on a leash. This trail goes along Lake Ontario through Sackets Harbor Battlefield and Cemetery, Madison Barracks and the historic village.

Saratoga Springs - 11km Walk (YR169) **Jan 1-Dec 31**
A Award availalbe
Sponsoring Club: AVA-410, Empire State Capital Volkssporters
POC: Ron Hersh, 518-885-6281. 128 Church Ave, Ballston Spa, NY 12020 or Beryl Wolf, 518-383-2880. 605-B Clifton Park Center Rd, Clifton Park, NY 12065

Start Point: National Museum of Racing and Hall of Fame, 518-584-0400. Union Ave. & Ludlow St. Saratoga Springs is 30 miles north of Albany. I-87 (Adirondack Northway) to exit 14. West on Union Ave (Rt 9P North). Museum will be on your right. Turn right on Ludlow St to parking lot in rear of museum.

Event Info: Sun 12-4:30; Mon-Sat 10-4:30. During racing season (July 26-Sept 2) the museum is open daily 9-5. Closed Thanksgiving, Christmas, Easter, & New Years. Trail is rated 1+, suitable for strollers & wheelchairs with help. Pets must be leashed. This trail follows city sidewalks in the area of Saratoga Race Track, through the main streets of historic Saratoga Springs and the Skidmore College Campus.

Schenectady - 10km Walk (YR250) **Jan 3-Dec 31**
B Awards available
Sponsoring Club: AVA-410, Empire State Capital Volkssporters
POC: Ellen McNett, 518-372-1270. 822 Union St, Schenectady, NY 12308.

Start Point: Schenectady Urban Cultural Park located at the Schenectady Museum. Nott Terrace Heights. Schenectady is located 20 minutes west of Albany & 30 minutes south of Saratoga. Exit 25 off NY State Thruway. Take Crosstown 890 to the Broadway exit, turning right on Broadway and then right on Millard. Crossing Rt 5, road becomes Nott Terrace. Continue thru one light and right on Nott Terrace Heights just pass train engine on display. Museum is on the right.

Event Info: Tues-Fri 10-4:30; Sat/Sun, 12-5. Closed Mondays and major holidays. Pets must be leashed. Trail is rated 1+, suitable for strollers & wheelchairs with assistance. This trail goes through historic stockade area, Union College and GE Realty Plot.

Utica - 10km Walk (YR1146) **Jan 1-Dec 31**
B Awards available
Sponsoring Club: AVA-838, Mohawk Valley Pathfinders
POC: Helene Labrie, 315-866-6908. PO Box 4486, Utica, NY 13504

Start Point: Mobil/ Nice 'n Easy, 315-724-7852. 1800 Genesee St. From I-90 take exit 31. After the tollbooth, bear left for Genesee St. Follow Genesee St through downtown for about 3 miles to Mobil/ Nice 'n Easy, one block south of the Burrstone Rd and Memorial Parkway intersection and is on the right hand of the street.

Event Info: Daily dawn to dusk. Trail is rated 1+, and is not suitable for strollers & wheelchairs. The walk takes you through Roscoe Conkling Park and passes many handsome homes on Genesee St.

Watkins Glen - (YR239) **May 31-Dec 31**
A Award available
Sponsoring Club: AVA-790, Fingerlakes Region Volkssport Club
POC: Doug Schmeig, 607-776-9522. 6392 Cameron Rd, Bath, NY 14810

Start Point: Castel Grisch State Winery & Restaurant, 607-535-9614. County Hwy 28, Watkins Glen. From the south and east, take I-81 to NY 17E, take Hwy 14 N from Elmira to Watkins Glen. From the north, take I-90 to I-390 through Corning to Elmira. From the west, take NY 17 to Elmira. At the north side of Watkins Glen, take Hwy 409 north for 3/4 mile, turn right on Hwy 28 and proceed to the junction of Hwys 23 & 28. Turn right and drive 1/4 mile to the start point.

Event Info: Daily, 10 a.m. to dusk. Trail is rated 3+. NO strollers, wheelchairs or pets. The route begins at Castel Grisch overlooking Seneca Lake. Walking downhill into Watkins Glen, the route goes through the State Park, climbing up over 800 steps through the glen. The trail then follows a rail line back to the start point. **Note:** The route through the glen is difficult and slippery. Walker must wear footwear in good condition, and pace themselves for the strenuous climb. Walkers can receive 10% off the meal price at the start point.

++West Point - 11km Walk (YR037) **Jan 1-Dec 31**
Sponsoring Club: AVA-505, Volkssport Club of West Point
POC: Farrell G. Patrick, 914-446-4709/Ann Walsh, 914-485-6558. PO Box 30, West Point NY 10996

Start Point: Hotel Thayer Gift Shop, 914-466-8681. From the north: I-84, exit at Newburgh. Rt 9W South. Exit at Rt 218 into Highland Falls. Proceed to Thayer Gate. Hotel is on the right. From the south: Palisades Pkwy north to Bear Mountain Circle. Rt 9W north. Exit onto Rt 218 through Highland Falls. Proceed to Thayer Gate. Hotel is on the right.

Event Info: Daily 8-2. Closed Thanksgiving, Christmas and New Years Day. Trail is rated 2, suitable for strollers but not wheelchairs due to steep hills. Pets are allowed if leashed. The hotel gives room discount package which includes breakfast and the walk award. Trail is entirely within limits of the US Military Academy. It goes through residential areas, main academic area, and past historic monuments, the cemetery and athletic facilities. You will have magnificent views of the Hudson River.

Youngstown - 10km Walk (YR253) **Apr 1-Nov 30**
A Award available
Sponsoring Club: AVA-788, Niagara Escarpment Volkssport Association
POC: Dorothy N. Socie, 716-731-2630. 2181 Violet Cir #1, Niagara Falls NY 14304-2901

Start Point: Gatehouse at Old Fort Niagara State Park; 716-745-7057. Use Robert Moses Pkwy North off the I-190 from NYS Thruway (I-90). From Lockport follow Rt 93 to Youngstown to the Fort. Box is at the Gatehouse.

Event Info: Daily, 9-4 except in July & August when it's 9-7. Trail is rated 2, not suitable for strollers or wheelchairs. Pets are not allowed. Ask for the volkssport discount. The route tours fort buildings dating to the early 1700s and goes thru the historic and picturesque village.

NORTH CAROLINA ━━━━━━━━━━━━━━━━━━━━━━━

Asheville - 10km Walk (YR1010) **Jan 2-Dec 31**
B Awards available
Sponsoring Club: AVA-046, The Asheville Amblers
POC: Sheila Taylor, 704-684-7080. PO Box 1383, Asheville, NC 28802

Start Point: Asheville Chamber of Commerce Visitors Center, 151 Haywood St. From I-240 take exit 4C. Turn right onto Haywood St and take an immediate right into Visitors Center parking lot.

Event Info: Mon-Fri 8:30-5:30; Sat/Sun 9-5. Closed Thanksgiving, Christmas and New Years. Trail is rated 2, not suitable for strollers or wheelchairs due to one steep hill. Pets must be leashed. The Visitor Center staff cannot make change or give volkssport information. Please pay by check. Route is on city streets and sidewalks winding through downtown and neighborhoods; famous for European resort architecture and Art Deco design.

Ashville - 11km Walk (YR1318) **Jun 1-Oct 15**
Credit Only Event
Sponsoring Club: AVA-046, Asheville Amblers
POC: Sheila Taylor, 704-684-7080. PO Box 1383, Asheville, NC 28802

Start Point: North Carolina Arboretum, PO Box 6617. From I-26 take exit 2 (Hwy 191). Turn south, past Biltmore Square Mall. Continue 2 miles. Turn right at Arboretum sign onto Bent Creek Ranch Rd. Bear left onto Wesley Branch Rd. Follow signs to Visitor Education Center.

Event Info: Mon-Fri, 8-5; Sat, 9-5; Sun, 12-5. Call ahead if in doubt. Trail is rated 2+ and is not suitable for strollers or wheelchairs. Pets are not allowed. Trail goes through formal gardens, woods and across a creek. It is hilly and rocky in spots.

Black Mountain - 10km Walk (YR1138) **Jan 1-Dec 31**
Credit Only Event
Sponsoring Club: AVA-046, The Asheville Amblers
POC: Sheila Taylor, 704-684-7080. PO Box 1383, Asheville, NC 28802

Start Point: Town Hardware & General Store, 103 West State St. Take exit 64 off I-40. Travel north on NC9 (Broadway St) to intersection of US 70 (State St). Turn west (left) on US 70; start is the first store on your left. Parking is available throughout the downtown area.

Event Info: Mon-Fri 8-7; Sat 8-5:30; Sun 1-5. Closed New Years, Easter, July 4th, Thanksgiving and Christmas. Trail is rated 1+, not suitable for wheelchairs or strollers. Pets must be leashed. Route travels thru historic downtown Black Mountain, thru wooded areas, around Lake Tomahawk and thru historic residential areas.

Boone - 10km Walk (YR898) **Jan 2-Dec 31**
Credit Only Event
Sponsoring Club: AVA-NC, Tarheel State Walkers
POC: Karen Procter, 910-945-5506. PO Box 844, Lewisville, NC 27023-0844
or Mary Lois Leith, 910-765-6668

Start Point: Visitor Information Center, 704-264-1299/1-800-852-9506. 1700 Blowing Rock Rd. Follow US 321 south from US 421 or NC 105 or US 321 north from Lenoir to the Visitor Center.

Event Info: Daily, 9-5. Closed Thanksgiving & Christmas. Trail is rated 2+, difficult for strollers and wheelchairs. Leashed pets.

Brevard - 10km Walk (YR600) **Jan 2-Dec 31**
B Awards available
Sponsoring Club: AVA-046, The Asheville Amblers
POC: Sheila Taylor, 704-684-7080. PO Box 1383, Asheville, NC 28802

Start Point: D. D. Bullwinkel's Store, 704-862-4700. 38 South Broad St. From I-40 at Asheville, take I-26 to exit 9 (Asheville Airport exit). Turn right and follow Hwy 280 (21 miles) to Brevard. This becomes Broad St in Brevard. Continue to start point on right side of street at corner of Jordan. Parking: Turn left on Jordan St to parking on left behind gas station. There are several free parking lots in downtown.

Event Info: Mon-Sat, 10-5:30. Closed on Sundays and all major holidays. Rated 1+, suitable for strollers. Pets are not allowed. Route is on city sidewalks and through the college campus. Look for white squirrels.

Burnsville - 11km Walk (YR1319) **Jun 1-Sept 30**
Credit Only Event
Sponsoring Club: AVA-046, Asheville Amblers
POC: Lucy Krupp, 704-682-4731. RR 4, Box 265, Burnsville, NC 28714

Start Point: Mt. Mitchell State Park, Hwy 128, Yancey County. Near mile marker 355, Blue Ridge Pkwy. From I-40 in Asheville, take VA Hospital exit. Follow signs to Blue Ridge Parkway. Go north approx 35 miles. Turn into Park entrance and drive to parking lot at Summit. Box is at the office.

Alternate Start Point: Snack Bar at Summit of Mt Mitchell, 2 miles past park office.

Event Info: Daily, 9-5. Call ahead to verify if open during holidays. Trail is rated 4+ and is not suitable for strollers or wheelchairs. Pets must be leashed. This is a back country hike at high elevation. Expect cool temperatures even in summer. It is recommended that you start early. 1/2 mile is rocky with a steep descent. Approx 3 miles is level with the remainder being typically up and down mountain hiking. Fantastic views. Bears and other wildlife in the area.

Buxton - 10km Walk (YR602) **Jan 2-Dec 31**
Credit Only Event
Sponsoring Club: AVA-NC, Tarheel State Walkers
POC: Karen Procter, 910-945-5506. PO Box 844, Lewisville, NC 27023-0844

Start Point: Dillon's Corner, 919-995-5083. Hwy 12. From Raleigh take US Hwy 64 East to Hwy 12 South. Take Hwy 12 south 45-50 miles to Buxton. Start is on the right across from the Comfort Inn.

Event Info: Daily 6am-10pm. Closed Christmas. May close during bad weather. Rated 2, not suitable for strollers or wheelchairs. Take bug repellent. Pets must be leashed. National Park Visitor Cener opens at 9 and closes at 5. This is a level trail on grass along the roadway, dirt trails, sidewalks and some sandy beach area.

Chapel Hill - 10km Walk (YR314) **Jan 2-Dec 31**
Credit Only Event
Sponsoring Club: AVA-786, Triangle Trailblazers
POC: Bill Cruse, 919-848-0005. 8304 Sleepy Creek Dr, Raleigh, NC 27613

Start Point: University of North Carolina Visitor Center, Morehead Planetarium (inside West entrance), 919-962-1630. East Franklin Street. From the west: Take exit 266 (Hwy 86) off I-40. This becomes Columbia St in Chapel Hill. Left on East Franklin. Planetarium is on right. From the east: exit I-40 on US 15-501 South. Take the right fork, Franklin St. Start is on the left (has a rose garden with a large sundial). Park in front at right end and get parking permit. Illegally parked cars will be towed at owners expense. You don't need a permit on weekends.

Event Info: Mon-Sat 10-5; Sun 1-5. Open most holidays with modified hours. Call ahead. Trail is rated 1, suitable for strollers and wheelchairs. Pets must be leashed. This is an almost level trail on campus walkways, through the Coker Arboretum and old neighborhoods with historic homes and charming cottages.

Charlotte - 10km Walk (YR894) **Jan 1-Dec 31**
Sponsoring Club: AVA-831, Metrolina Walkers
POC: Judy Burns, 704-847-4821. 102 Lakenheath Lane, Matthews, NC 28105

Start Point: Charlotte Visitor Center, 704-334-2282. 330 South Tryon St. From I-77, exit 9(B) onto I-277 (John Belk Fwy). Take 2nd exit onto College (Follow Visitor Center signs). At Stonewall St, 1st street, turn left to Tryon St, one block. Right onto Tryon for 2 blocks to start on the left.

Event Info: Mon-Fri 8:30-5; Sat 10-4; Sun 1-4. Closed New Year's, Thanksgiving, & Christmas. Trail is rated 1+, suitable for strollers and wheelchairs. Pets are allowed on a leash. The parking lot behind the Visitors Center has a fee except on weekends. This trail is mostly flat with a couple of rolling hills. It is on city sidewalks.

Corolla - 10km Walk (YR1139) **Jan 2-Dec 31**
Creidt Only Event
Sponsoring Club: AVA-NC, Tarheel State Walkers
POC: Karen Procter, 910-945-5506. PO Box 844, Lewisville, NC 27023-0844 or Steve/Janet Blough, 717-795-9396.

Start Point: Sun Realty, 919-453-8822. Rt 12. From Norfolk VA: 168 south towards Nags Head. 168 becomes 158 in NC. Continue on 158 until crossing onto the island. Go to 4th traffic light and turn left onto Rt 12 toward Duck and Corolla. After passing the Corolla lighthouse on your left, watch for Sun Realty on your right, just past the Currituck County Satelite Office. From west & south: Take US64 east through Manteo to Nags Head. Turn left on 158 and proceed 15 miles north and turn right on Rt 12. Follow directions above at Rt 12.

Event Info: Daily 9-5. Closed New Years Eve & Day, Thanksgiving, Christmas Eve & Day. Trail is rated 1+, not suitable for strollers and wheelchairs. Pets must be leashed and cleaned-up after. Insect spray is recommended and please carry water. The start point has rentalhomes available year round. The route is on pavement, sidewalks, and sand & gravel paths. You will pass varied styles of architecture including a Hunt Club from the 20s. Corolla is home to herds of wild horses descendents from Spanish mustangs marooned in the 1600s.

Durham - 10km Walk (YR940) **Jan 2-Dec 31**
Credit Only Event
Sponsoring Club: AVA-786, Triangle Trailblazers
POC: Bill Cruse, 919-848-0005. 8304 Sleepy Creek Drive, Raleigh, NC 27613

Start Point: 9th Street Active Feet, Inc. 919-286-5101. 705 Ninth St. From either I-85 or I-40 take the Durham Freeway, State Route 147, take Exit 14, Swift Ave to Ninth St. Follow signs to "Ninth St". There is a parking lot next to the Ninth Street Active Feet Store.

Event Info: Daily 10-7. Closed major holidays. Trail is rated 1+, suitable for strollers and wheelchairs. Pets are allowed. The trail is predominently on sidewalks with only slight hills. It passes through downtown Durham as well as the East and West campus of Duke University.

Elizabeth City - 10km Walk (YR895) **Jan 2-Dec 31**
Sponsoring Club: AVA-NC, Tarheel State Walkers
POC: Karen Procter, 910-945-5506. PO Box 844, Lewisville, NC 27023-0844 OR Sharon Goehring, 919-331-7893. 1826 Darian Dr, Elizabeth City, NC 27909

Start Point: The Main Thing, 919-331-1112. 507 East Main. From south on Hwy 17 Bypass, turn right (east) on Main. Go about 14 blocks to Water St. Turn right to the Public Parking lot on right side between Church St & Ehringhaus. From East on US 158 turn left on Water St and proceed to parking lot.

Event Info: Mon & Tues, 7-6; Wed-Fri, 7am-7:30pm; Sat 7-5. Closed Sunday & major holidays. Rated 1, suitable for strollers & wheelchairs. Pets must be leashed. Distance begins at the parking lot. Exit parking lot onto Church St to Poindexter, the street away from Water St. Right (or straight) on Poindexter to Main St (2 blocks). Left on Main St to the start, a store and cafe on the left approx 1/2 block. Elizabeth City is the home of the Moth boat, a one person sailboat. You will walk along the docks and on city sidewalks through residential areas passing many old homes.

Ft Bragg - 11km Walk (YR892) **Jan 1-Dec 31**
Sponsoring Club: AVA-NC, Tarheel State Walkers
POC: Karen Procter, 910-945-5506. PO Box 844, Lewisville, NC 27023-0844

Start Point: 82nd Airborne War Memorial Museum, Gift Shop, 919-432-5307. Bldg 6841, Ardennes & Gela Sts. Drive to Ft Bragg on NC Hwy 24 (also called Bragg Blvd) and enter the post on Gruber Road. Follow signs to museum. There are signs on I-95 and NC24 showing the way to Fort Bragg.

Event Info: Tue-Sat, 10-4:30; Sun, 11:30-4. Closed Mondays, New Year's & Christmas. There is a mounted box near the door with maps & start cards for early walkers. Trail is rated 1+, suitable for strollers and wheelchairs. Pets must be leashed. Route is on sidewalks through the post and residential areas. You will also go by the JFK Museum and Iron Mike Statue.

Greensboro - 10km Walk (YR1320) **Jan 1-Dec 31**
Credit Only Event
Sponsoring Club: AVA-284, Winston Wanderers
POC: Karen Procter, 910-945-5506. PO Box 844, Lewisville, NC 27023-0844 OR Sandra Barnes, 910-288-2023. 3750 Greene's Crossing, Greensboro, NC 27410

Start Point: Colonial Heritage Center, Tannenbaum Park, 910-545-5315. 103 Green Acres Lane. From I-40 take exit 213 (Guilford College Rd). Follow signs to Guilford Courthouse National Military Park. After crossing Battleground Ave (Hwy 220), Tannenbaum Park is on the right on New Garden Rd.

Alternate Start Point: Guilford Courthouse National Military Park Visitor Center, 2332 New Garden Rd. Continue on New Garden Rd past entrance to Tannenbaum Park to Guilford Courthouse Park entrance. (Maps & Start Cards Only)

Event Info: Tue-Fri, 9-5; Sat, 10-5; Sun, 1-5. Closed Mondays and legal holidays. Trail is rated 1+. Some gravel paths may make it difficult for wheelchairs and strollers. Pets are allowed on a leash. This walk starts at Tannenbaum Park, which has the oldest house in Guilford County. It was there when the Revolutionary battle was fought at Guilford Courthouse in 1776. The trail, on park roads, gravel paths and paved greenways, winds around parks, past a lake and, of course, a maze of monuments in the Guilford Courthouse National Park.

Maggie Valley - 10km Walk (YR601) **Jan 1-Dec 31**
Credit Only Event
Sponsoring Club: AVA-778, Greenway Walkers
POC: Tim Plowman, 704-456-9207(days) 704-456-6805(eves). PO Box 1366, Waynesville, NC 28786

Start Point: Pick up map & start card at Mast General Store, 704-452-2001. 148 N Main St. From Asheville, I-40 west. Right on Exit 27 (Waynesville, Clyde, Hwy 19-23) to exit 102 (Hwy 276). Turn right on Russ Ave (Hwy 276) which becomes Walnut. Continue to Main St, turn right. At Miller St, turn right. Park in large lot at corner of Miller and Montgomery. From Tennessee: I-40 east, exit 20. Go south on 276 to light. Left on 19-23. Go to next light and turn right on Dellwood Rd (276 South which becomes Russ Ave then Walnut St). Turn right on Main St and right again on Miller St.

Event Info: Mon-Sat 10-5; Sun 1-5. Closed New Years, Thanksgiving, Easter and Christmas. Trail is rated 1+ and has a gradual hill. It is suitable for strollers and wheelchairs. Pets must be leashed. Route is entirely on sidewalks from one end of Maggie Valley to the other. There is a slight grade but otherwise it is rather flat. Many attractions on trail including Ghost Town in the Sky.

Morehead City - 10km Walk (YR896) **Jan 1-Dec 31**
Credit Only Event
Sponsoring Club: AVA-NC, Tarheel State Walkers
POC: Karen Procter, 910-945-5506. PO Box 844, Lewisville, NC 27023-0844

Start Point: Crystal Coast Visitor Center, 919-726-8148. Hwy 70 Between 34th & 33rd. From New Bern, go East on Hwy 70. Follow signs to Visitor Information Center. By ferry from Ocracoke to Cedar Island (reservation suggested), south on Hwy 12 and then Hwy 70 to VC at Morehead City.

Alternate Start Point: Mary's Flowers & Pastries. 919-808-2077. 801 Arendell St (Hwy 70). From the Visitor Center, proceed on Hwy 70 to the corner of 8th & Hwy 70. Open Mon-Sat 8am-9pm. Closed Sunday & major holidays.

Event Info: Mon-Fri 9-5; Sat/Sun 10-5. Weekend hours may change from Nov-Apr. Call 1-800-SUNNY NC to verify. Closed major holidays. Trail is rated 1, suitable for strollers and wheelchairs. Pets are allowed on a leash. Route is on residential streets and along the wharf.

Mount Airy - 10km Walk (YR891) **Jan 1-Dec 31**
Sponsoring Club: AVA-NC, Tarheel State Walkers
POC: Karen Procter, 910-945-5506. PO Box 844, Lewisville, NC 27023-0844.

Start Point: Mount Airy Visitor Center, 615 N. Main. From I-77: Exit 100 to Hwy 89 east. Take 89 to Renfro St turn left. Follow Renfro just beyond Independence Blvd, turn sharp left onto N Main St. Visitors Center is two story blue house on right side of street. From 52 South: Take 52 North to Bus 52 (becomes Renfro St). Follow Renfro just beyond Independence Blvd, turn sharp left onto N Main St.

Event Info: Mon-Sat 9-4; Sun 1-4. Closed major holidays. Trail is rated 1+, suitable for strollers but wheelchairs may have trouble with curbs and one hill. Pets must be leashed. Route is on city sidewalks through downtown and residential areas. Walk past Snappy Lunch and Floyd's Barber Shop where Andy Griffith went.

New Bern - 10km Walk (YR1140) **Jan 1-Dec 31**
Sponsoring Club: AVA-NC, Tarheel State Walkers
POC: Karen Procter, 910-945-5506. PO Box 844, Lewisville, NC 27023-0844

Start Point: Craven County Convention & Visitors Bureau, 919-637-9400/800-437-5767. 219 Pollock St. US 17 South into New Bern. Follow US 70 Business to Pollock St, first traffic light, turn right to Visitor Center on left. US 17 North into New Bern. At east Front St turn right. At first traffic light take right onto Pollock St. Follow signs to Visitor Center from US 70.

Event Info: Mon-Fri 8-5; Sat 10-5; Sun 11-4. Closed Thanksgiving, Christmas and New Years. Trail is rated 1+ with some slight hills. Pets must be leashed. It is suitable for strollers but wheelchairs might have trouble with curbs. Pick up a copy of the New Bern Heritage Tour Brochure at the Visitor Center for detailed historic site information along the walk. Route goes through historic neighborhoods, along the river front, pat the Tryon Palace, Capitol Building and home of the Colonial Governor of NC. There is an admission charge to enter.

Pilot Mountain - 10km Walk (YR1141) **Apr 1-Dec 15**
Credit Only Event
Sponsoring Club: AVA-284, Winston Wanderers
POC: Karen Procter, 910-945-5506. PO Box 844, Lewisville, NC 27023-0844.

Start Point: Pilot Mountain State Park Visitor Center, 910-325-2355. Rt 3, Box 21. Off US 52, 14 miles south of Mount Airy and 24 miles north of Winston-Salem.

Alternate Start Point: Mt Airy Visitor Center, 800-576-0231. 615 N Main St. Mon-Sat 9-4; Sun 1-4. Closed major holidays.

Event Info: Mon-Fri 9-5. Start point is closed Weekends. Use alternate start point. Park is open daily 8-5. It sometimes closes for extreme inclement weather. Call park first if in doubt. Trail is rated 3+ and is not suitable for strollers or wheelchairs. Pets must be leashed. IVV Stamp is available at both start points. Map and start card can also be picked up ath the Winston-Salem Visitor Center. Since mountain trails get slippery, a walking stick will be useful. As with any nature walk, use insect repellent in summer and carry water at all times. This trail is a hikers delight but is NOT suitable for small children. You will walk down a mountain on dirt and rock trails; also climb over some rocks and return to summit on a paved park road. From the observation platform, you can see the cities of Winston-Salem, Greensboro & High Point.

Raleigh - 11km Walk (YR728) **Jan 2-Dec 31**
Credit Only Event
Sponsoring Club: AVA-786, Triangle Trailblazers
POC: Bill Cruse, 919-848-0005. 8304 Sleepy Creek Dr, Raleigh, NC 27613

Start Point: Capitol Area Visitor Center, 919-733-3456. 301 N Blount St. Located in downtown Raleigh across from the executive mansion. From the west, exit onto Wade Ave off of I-440 (Beltline). Follow Wade as it merges into Capital Blvd, exit to right for Peace St. Turn left on Peace St to Blount St. Right on Blount to Lane. The Visitor Center is on the right corner. From the east, exit onto New Bern Ave off of I-440 (Beltline). New Bern eventually becomes Edenton; stay on Edenton, turn right on Person, then left on Lane for one block. (Cross over Blount to reach the Visitor Center). There is limited parking behind the Visitor Center, off of Lane St. Volksmarchers may park there, when space permits. Parking is available 8-5 at the State Government Visitors' lots located two blocsk northeast of the Visitor Center on the corner of Wilmington & Polk Sts, and three blocks NW of the center on Salisbury St.

Event Info: Mon-Fri 8-5; Sat 9-5; Sun 1-5. Rated 1+, suitable for strollers & wheelchairs. Pets are allowed on a leash. The trail is predominently along city streets and greenway trails. It passes through the campus of NC State University and Cameron Village Shopping Center.

Raleigh - 10km Walk (YR597) **Jan 2-Dec 31**
Credit Only Event
Sponsoring Club: AVA-786, Triangle Trailblazers
POC: Bill Cruse, 919-848-0005. 8304 Sleepy Creek Dr, Raleigh, NC 27613

Start Point: Capital Area Visitor Center, 919-733-3456. 301 N Blount St. Located in downtown Raleigh across from the executive mansion. From the west, exit onto Wade Ave off of I-440 (Beltline). Follow Wade as it merges into Capital Blvd, exit to right for Peace St. Turn left on Peace St to Blount St. Right on Blount to Lane. The Visitor Center is on the right corner. From the east, exit onto New Bern Ave off of I-440 (Beltline). New Bern eventually becomes Edenton; stay on Edenton, turn right on Person, then left on Lane for one block. (Cross over Blount to reach the Visitor Center).

NORTH CAROLINA, cont.

Alternate Start Point: (For start card & map only) The Oakwood Inn, 411 N Bloodworth St, in downtown Raleigh. For reservations only: 919-832-9712. You will pay and get your books stamped only at the Visitors Center.

Event Info: Mon-Fri 8-5; Sat 9-5; Sun 1-5. Closed major holidays. Trail is rated 1+, suitable for strollers and wheelchairs. Pets are allowed on a leash but not in public buildings. Limited parking behind Visitor Center. Route is mostly flat, through historic Oakwood neighborhoods, the Capitol Building, and past Museums of Natural Science and History. Also goes through Mordecai Park.

Raleigh - 10km Walk (YR994) **Jan 2-Dec 31**
Credit Only Event
Sponsoring Club: AVA-786, Triangle Trailblazers
POC: Bill Cruse, 919-848-0005. 8304 Sleepy Creek Dr, Raleigh, NC 27613

Start Point: William B. Umstead State Park, Park Office, 919-787-3033. Hwy 70 W. Located between Raleigh and Durham, 10 miles west of Raleigh. Follow signs to park office (2nd left).

Alternate Start Point: Sports & Rec, 8600 Glenwood Ave (US Hwy 70 W). 1/2 mile east of park entrance.

Event Info: Daily 8-6. Closed major holidays. Trail is rated 4, no strollers or wheelchairs. Pets are allowed. Natural surfaced, wooded trail with some significant hills.

Salisbury - 10km Walk (YR599) **Jan 1-Dec 31**
A Award available
Sponsoring Club: AVA-217, Rowan Roamers
POC: Mary Anne Laningham, 704-633-1447. 327 Bethel Dr, Salisbury, NC 28144 OR Robert Pruehsner, 704-633-3247. 1918 Baker Court, Salisbury, NC 28144

Start Point: Rowan County Visitor Center, 704-638-3100/1-800-332-2343. 132 E. Innes St. From I-85 exit 76B. West on E. Innes .9 miles to Visitor Center on the NW corner of Innes/Lee (one block from the "Square").

Alternate Start Point: For Start Card & Map Only: Days Inn Motel, 704-633-4211. 1810 Luthern Synod Dr. Exit 75 from I-85 at Jake Alexander Blvd.

Event Info: Mon-Fri 9-5; Sat 10-4; Sun 1-4. Closed New Years, Easter, Thanksgiving and Christmas. Trail is rated 1+, suitable for strollers and wheelchairs. Pets must be leashed. Route goes through a historic area, National Cemetery, site of Civil War prison and through the city park.

Troutman-11km Walk (YR1207) **Jan 1-Dec 31**
Credit Only Event
Sponsoring Club: AVA-NC, Tarheel State Walkers
POC: Karen Procter, 910-945-5506. PO Box 844, Lewisville, NC 27023-0844

Start Point: Duke Power State Park Office, 704-528-6350. 159 Inland Sea Lane. From the north, exit 45 off I-77 (Barium Springs). Right on Amity Hill Rd for 200 yards, left on Murdock Rd. Go through the 1st traffic light and turn left on the 2nd rd, Monbo. About 3 miles to Bethel Baptist Church on the right. Immediately past church, left on Saint Johns Rd, Follow sign to Park Office. From the south, Exit 42 off I-77. Follow signs to Park, 8 miles and follow signs to Park Office. IVV Stamp is available at both start locations.

Alternate Start Point: Perth Bait & Tackle Shop, Perth Rd. 704-528-4826. From I-77 MUST USE Exit 42. Follow signs to Park. On the right side of Perth Rd before entrance to Park. Open daily, 6am-8pm. IVV Stamp is available at both start locations.

Event Info: Mon-Fri, 8-5. Closed Sat, Sun & Legal Holidays. Park is open daily, 8-5. Park is closed on Thanksgiving, Christmas, & New Year's Day and sometimes due to extreme inclement weather. Call Park first if in doubt. Trail is rated 3 and is not suitable for strollers and wheelchairs. Pets must be leashed. Since hilly, wooded trails can get slippery, a walking stick will be useful. As with any nature walk, use insect repellent in summer and carry water at all times. Discover Lake Norman, the largest man-made lake in the state. The walk is on nature trails, some by the lake, in a wooded area with some moderate rolling hills.

Waynesville - 10km Walk (YR585) **Jan 1-Dec 31**
Credit Only Event
Sponsoring Club : AVA-778, Greenway Walkers
POC: Tim Plowman, 704-456-9207(days) 704-456-6805(eves). PO Box 1366, Waynesville, NC 28786

Start Point: Mast General Store, 148 N. Main St; 704-452-2101. From Asheville, I-40 west. Right on Exit 27 (Waynesville, Clyde, Hwy 19-23) to exit 102 (Hwy 276). Turn right on Russ Ave (Hwy 276) which becomes Walnut. Continue to Main St, turn right. At Miller St, turn right. Park in large lot at corner of Miller and Montgomery. From Tennessee: I-40 east, exit 20. Go south on 276 to light. Left on 19-23. Go to next light and turn right on Dellwood Rd (276 South which becomes Russ Ave then Walnut St). Turn right on Main St and right again on Miller St.

Event Info: Mon-Sat 10-5; Sun 1-5. Closed on New Year's, Easter, Thanksgiving & Christmas. Trail is rated 2, suitable for strollers but not wheelchairs. Pets are allowed. Trail goes through town, past historical sites and quiet neighborhoods.

Wilmington - 10km Walk (YR893) **Jan 1-Dec 31**
Credit Only Event
Sponsoring Club: AVA-NC, Tarheel State Walkers
POC: Karen Procter, 910-945-5506. PO Box 844, Lewisville, NC 27023-0844

Start Point: New Hanover County Courthouse - Cape Fear Coast Visitor Center, 800-222-4757. 24 N Third. From west on I-40, after I-40 ends, take first exit (marked Wilmington/Wrightsville Beach 17/74). At traffic light, make left onto Hwy 17 South (Market St) and follow Hwy 17 Business to Third. From the north, take Hwy 17 Business to Third. Proceed as from west. From the south, Hwy 74, 76 & 17 North. Cross the Cape Fear River Bridge, take a left at stoplight onto Third St; cross Market St and the Visitor Center is on the right. Parking deck for walkers is located 1/2 block past the Visitor center on the left for a minimal fee. Street parking with time limits also available.

Event Info: Mon-Fri 8:30-5; Sat 9-4; Sun 1-4. Closed Thanksgiving & Christmas. Trail is rated 1+, suitable for strollers and wheelchairs. Pets must be leashed. Route is on sidewalks and passes through historic residential areas, along the waterfront and out to Cape Fear Museum. It also goes by the Transportation Museum, USS North Carolina and many shops and the old City Market. Look for movies being made along the way!

Winston-Salem - Four 10km Walks (YR073, YR237, YR081 & YR1137) **Jan 2-Dec 31**
Sponsoring Club: AVA-284, Winston Wanderers
POC: Karen Procter, 910-945-5506. PO Box 844, Lewisville, NC 27023-0844

Registration: Winston-Salem Visitor Center, 910-777-3796/1-800-331-7018. 601 N Cherry St. From Business I-40 take the Cherry St exit and follow signs to Visitor Center, which is in the City Market Bldg. Drive to various starts for the events listed below:

Start Point: **YR073:** Drive 3 miles to Historic Bethabara Park. **YR081:** Start at Registration Point. **YR237:** Drive 3 miles to Salem Lake and **YR 1137** drive 10 miles to Tanglewood Park. Maps are available at registration point. Maps and start cards may also be picked up at Salem Inn, 127 S Cherry St. The Salem Inn gives a Volksmarcher discount.

Event Info: **YR 073:** Mon-Fri 9-5; Sat/Sun 10-5. Closed New Years, Easter, Thanksgiving and Christmas (may also be closed on the days prior). Trail is rated 3, not suitable for strollers or wheelchairs. Pets are not allowed. A small section of trail is subject to flooding during heavy rains. A walking stick or cane is recommended. The Salem Inn gives a discount to volkssporters. This is an easy to moderate walk with some hills of short duration. On scenic greenway and through historic wooded areas on natural trails. **YR081:** Same hours and holidays as above. Trail is rated 2, suitable for strollers but might be difficult for wheelchairs. Pets must be leashed. Books can be stamped only at the Visitor Center. Route is downtown, through the historic west end and Old Salem. See a reconstructed Moravian Village. Some moderate hills. **YR237:** Same hours and holidays listed above. Trail is rated 2+, sitable for strollers. After heavy rains, the trail may need to be altered. Route is on secluded, peaceful, wooded, dirt and paved paths around Salem Lake. It has a couple of hills of short duration. **YR1137:** Same hours and holidays apply. Trail is rated 2, not suitable for strollers or wheelchairs. Pets must be leashed. There is a $2.00 entrance fee into the Park. A campground, Bed & Breakfast as well as a Lodge is available. This is an easy to moderate walk on park roads, past the lake and through the rose garden of Manor House. Also follows horse trails along Yadkin River.

NORTH DAKOTA

Bismarck - 10km Walk (YR939) **Jan 1-Dec 31**
B Awards available
Sponsoring Club: AVA-406, Koda Manipe Volkssport Club
POC: Mike Starr, 701-223-4355/701-224-5912. 1429 Portland Dr, Bismarck, ND 58504

Start Point: Ramada Hotel, 701-223-9600. South side of Memorial Hwy.

Event Info: Daily dawn-dusk. Trail is rated 1+ and is suitable for strollers and wheelchairs. Pets must be leashed. Walk in North Dakota's State Capitol. The Observation Deck in the Capitol is on the 19th floor. The view is outstanding. Ther Heritage Center is on the Capitol Grounds. Route follows city streets and sidewalks.

Fargo - 10km Walk (YR191) **Apr 1-Nov 15**
A Award available
Sponsoring Club: AVA-032, Red River Volkssport Association
POC: Don/Glenna Scoby, 701-235-3389. 3302 North 2nd St #22, Fargo ND 58102

Start Point: Super 8 Downtown, 301 3rd Ave N. 1-800-437-4682. Located near the Red River in downtown Fargo, north of the Civic Center. YR191 start here and you can register for YR762 here and then drive across the river to the start in Moorhead Minnesota. Get two states with one stop. See Minnesota listing for additional information on this event.. Follow the directions on the trailmap to cross the Red River Bridge to the Heritage Hjemkomst Center Parking Lot where the trail starts.

Event Info: Daily, 6-dusk. You must be off the trail by dark. Trail is rated 1, suitable for strollers & wheelchairs. Pets must be leashed. The River Inn offers special rates for volkssporters. Mention when registering. The trail consists of city sidewalks past many beautiful historic homes and city park trails following the north flowing Red River. During flooding season an alternate route is available. Most of the trail is shaded.

Ft Ransom - 10km Walk (YR160) **May 1-Oct 15**
B Awards available
Sponsoring Club: AVA-406, Koda Manipe Volkssport Club
POC: Wayne Beyer, 701-642-2811. 120 North 4th St, Wahpeton ND 58075

Start Point: Fort Cafe on Main St; 701-973-2301. Fort Ransom is 30 miles S of Valley City, 18 miles NW of Lisbon and 2 miles N of the town of Fort Ransom along the Walter Hjelle Pkwy.

Event Info: Mon-Sat, 7-3; Sun, 10-3. Trail is rated 3, not suitable for strollers or wheelchairs. Pets must be leashed. Dirt, grass & gravel trails through heavily wooded areas along Sheyenne River. Native prairie, summer wildflowers & autumn foliage.

Medora - 10km Walk (YR645) **May 1-Sep 30**
A Award available
Sponsoring Club: AVA-794, Theodore Roosevelt Medora Foundation
POC: Kathy James, 701-623-4545. Box 367, Medora, ND 58645

Start Point: Badlands Motel Office, 701-623-4444. 501 Pacific Ave. Traveling west on I-94 take exit 27. Drive approximately 1 1/2 miles. Badlands Motel will be on the right. Traveling east on I-94, take exit 24. Drive approximately 3 miles to start on the left.

Event Info: Daily, 6am-dusk. Trail is rated 1+, suitable for strollers & wheelchairs. Pets must be leashed. This course will lead through residential areas of Medora as well as business areas. Numerous historical sites will be located along the route. Mostly on city sidewalks or paved streets with fairly flat terrain. The town has been restored to its glory days when Theodore Roosevelt & the Marquis De Mores worked & roamed the beautiful North Dakota Badlands.

Wahpeton - 10km Walk (YR161) **Jan 1-Dec 31**
B Awards available
Sponsoring Club: AVA-406, Koda Manipe Volkssport Club
POC: Wayne Beyer, 701-642-2811. 120 North 4th St, Wahpeton ND 58075

Start Point: Comfort Inn, 209 South 13th St; 701-642-2811. Wahpeton is located in southeastern North Dakota. 10 miles east of I-29 (Hwy 13), or 25 miles west of I-94 (Hwy 210).

Event Info: Daily, 7-6. Trail is rated 1, suitable for strollers & wheelchairs. Pets must be leashed. This walk meanders through Wahpeton, North Dakota & Breckenridge, Minnesota. Points of interest include Chahinkapa Zoo, Prairie Rose Carousel, Red River of the North, Junior College Campus and Rodger Ehnstrom Nature Center.

OHIO ━━

Bexley - 10km Walk (YR1294) **Jan 1-Dec 31**
A Award available
Sponsoring Club: AVA-733, De'Fence Walkers
POC: Jean Thomas, 614-864-JEAN(5326), PO Box 13543, Columbus, OH 43213-0543

Start Point: Friendly Restaurant, 2790 E Main St. From I-70 westbound, take exit 105B, James Rd. Travel north 1.7 miles to East Main St. Turn left at East Main. Travel 0.5 miles to start on your right. From I-70 eastbound, take exit 103A, Bexley/East Main St. Travel north 0.6 miles to East Main St. Turn right on East Main and travel one mile to start on your left. Registration is sefl-service. Look for box in window.

Event Info: Mon-Thurs 7am-10pm; Fri & Sat, 7am-11pm; Sun 8am-10pm. SUMMER HOURS: Mon-Sat 7am-11pm; Sun 8am-10pm. Closed Thanksgiving & Christmas. Trail is rated 1. It is suitable for strollers and wheelchairs if they can navigate some high curbs. Pets must be leashed. Bexley is a small city surrounded on all sides by the large city of Columbus. The walk passes by many lovely homes with spacious grounds including the Governor's Mansion and highlights the city's historical sites and educational institutions.

Cincinnati (Downtown) - 11km Walk (YR303) **Jan 6-Dec 31**
Credit Only Event
Sponsoring Club: AVA-815, Mid America Walking Association
POC: Ted Ballman, 513-385-1279. PO Box 53921, Cincinnati, OH 45253-0921

Start Point: Tischbein Pharmacy, 513-721-0234. Dixie Terminal Bldg, 4th & Walnut. From I-75 S, exit 5th St to Walnut. Right on Walnut to 4th. From I-75 N, I-71 N (KY) cross over the Ohio River following I-71 to Main St (exit 1D). Main to 4th, left on 4th to Walnut. From I-71 S, thru tunnel to Elm/Third St exit (Exit 1B), right on 3rd to Main and left on Main to 4th. Left on 4th to Walnut.

Event Info: Mon-Fri 8-5. Closed Saturdays, Sundays and major holidays. Trail is rated 2+, no strollers, wheelchairs or pets. This route is a city walk with steps and some hills. Great views of downtown from Mt Adams.

Cincinnati (Hyde Park) - 10km Walk (YR270) **Jan 4-Dec 31**
Credit Only Event
Sponsoring Club: AVA-815, Mid America Walking Association
POC: Ted Ballman, 513-385-1279. PO Box 53921, Cincinnati, OH 45253-0921

Start Point: Bob Roncker's Running Spot, 513-321-3006. 1993 Madison Rd. From south, I-71 to Dana (exit 5). Left on Duck Creek Rd (.7 miles) to Dana. Right (.4 miles) to Madison. Right (.7 miles) to Bob Roncker's. From north, exit I-71 at Dana (exit 5). Left on Dana (.4 miles) to Madison. Right (.7 miles) to Roncker's.

Alternate Start (Sundays & Holidays Only): Graeter's, 2404 Erie Ave. Sun, 9am-10pm; Holidays noon-4. Closed Thanksgiving, Christmas & New Years.

Event Info: Mon-Fri 11-7; Sat 10-4. Closed Sundays, New Years, Memorial Day, July 4th, Labor Day, Thanksgiving & Christmas. Trail is rated 2, not suitable for strollers or wheelchairs. Pets must be leashed and there is a clean-up law. The checkpoint is open Mon-Sat, 9am-10pm. Water & restroom at start; water only at checkpoint. No restrooms at Graeter's. This is a revised trail from last year. It goes through residential sections with old homes on paved surfaces with a few gradual hills.

Cincinnati (North College Hill) - 10km Walk (YR832) **Jan 1-Dec 31**
Credit Only Event
Sponsoring Club: AVA-815, Mid-America Walking Association
POC: Ted Ballman, 513-385-1279. PO Box 53921, Cincinnati, OH 45253-0921

Start Point: Perkins Family Restaurant, 513-522-3008. 7124 Hamilton Avenue. From I-275 (north), exit south onto Hamilton Ave for 3 miles to Perkins. From I-74 exit north onto North Bend Rd. Continue on North Bend as it makes a 90 degree right turn at Cheviot Road. Proceed on North Bend past Colerain Ave to Hamilton Ave and turn left onto Hamilton to start (past Galbraith Rd). From I-75, exit Galbraith Rd. Go west on Galbraith, crossing Winton to Hamilton Ave. Go right on Hamilton to Perkins.

Event Info: Daily dawn to dusk. Extremely busy Sundays until about 2pm. Either start very early or be extremely patient while they assist their customers. Trail is rated 2, not suitable for strollers or wheelchairs. Pets must be leashed and the "pooper scooper" law is enforced. Route is mostly paved with a few hills through residential areas.

Cincinnati (Sharonville) - 10/11km Walk (YR301) **Jan 1-Dec 31**
Credit Only Event
Sponsoring Club: AVA-548, Northern Kentucky Trotters
POC: Carol Fairbanks, 606-491-2664. 600 Garrard St, Covington, KY 41011

Start Point: Ameristop, 11114 Main St. I-75 north or south, take Sharon Rd exit #15 and turn east to Sharonville. Cross Reading Rd and bear left onto Main St. After crossing Creek Rd, turn left into parking lot. Star will be directly across Main St. Please do not park in Ameristop lot. From east or west, take I-275 to Rt 42 (exit 46) and turn left. Drive about 2 miles to Sharonville. After road splits into one way, look for Creek Rd and turn left. Go one block to Main St and turn left. Turn left immediately into city parking lot, across the street from the start.

Event Info: Daily dawn to dusk. Trail is rated 1+. It is not suitable for strollers or wheelchairs. Pets are allowed if leashed. Route is mostly paved on hike/bike trail with some woods and roads. Trail follows around a beautiful lake and through a geological gorge trail.

Cincinnati (White Oak) - 10km Walk (YR268) **Jan 2-Dec 31**
Credit Only Event
Sponsoring Club: AVA-815, Mid America Walking Association
POC: Ted Ballman, 513-385-1279. PO Box 53921, Cincinnati, OH 45253-0921

Start Point: Ashland, 513-385-5954. 6050 Cheviot Rd. I-74 exit North Bend Rd. North on North Bend (at Thriftway North Bend bears to the right and Cheviot Rd will go straight). Continue straight on Cheviot Rd to Ashland (right side of street beyond White Oak Shopping Center). From I-275 exit Colerain, South (toward Malls) for six lights to Poole Rd. Right on Poole to Cheviot Rd. Left on Cheviot to start approximately 2.5 miles on left.

Event Info: Mon-Sat 7am-10pm; Sun 8-8. Closed major holidays. Trail is rated 2, suitable for strollers and wheelchairs. Pets must be leashed. It is paved, mostly residential with some hills.

Cincinnati (Winton Woods) - Four 10km Walks (YR855) **Jan 1-Dec 31** (YR1112) **Apr 1-Jun 30**   (YR1113) **Jul 1-Sep 30**   (YR1114) **Oct 1-Dec 31**
B Awards available
Sponsoring Club: AVA-098, Zinzinnati Wanderers
POC: Jerry Bocock, 513-851-7310. 618 Waycross Rd, Cincinnati, OH 45240

Start Point: Winton Woods, 513-521-PARK. 10245 Winton Rd. From I-275 take exit #39 (Winton Rd). Go south for about 3 miles to park entrance on the right. Take first left to Winton Centre. Contact Hamilton County Park Ranger Dispatcher.

Event Info: Daily 8-dusk. Must be finished by dark. Vehicle permit is required; $3.00/annual or $1.00/day. All trails are rated 2+, not suitable for strollers or wheelchairs. Pets must be leashed. All routes are along park trails and roads.

Cleveland - 10km Walk (YR1082) **Jan 2-Dec 31**
A Award available
Sponsoring Club: AVA-049, Valley Vagabonds, Inc.
POC: Deva Simon, 216-572-1675. 13317 Tradewinds, Strongsville, OH 44136

Start Point: Tower City Drug - Tower City Center, Public Square. 216-566-9157. Located in downtown Cleveland. From I-71 or I-90 take the Ontario exit in downtown Cleveland. At the 3rd stoplight go left on to Huron Rd. Tower Center Parking will be on the left. Enter Tower City Center and go to level with Food Court & Fountain. Proceed to Tower City Drug which is across from Dillards. Can also be reached by RTA public transit. Park at W 150th St. Exit off I-71 and ride to Tower City Center ($1.50).

Event Info: Mon-Fri 5:30am-8pm; Sat 10-8; Sun noon-6. Holidays, 11-6. Closed Easter, Thanksgiving, Christmas and New Years. Trail is rated 1+, suitable for strollers and wheelchairs. Pets are not allowed. Trail is mainly flat with just two hills. The trail will pass landmarks -- Terminal Tower, Soldiers & Sailors Monument, Rock & Roll Hall of Fame, Science Center, Jacobs Field, Gund Arena, the Flats, The Warehouse District and many more.

Cleveland (Berea) - 10km Walk (YR538)   27km Bike (YR856) **Jan 1-Dec 31**
Walk has an A Award available   Bike has B Awards available
Sponsoring Club: AVA-049, Valley Vagabonds, Inc.
POC: Deva & Al Simon, 216-572-1675. 13317 Tradewinds, Strongsville, OH 44136

Start Point: Elias Big Boy Restaurant, 216-234-3315. 442 W. Bagley Rd. 15 miles SW of Cleveland. From east/west, take I-480 to I-71 south. Exit Bagley Rd (west). 2.7 miles to W Valley Plaza.

Event Info: Mon-Fri 6am-midnight; Sat/Sun/Holidays 24 hrs. Participate during daylight hrs only. Closed Christmas. Both trails are rated 1+.   The walk is suitable for strollers and wheelchairs. Pets must be leashed. It has two trails available. Only one event credit even if doing both trails. The walk trails are on city streets and paved all-purpose trails. They go through historic Berea and an adjacent Metropark.   Bikers must sign waiver and should wear helmets. The bike trail is on hard surface all-purpose trails in the metropark.

Columbus - 25/50km Bike (YR714) **Apr 5-Nov 9**
B Awards available
Sponsoring Club: AVA-522, Heart of Ohio Hikers
POC: Max Rhoades, 614-451-2905. 599 Lummisford Lane N, Columbus OH 43214

Start Point: McDonald's Restaurant, 3095 North High St. McDonald's is in the NW corner of High St and W Weber. Two miles N of OSU. From I-71 north or south, exit at Weber Road. Turn west and follow Weber to High St. Turn right on high St about a block to the intersection of West Weber and High St.

Event Info: Mon-Sat 6-dusk; Sun 7-dusk. Rated 1+. Participants must sign waiver. This paved trail is almost all on the Olentangy Bike Path. There are a few sharp turns. The trail is very scenic and for the most part parallels the Olentangy River. The 50km trail repeats the 25km trail.

Columbus - 10km Walk (YR293) **Jan 2-Dec 31**
Sponsoring Club: AVA-090, German Village Wander Volk
POC: Russ Brown, 614-837-9126. 3557 Cadell Rd, Columbus, OH 43232-6006

Start Point: Brown Bag Deli, 898 Mohawk St (SE corner of Market & Mohawk). From I-70 westbound take exit 100B (High St/Rt 23). Turn left at 3rd St. Take 3rd to Whittier St and turn left. Proceed to Mohawk St. From I-71 southbound take exit 108A (Main St). Go straight from exit, crossing Main St. You will be on Rich St. Turn left at 3rd St to Whittier St and turn left. Proceed to Mohawk. From I-71 northbound and I-70 eastbound take exit 100A (High St/Front St). proceed straight on Livingston Ave to 3rd St. Turn right at 3rd. Take 3rd to Whittier St and turn left. Proceed to Mohawk.

Event Info: Mon-Fri, 9-8:30; Sat 9-8; Sun 11-6. Closed Easter, Memorial Day, July 4th, Labor Day, Thanksgiving, Christmas and New Years. Trail is rated 1. It would be difficult for strollers and wheelchairs. Pets must be leashed. This unique 10km walk will explore historic German Village and downtown Columbus. The trail passes a replica of the famous Santa Maria, Christopher Columbus' Flagship. Trail includes brick sidewalks. The Santa Maria is not open during the winter.

Conneaut - 10km Walk (YR857) **Jan 1-Dec 31**
A Award available
Sponsoring Club: AVA-049, Valley Vagabonds, Inc.
POC: Deva Simon, 216-572-1675. 13317 Tradewinds, Strongsville, OH 44136

Start Point: Markko Vineyard, 216-593-3197. RD 2, South Ridge Rd. From I-90, exit #235. Go north on Rt 193 to Kingsville. Turn right on Main St. Bear right at first Y and then bear left about 100 ft onto South Ridge Rd. Follow South Ridge aproximately 3 miles and you will see the vineyard on your left.

OHIO, cont. ——————————————————————

Event Info: Mon-Sat 9-6. Closed Sundays & holidays. Between 9 & 11 they may be in the vineyard. Gray start box will be located on outside of the north door or inside. Trail is rated 1+ and is suitable for strollers & wheelchairs. Pets are allowed. This event has two routes. Only one event credit even if doing both routes. Covered Bridge trail is on country roads and passes two covered bridges. The Bicentennial trail is located in downtown Conneaut, through a park, along a beach with a boardwalk and some sand, through the marina and historical district.

Dresden - 10km Walk (YR954) **Jan 1-Dec 31**
B Awards available
Sponsoring Club: AVA-514, Westerville Boot-n-Leggers
POC: Fleur Sells, 614-890-2699. 162A Brandywine, Westerville, OH 43081

Start Point: Dresden Village Association, 709 Main St. From the north: I-77 S to SR 36 W to Coshocton. Rt 16 S to Rt 60 S to Dresden. From the south: I-77 N to I-70 W to Zanesville to Rt 60 N to Dresden. From the east: I-70 W to Zanesville to Rt 60 N to Dresden. From the west: I-70 E to Zanesville to Rt 60 N to Dresden.

Event Info: Mon-Sat 10-5; Sun 1-5. Closed all holidays. Trail is rated 1+, suitable for strollers and wheelchairs. No pets are allowed. Route is through the historic village of Dresden, mostly on sidewalks with some dirt roads by the river. Dresden is the home of Longberger Baskets and has the world's largest woven basket.

Findlay - 10/20/30km Walk (YR1111) **Jan 1-Dec 31**
B Awards available
Sponsoring Club: AVA-432, Blanchard Valley Volkssporters
POC: Frank Reigel, 419-523-4799. 7718 J-6, Ottawa, OH 45875

Start Point: Days Inn, 1305 West Main Cross St. Located at the SE corner of the intersection of I-75 and Ohio SR 12, freeway exit 157.

Event Info: Daily 8-dusk. Trail is rated 1+, suitable for strollers and wagons but wheelchairs may have trouble with curbs. Pets must be leashed and you must provide clean-up. Please pay by check only, to Blanchard Valley Volkssporters, NO CASH. This is an easy route on city streets and sidewalks. Some gravel, trails, boardwalks, steps and gentle hills possible. Only one event credit even if doing all routes.

Hamilton - 10km Walk (YR1286) **Jan 1-Dec 31**
B Awards available
Sponsoring Club: AVA-164, Miami Indian Trekkers
POC: Gerald McCormick, 513-868-7471. 21 Fairborn Court, Hamilton, OH 45013 OR Dr. S. K. Norman, 513-863-4528. 55 Cove Ct, Hamilton, OH 45013

Start Point: Hamiltonian Hotel, 1 Riverfront Plaza. From Rt 4 (north or south) turn west on High Street. Continue to Front St - just past Elder-Beerman. Turn rightand go one block to Riverfront Plaza. Parking is available.

Event Info: Daily, 9am-dusk. Must be finished by dark. Closed Christmas & Easter. Trail is rated 1+ and is suitable for strollers and wheelchairs. Pets must be leashed. Route goes through historical areas of Hamilton and along the Miami River.

Harrison (Miami Whitewater Forest) - Two 10km Walks (YR1115) **Apr 1-Jun 30** (YR 1116) **Jul 1-Sep 30**
B Awards available
Sponsoring Club: AVA-098, Zinzinnati Wanderers
POC: Jerry Bocock, 513-851-7310. 618 Waycross Rd, Cincinnati, OH 45240-3821

Start Point: Boathouse, Harbor Point Pavilion, 513-521-PARK. Miami Whitewater Forest. From I-74 (west of Cincinnati) take exit 3 (Dry Fork Rd). Turn north (away from Harrison) to the first stop sign (about 1 mile). Turn right onto West Rd. Proceed to park entrance on the left. Enter park and follow signs to Harbor Point. Boat House is on the right end of the building complex.

Event Info: Daily 8-dusk. Must be finished by dark. Both walks are rated 3, not suitable for strollers or wheelchairs. Pets must be leashed. Routes follow park trails and roads. Events are subject to a motor vehicle permit fee of $3.00 yearly or $1.00 daily.

Marietta - 10km Walk (YR937) **Jun 1-Dec 31**
A Award available
Sponsoring Club: AVA-804, Flusstalvolk
POC: Sandia Sommer, 614-373-8685. 519 Seventh St, Marietta, OH 45750

Start Point: Lafayette Hotel, 101 Front St. From I-77 take exit 1 at Marietta. Turn right on Rt 7 south to Greene St. Continue on Greene to Front St. From Routebo: follow Rt 60 to Rt 7 (see above). Rt 7 North: Follow Rt 7 South to Greene. (See above). Rt 7 South: Follow Rt 7 North to Front. Turn right on Rt 60 to Greene. Turn right on Greene St to Front St.

Event Info: Daily, dawn to dusk. Trail is rated 1+, suitable for strollers but not wheelchairs. Pets are allowed. Points of interest include Mound Cemetery and 20 other indian mounds.

Marion - 10km Walk (YR1196) **Jan 1-Dec 31**
B Awards availalbe
Sponsoring Club: AVA-514, Westerville Boot-n-Leggers
POC: Jim Spurgeon, 614-471-5777(W) 614-891-0275(H). 3370 E Powell Rd, Lewis Center, OH 43035

Start Point: Harding Motor Lodge, 614-383-6771. 1065 Delaware Ave. Rt 23 (north or south) to Rt 95 West (Mt Vernon Ave). Turn left on Vernon Heights Blvd, left on Delaware Ave to start.

Event Info: Daily 8-8. Trail is rated 1 but is not suitable for strollers or wheelchairs. Pets are allowed on a leash. Route is mostly sidewalks with some grassy areas in the park. Walk to President Harding Memorial and home and other attractions in Marion. Harding was the 29th President and the first one that women could vote for.

Maumee - 10km Walk (YR329) **Apr 6-Nov 26**
B Awards available
Sponsoring Club: AVA-532, Maumee Valley Volkssporters
POC: Kitty Hall, 419-885-4703. 4802 Wickford Dr E., Sylvania, OH 43560

Start Point: Jacky's Depot, 419-893-0216. Allen & W Dudley St. From Ohio Turnpike I-80/I-90 exit #4 south on S Reynolds to Maumee. Reynolds Rd changes to Conant St in Maumee. After crossing Rt 24 go three blocks to W Dudley, turn right one block to Allen and start location. From I-475 take Maumee exit--Rt 24 east to Conant St (3rd light). Turn right on Conant 3 blocks to W. Dudley. Turn right one block to Allen & start location.

Event Info: Mon-Sat 10-6. Closed Easter. Trail is rated 1+. Strollers and wheelchairs will have difficulty with steps at the Canal locks. Pets must be leashed. Route follows city streets & park paths with a few steps at the canal lock.

Middletown - 10km Walk (YR199) **Jan 1-Dec 31**
Sponsoring Club: AVA-229, Bulls Run Ramblers
POC: Bob/Judy Hawkins, 513-746-9394. 7754 Martz Paulin Road, Franklin, OH 45005 or Vicki L. Daniel, 513-424-0186. 2109 Erie Ave, Middletown, OH 45042-2307

Start Point: Manchester Inn, 513-422-5481. 1027 Manchester Ave. From I-75 north or south, take Rt 122 and follow west to downtown Middletown, approximately 5 miles. After crossing Verity Parkway at the Post Office, the next light is Main Street. Turn left on Main and look for the Inn parking signs on the left in the middle of the block.

Event Info: Daily dawn to dusk. Trail is rated 1+. Strollers can get by but not wheelchairs. Leashed pets only. The course is mostly paved, winding through several city parks, residential areas and part of the downtown area.

Oxford - Two 10km Walks (YR1287 & YR1288) **Jan 1-Dec 31**
B Awards available
Sponsoring Club: AVA-164, Miami Indian Trekkers
POC: Virginia Lee, 513-523-7087. 304 West Chestnut #2, Oxford, OH 45056. OR Jerry McCormick, 513-868-7471. 21 Fairborn Ct, Hamilton, OH 45013

Start Point: Amerihost Inn, 513-523-0000. 6 East Sycamore St. From High Street in downtown Oxford, turn north on Main St for four blocks. Motel is at corner of Main & Sycamore. Oxford is 20 miles north of Cincinnati on Rt 27; 30 miles south of Richmond, IN on Rt 27; 30 miles SW of Dayton, OH on Rt 73.

Event Info: Daily, dawn to dusk. Must be finished by·dark. **YR1287** is rated 1 and is suitable for strollers & wheelchairs. Pets must be leashed. Route is mostly on sidewalks, through the business district and residential areas of Oxford. Past historic homes and the McGuffey Museum. **YR1288** is rated 1+ and is not suitable for strollers or wheelchairs. Pets must be leashed. This route is mostly on sidewalks through the campus of Miami University and the campus of Western College.

Spring Valley - 10/20km Walk (YR1078) 25/50km Bike (YR1079) **Jan 1-Dec 31**
B Awards available
Sponsoring Club: AVA-526, Xenia Peg Legs
POC: Paul/Linda Blanton, 513-372-1302. 92 Kinsey Rd, Xenia, OH 45385-1537

Start Point: Spring Valley General Store, 1616 W Spring Valley Paintersville Rd. Located on the NW corner of Rt 42 & Spring Valley Paintersville Rd approximately 7 miles south of Xenia. From the north, take I-70 to Rt 68 south to Xenia. Then take Rt 42 south to Spring Valley. From the south, take I-71 to Rt 48 northto Rt 42 north to Spring Valley. From the east and west, take Rt 35 to Xenia and then south on Rt 42 to Spring Valley.

Event Info: Daily 8-dusk. Closed Christmas. Only one event credit even if doing more than one distance. All trails are rated 1. The walks are suitable for strollers and wheelchairs. Pets are allowed on a leash. For all events, you will pick up your start cards and the General Store and drive to Walton Park for the events. Please pay by checks made payable to the club. Bikers must sign a waiver and should wear helmets. All routes follow a bike trail.

Wapakoneta - 10km Walk (YR690) **Jan 1-Dec 31**
B Awards available
Sponsoring Club: AVA-675, Four Seasons Pathfinders
POC: Jay Koenig, 419-738-3532. 105 Hamilton Rd, Wapakoneta OH 45895

Start Point: Holiday Inn, I-75 & Bellefontaine St. From I-75 north or south, use exit 111 and go west. Holiday Inn is the first traffic light to the right. US 33 east and west, go north on I-75, stay in the right lane as exit 111 is immediately on the right. Turn left and the Inn is the first light to the right.

Event Info: Daily dawn to dusk. Trail is rated 1, suitable for strollers and wheelchairs. Pets must be leashed and are not allowed in the start/finish or checkpoint. Route will be on city streets and sidewalks, mainly through residential areas and downtown Wapakoneta.

West Carrollton - 10/20km Walk (YR005) 25/50km Bike (YR004) **Jan 1-Dec 31**
B Awards available
Sponsoring Club: AVA-OH, Ohio Volkssport Assn.
POC: Jack Majni, 513-438-9235. 6640 Green Branch Dr #5, Centerville, OH 45459

Start Point: Whitman's Bike Shop, 5641 Marina Dr. On I-75 take exit 47 right to West Carrollton. Right on Marina Dr and start is on the left. From the south on I-75, exit 47 for Moraine-Kettering to first traffic light. One block beyond light to Winwood Ave turn left. One block and turn left on Kettering Blvd. Stay to right to W Carrollton. When road merges, use extreme caution and go into rightlane. Right on Marina Dr to start.

Event Info: Mon-Fri 10-7; Sat 10-5; Sun 11-4 (only open Sundays from Apr-Aug). Call to confirm. Walk is rated 1+, suitable for strollers and wheelchairs. The bike is rated 1+. Pets are allowed but must be leashed. Bikers must sign a waiver and should wear a helmet. All payments by check only.

Westerville - 10km Walk (YR077) **Jan 1-Dec 31**
B Awards available
Sponsoring Club: AVA-514, Westerville Boot-n-Leggers
POC: Jim Spurgeon, 614-471-5777(wk) 614-891-0275(hm). 3370 E Powell Rd, Lewis Center, OH 43035

Start Point: Westerville Athletic Club, 934 S State St. From the north: I-71 S to I-270 E to Rt 3 N (State St). From the south: I-71 N to I-270 E to Rt 3 N (State St). From the east: I-70 W to I-270 N to Rt 3 N (State St). From the west: I-70 E to I-270 N to Rt 3 N (State St). N State St to Heatherdown, left on Heatherdown to Athletic Club.

Event Info: Mon-Fri, 6am-11pm; Sat/Sun 8am-11pm. Trail is rated 1+. Strollers and wheelchairs may have difficulty. Pets are allowed on a leash. Route is on sidewalks and through park areas. It goes through historic Westerville and the Otterbein College Campus. Westerville was headquarters for the Anti-Saloon League. It's now home to the American Motorcycle Assn.

Wilmot - 10km Walk (YR376) **Jan 2-Dec 30**
B Awards available
Sponsoring Club: AVA-544, Gemutlich Wanderers
POC: Earl Franks, 330-359-2716. 501 N Market St, Shreve, OH 44676

Start Point: The Wilderness Center, Interpetive Bldg, 330-359-5235. 9877 Alabama Ave, SW. From the north take Rt 21 south to Rt 62 west to Wilmot and Rt 250 west to the Center. From the south take Rt 21 north to Rt 250 west through Wilmot to the Center.

Event Info: Tues-Sat 9-2; Sun 1-2. You must finish by 5. **The parking lot is locked at 5pm.** Closed Mondays, New Year's Eve and Day, Presidents' Day, Thanksgiving, Christmas Eve and Day. Open Easter Sunday, Memorial Day, 4th of July & Labor Day but closed the Tuesday following these holidays. Trail is rated 2+ and is not suitable for strollers or wheelchairs. Pets are not allowed. The trail will pass through upland forest, bottomland woods, prairie plantings and marshes. Sigrist Woods Trail wanders among some of the oldest trees in Ohio. This unique woods has been designated an Ohio Natural Landmark. There is a viewing pier on the lake, a wildlife observation tower, a wildlife viewing blind, boardwalks and bridges crossing streams.

Xenia - Two 10/20km Walks (YR279 & YR956) 30/60km Bike (YR280) **Jan 1-Dec 31**
B Awards available
Sponsoring Club: AVA-526, Xenia Peg Legs
POC: Paul & Linda Blanton, 937-372-1302. 92 Kinsey Rd, Xenia, OH 45385-1537

OHIO, cont.

Start Point: Heritage Bike Shop, 937-372-2555. 594 N Detroit St. From the north on I-75: I-70E to I-675 to 235 Xenia exit 235 to 68, right on 68 to Xenia. Start is on the right. From the south: I-75 to Rt 35 Xenia exit. 35 to Detroit St, left to start. From I-71 take 35 exit to Xenia, right on Detroit St to start. From I-70, exit 68 south to Xenia to Heritage on the right. Rt 68 is Detroit St in Xenia.

Event Info: Mon-Sat 9-5. Closed Sundays & all holidays. All trails are rated 1. Walks are suitable for strollers and wheelchairs. Pets must be leashed. Bikers must sign waiver and should wear a helmet. YR956 (walk) is done on a bike trail. The bike is done on a bike trail & YR279 (walk) is a town walk on city streets.

OKLAHOMA

Bartlesville - 10/11/21km Walk (YR718) **Jan 1-Dec 31**
Credit Only Event
Sponsoring Club: AVA-291, Green Country Wander-Freunde, Inc.
POC: William Dum, 918-335-0709. 5837 SE Whitney, Bartlesville, OK 74006-6042

Start Point: Johnstone Park. Located 40 miles northeast of Tulsa close to the Kansas Border. It is accessible by US Hwy 75 (north & south) or US Hwy 60 (east & west).

Register: Holiday Inn, 918-333-8979. 1410 SE Washington Blvd. 1/8 mile north of the intersection of Hwy 60 East and Hwy 75 (on the east side of Hwy 75). Drive to Johnstone Park for start/finish.

Event Info: Daily, dawn to dusk. Trail is rated 1+. Strollers & wheelchairs could have trouble with curbing. Pets are allowed. Three routes are available but you can receive only one event credit even if doing all routes. The walk runs along the Caney River, along paved streets in residential & business areas. You will pass historic bldgs & landmarks. Mostly flat with a few slight grades.

Lawton - 10km Walk (YR222) **Jan 1-Dec 31**
A Award available
Sponsoring Club: AVA-316, Holy Family Walkers
POC: George Snyder 405-357-2930. 1714 NW 49th St, Lawton OK 73505

Start Point: The Ramada Inn, 601 NW 2nd St; 405-355-7155. From the south & east, exit I-44 at Exit 37. Go left to 2nd st, then right to Ferris. Inn is on your right. From the north, eixt I-44 at Exit 39B and continue south 1/2 mile. Inn is on your left at Ferris (the first light). From the west follow US 62 through north Lawton to the Wichita Falls/Lawton exit. Take the right fork (Lawton/Bus 281) to the first traffic light (Ferris Ave). Inn is on your left.

Event Info: Daily, dawn to 3 hours before sunset. Trail is rated 2. Strollers & wheelchairs will experience some difficulty with curbs, grass & natural paths. Pets must be leashed. Volkssporters can receive the corporate discount rate. Trail goes through residental areas, three city parks and is mostly on flat surfaces with some grass.

Norman - 11km Walk (YR262) **Jan 1-Dec 31**
B Awards available
Sponsoring Club: AVA-026, Wandergruppe Walking Club
POC: Al Heberlein 405-843-5731. 1008 NW 49th St, Oklahoma City OK 73118

Start Point: Thunderbird Lodge, 1430 24th Ave, SW; 405-329-6990. From I-35 exit at 108B (Lindsey). Travel about 3/4 of a mile east to the first light at 24th Ave. Turn right on 24th and about 1/3 mile down, the Lodge is on your right. Start point is at the Registration Desk.

Event Info: Daily, dawn to dusk. Rated 1. Curbs & grassy areas may be difficult for strollers & wheelchairs. Pets must be leashed. Trail is basically on sidewalks & city streets. It begins in a residential area and then encompasses the University of Oklahoma Campus, then a business area & back to motel.

OKLAHOMA, cont. ━━━━━━━━━━━━━━━━━━━━━━━━━━━━

Oklahoma City - 10/13km Walk (YR064) **Jan 1-Dec 31**
A Award available
Sponsoring Club: AVA-232, Frontier Walkers, Inc.
POC: Marvin Baker, 405-329-0808 (h) 405-325-5325 (w). 300 Hal Muldrow Dr #227, Norman, OK 73069

Start Point: Crystal Bridge Building in the Myriad Botanical Gardens, Reno & Harvey Sts, 405-297-3995. From I-40 eastbound, exit at Walker and go north to Reno, then east to the Myriad Gardens. From I-40 westbound, exit at Robinson and go north to Reno, then west to the Myriad Gardens. Visitor parking lot on east side of gardens. Ask for walk registration materials at ticket counter in the Crystal Bridge Building.

Event Info: Daily, 9-6. Closed Christmas. Trail is rated 2, not suitable for strollers or wheelchairs. Pets are allowed. Walk passes through downtown Oklahoma City including the Murrah Building bombing site, elite residential neighborhoods undergoing restoration, the State Capitol, and the bricktown entertainment district. A 3km option explores the Oklahoma Health Sciences Center.

Oklahoma City - 11km Walk (YR350) **Jan 1-Dec 31**
A Award available
Sponsoring Club: AVA-232, Frontier Walkers, Inc.
POC: Chris Papahronis, 405-634-7222. PO Box 25233, Oklahoma City, OK 73125

Start Point: Conoco Food Mart, 405-842-2887. 6401 N. Western. From I-40 take I-235 North. Exit at North 63rd St. Turn west for approximately one mile to the corner of 63rd & North Western Ave. The Conoco Food Mart is on the NW corner of the intersection. From I-44 take Western Ave north to 63rd St. Ask clerk for "walkbox".

Event Info: Daily, 6:30am-11pm. Trail is rated 1+, not suitable for strollers or wheelchairs. Pets are allowed. Course follows residential streets through beautiful Nichols Hills with its many beautiful homes.

Oklahoma City - 10km Walk (YR518) & 25km Bike (YR059) **Jan 1-Dec 31**
A Awards available for both events
Sponsoring Club: AVA-232, Frontier Walkers, Inc.
POC: Chris Papahronis, 405-634-7222 (days only). PO Box 25233, Oklahoma City, OK 73125

Start Point: Oklahoma City Sports Unlimited, 405-749-1811. 9225 N May Ave. From I-44 in Oklahoma City, take Hefner Pkwy north to Britton Rd. Go east on Britton approx 1/2 mile to May Ave. Store is in the shopping plaza on the SW corner of Britton & May. Ask at service desk for "walkbox".

Event Info: Mon-Fri, 9:30-9; Sat, 9-9; Sun, 11-6. Closed Christmas & Easter. Both events are rated 1+. They are not suitable for strollers or wheelchairs. Pets are not allowed. Both events go around Lake Hefner on paved park trails and streets.

Sulphur - 10/14km Walk (YR117) **Jan 2-Dec 31**
B Awards available
Sponsoring Club: AVA-026, Wandergruppe Walking Club
POC: Al Heberlein 405-843-5731. 1008 NW 49th St, Oklahoma City OK 73118

Start Point: Travertine Nature Center, Chickasaw National Recreation Area; 405-622-3165. Southbound on I-35, exit at exit 55. Go east on Hwy 7 through Davis & 8 miles to Sulphur. Northbound on I-35, take exit 51 & go north on Hwy 77 to Davis. Turn east on Hwy 7 & go east 8 miles to Sulphur. In Sulphur, at the stop sign (Hwy 177) turn right & follow park signs.

Event Info: 8-5 September-May; 8-9 June-August. Closed Christmas & New Year's. Trail is rated 1+. Difficult for strollers & wheelchairs in some parts. Pets must be leashed and are not allowed in the Nature Center building and on a portion of the trail by the spring headwaters. The walk is along graveled park trails and blacktop park roads. There are some gentle hills & short flights of trail stairs. Trails are mostly shaded & pass many springs.

Tulsa - 10km Walk (YR009) **Jan 1-Dec 31**
B Awards available
Sponsoring Club: AVA-291, Green Country Wander-Freunde, Inc.
POC: Shirley Schelper, 918-481-1860/Frank Sober, 918-481-1718. PO Box 701856, Tulsa, OK 74170-1856

Start Point: Med-X Drug Store #11, 918-743-9968. 1714 S Utica Square at 21st St. Located in the Utica Shopping Center located approximately 3 miles southeast of Downtown Tulsa at the se corner of 21st St & Utica Ave across the street from St Johns Hospital.

Event Info: Daily, dawn to dusk. Trail is rated 2, moderately easy and is suitable for strollers & wheelchairs. Pets are allowed. The average steady walker can complete the trail in three hours or less. The trail winds through Utica Square and the beautiful Maple Ridge residential area.

Tulsa - 10km Walk (YR079) **Jan 1-Dec 31**
B Awards available
Sponsoring Club: AVA-291, Green Country Wander-Freunde, Inc.
POC: Shirley Schelper, 918-481-1860/Frank Sober, 918-481-1718. PO Box 701856, Tulsa, OK 74710-1865

Start Point: Keystone State Park Store, 918-865-4477. 15 miles west of Tulsa on Hwy 51-A. Hwy 51-A crosses the Keystone Park Lake between Hwys 51 & 64. The Park Store is located just inside the park entrance.

Event Info: Daily, 8-dusk. Trail is rated 4. No strollers or wheelchairs. Pets are not allowed. Part of trail goes along the lake and is rugged, part goes along a training path and the rest is on blacktop road.

Tulsa - 10km Walk (YR973) **Jan 1-Dec 31**
A Award available
Sponsoring Club: AVA-291, Green Country Wander-Freunde, Inc.
POC: Frank Sober, 918-481-1718, 3791 E 82nd St, Tulsa, OK 74137-1634

Start Point: Thornton Family YMCA, 918-622-4500. 5002 S Fulton. From I-44 exit south on Yale Ave. Turn left at 51st St & again left at South Fulton. The YMCA is on the left side. Free parking available. Register here, pay fees, if any & pick up your start card.

Event Info: Mon-Fri dawn to dusk; Sat 8-6; Sun 1-6. Trail is rated 3, suitable for strollers & wheelchairs. Pets are not allowed. There are two trails available. Only one event credit even if doing both trails. The course winds its way through La Fortune Park, around the picturesque grounds of the Double Tree Hotel and St Francis Hospital. You may walk around La Fortune Park twice or choose the neighborhood walk.

Tulsa - 25km Bike (YR148) **Jan 1-Dec 31**
B Awards available
Sponsoring Club: AVA-291, Green Country Wander-Freunde, Inc.
POC: Dorothy Brown, 918-437-8404. 11322 E 4th, Tulsa, OK 74128-2006

Start Point: The Wheel Bicycle & Emporium, 918-587-5927. 815 Riverside Dr. Located at 11th St & Riverside Dr. This is in the Tulsa Parks Area which is about 1/2 mile south and a little west of the city.

Event Info: Apr-Aug, Wednesday & Sunday 10-7. Sept-Mar, Wednesday & Saturday 10-6. Call to verify times (918-587-5927). Trail is rated 2+ and is not suitable for strollers or wheelchairs. No pets are allowed. Trail follows scenic areas along the east bank of the Arkansas River. It is an easy ride for the average cyclist.

OREGON ━━━━━━━━━━━━━━━━━━━━━━━━━━━━━━━━━━━

Albany - 10km Walk (YR215) 11/13km Walk (YR795) 10km Walk (YR377) **Jan 1-Dec 31**
B Awards available
Sponsoring Club: AVA-474, Albany Fitwalkers
POC: Phoebe Harrison, 541-926-1735/Pat Leahy, 541-928-6832. 1410 Lehigh Way, Albany, OR 97321

Start Point: Pop's Branding Iron Restaurant, 901 Pacific Blvd SE. From North on I-5, exit 234B Pacific Blvd. From South on I-5, exit 233 (Hwy 20/Santiam Hwy). Turn west on Santiam Hwy. Stay in left lane and you will have to turn left on Pacific Blvd (no choice)...follow Pacific Blvd to Madison. Be in right lane. Pop's is on the right just before the BP Station. Please park towards the back of the lot.

Event Info: Daily, dawn to dusk. Closed after 3pm on Christmas Eve and all day on Christmas Day. **YR215** is rated 1, suitable for strollers and wheelchairs but all curbs are not cut. Pets are allowed if leashed. It goes through historic downtown, along the river in Monteith Park and in the historic homes district. It is on city streets and bike paths. **YR795** is also rated 1, suitable for strollers & wheelchairs but may have difficulty with curbs. It goes through parks, by five lakes, along city streets and bike paths along streams. Lots of beauty and hungry ducks and maybe some nutria. **YR377** is rated 1+ and is suitable for strollers but wheelchairs may have difficulty with hwy shoulders. Pets are allowed. It goes over the Willamette River then along the golf course and a residential area in North Albany.

Ashland - 10km Walk (YR063) **Jan 2-Dec 31**
B Awards available
Sponsoring Club: AVA-486, Ashland Hillclimbers
POC: Linda Vanderlip 541-482-4674. 325 W. Nevada St, Ashland OR 97520

Start Point: Ashland Rexall Drug, 275 E Main St. From I-5 take exit 19--follow signs to town. The exit will put you onto Valley View Rd for approximately 4 blocks. At Old Hwy 99 turn left. This road will take you directly to the Drug Store but it changes names from Hwy 99 to N Main to E Main in the process. Store is located in the business area in the center of town on your left.

Event Info: Daily 9-3 hours before dark. Finish by dark. Closed major holidays. Trail is rated 3. Very difficult for strollers and wheelchairs. Pets must be leashed and must take the alternate route through Lithia Park. Trail goes down main boulevard to college campus, through residential neighborhoods, Lithia Park and the Shakespeare Festival area.

Astoria - 10/13km Walk (YR475) **Jan 1-Dec 31**
Credit Only Event
Sponsoring Club: AVA-679, Turnaround Trekkers
POC: Doris Larremore, 503-325-4734. PO Box 975, Seaside, OR 97138-0975

Start Point: Columbia Memorial Hospital, 2111 Exchange. Follow the signs from Hwy 101 or Hwy 30 to Astoria. Follow Hwy 30 through town. Turn south one block on 20th. Box is in lobby. Register here and then drive to Peter Pan Market, 712 Niagara for start. As you exit hospital parking lot, turn left to 16th St. Turn left on 16th to Jerome. Turn right on Jerome to 15th. Turn left on 15th to Niagara. Turn right on Niagara to start.

Event Info: Daily dawn to dusk. Trail is rated 2+ and is not suitable for strollers or wheelchairs. Pets must be leashed. This event has an alternate 3km route. Only one event credit even if doing both the 10km and 13km trail. It is mostly on city streets with some stairs. There is a short wood chip trail on the alternate 13km route.

Beaverton - 10km Walk (YR1025) 11km Walk (YR1026) **Jan 1-Dec 31**
Credit Only Events
Sponsoring Club: AVA-549, Cedar Milers
POC: Colleen/Dale Seed, 503-579-3012. 12595 Colt Court, Beaverton, OR 97008

Start Point: Beaverton Fire Dept Station #2, 13900 SW Brockman Rd. I-5 northbound, take Hwy 217 to the Scholls Ferry/Progress exit. Turn right on Scholls Ferry. Turn left on Hall Blvd and left on Greenway Blvd. Greenway becomes Brockman at 125th. Proceed to Fire Station on left. I_5 southbound, take I-405 south. Exit Hwy 26 to Hwy 217. Take Hwy 217 south to the Progress exit. Turn right on Hall & left on Greenway. Greenway becomes Brockman at SW 125th. Proceed to Fire Station on left.

Event Info: Daily, dawn to dusk. Both trails are rated 2 and are suitable for strollers and wheelchairs. Pets are allowed on a leash. YR1025 is the Murrayhill Stroll and follows sidewalks & bike paths. It goes through residential areas including Murrayhill Lake & fountain. YR0126 is the Greenway Park Trail and follows sidewalks & bike trails. The trail meanders through Greenway Park & lovely residential areas including the new Carr Estates.

Canby - 12/15km Walk (YR797) **Jan 1-Dec 31**
Credit Only Event.
Sponsoring Club: AVA-567, The Walking Connection
POC: Phyllis Stuart, 503-266-3747. PO Box 2629, Wilsonville, OR 97070-2629

Start Point: Francesca's Coffee House & Candy Shop, 248 NW First St. From I-5 northbound, take exit 278 (Aurora/Donald). Right on Ehlan Rd to Aurora (3 miles). turn left on Hwy 99E to Canby (3.5 miles). Left on Grant (Texaco Station) to First. Right to Francesca's. From I-5 southbound, take exit 282A (Canby/Hubbard) to 1st traffic light. Turn left on Arndt Rd. Follow Canby Truck Route to 99E. Follow directions above. From I-205, take exit 9 (Oregon City). Follow signs and Hwy 99E to Canby (10 miles). Turn right on Grant, right on 1st to Francesca's. Parking is available across the street.

Event Info: Mon-Fri 6-6; Sat 7:30-6; Sun 8:30-2. Closed Easter, Memorial Day, July 5 (Open July 4), Labor Day, Thanksgiving and December 25 & 26. Trail is rated 1+, suitable for strollers and wheelchairs with a little difficulty from narrow shoulders and uncut curbs. Pets must be leashed. Walkers need to walk on the left unless directed to do otherwise. There are some very narrow shoulders. Plan to walk the extra 3km along the river to Beer Can Beach. Ride the ferry (free to walkers) and take the kids on the miniature ralroad at Flower Farm.

Cannon Beach - 10km Walk (YR434) **Jan 1-Dec 31**
Credit Only Event
Sponsoring Club: AVA-679, Turnaround Trekkers
POC: Mel Hickman, 503-738-5859. PO Box 975, Seaside, OR 97138-0975

Start Point: Tolovana Inn, 3400 S. Hemlock. Follow the signs from Hwy 101 or Hwy 26 to Tolovana exit (south end of Cannon Beach), to the intersection of Hemlock & Warren Way--Tolovana Inn is on the SW corner of the intersection. Drive through "portico" and over speed bump. Keeping to the right, continue to far end of parking area. Start box is located in basement of Bldg 4. Use outside stairway. Box will be in the far right corner of room, just past soft-drink machine. Lift cover to find two drawer file cabinet. After registering, drive back out of Inn parking. Cross Warren Way and park in parking lot at the park. PLEASE do not leave your vehicle at Tolovana Inn. Hemlock is the main street through the business district of Cannon Beach.

Event Info: Daily, 7-dusk. Trail is rated 2. It is not suitable for strollers or wheelchairs. Pets are allowed but you must clean up after them. Route is mostly on city streets except for 2km on the beach.

Charleston - 10km Walk (YR420) **Feb 1-Nov 30**
Credit Only Event
Sponsoring Club: AVA-507, South Coast Wavewalkers
POC: Ann Inman, 541-756-7828. PO Box 284, Coos Bay, OR 97420

Start Point: Davey Jones Locker market. From I-5 take exit 162 to Oregon Hwy 38 (or exit #116 to Oregon Hwy 42). Go west to US Hwy 101. Proceed to Coos Bay/North Bend & follow signs to Charleston. Start is just across the Charleston Bridge on the right. Then drive to Shore Acres State Park.

Event Info: Daily, dawn to dusk. Trail is rated 3 with an alternate that is rated 4+. Only one event credit even if doing both routes. Neither route is suitable for strollers or wheelchairs and pets are not allowed. An entry fee is charged per car. The route rated 3 is along forest and ocean cliffs. Great views of Sunset Bay State Park. The 4+ trail goes up the mountain and affords great views of the Pacific Ocean. Both routes take you through exotic Shore Acres State Park which has more than seven acres of formal rose & oriental gardens. Park closes at dusk.

Coos Bay - 10km Walk (YR177) **Feb 1-Nov 30**
Credit Only Event
Sponsoring Club: AVA-507, South Coast Wavewalkers
POC: Ann Inman, 541-756-7828. PO Box 284, Coos Bay, OR 97420

Start Point: McKay's Market, Corner of 7th & Central. From I-5 take Oregon Hwy 38 or 42 to Hwy 101, then to Coos Bay. Turn west at the Wells Fargo Bank (Commercial St) following signs to Ocean Beaches. This road connects with Central just at McKay's Market.

Event Info: Daily, 8-dusk. Trail is rated 1+ and is suitable for strollers & wheelchairs. Pets are allowed. Trail is along city streets, the bay front and Coos Bay Avenue of Flags. Go through Mingus Park which includes the Choshi Japanese Gardens.

Corvallis - 10km Walk (YR999) 25/50km Bike (YR998) **Jan 1-Dec 31**
Credit Only Events
Sponsoring Club: AVA-499, Corvallis Cruisers
POC: Clark E. Elwell, 541-753-6744. 1208 NW Grant Ave, Corvallis, OR 97330

Start Point: Cub Foods - Timberhill Shopping Center, 2335 NW Kings Blvd. I-5 north or south, exit 228, Hwy 34 west to Corvallis. Cross Willamette River bridge. Street becomes Harrison. Follow Harrison to street past 18th St (Kings Blvd). Right on Kings Blvd past Circle Blvd to Timberhill Shopping Center. Turn right into center. Park away from busy sections. Ask for our registration book at the Video Dept.

Event Info: Daily dawn to dusk. Call on major holidays to verify hours. The walk is rated 3 and is not suitable for strollers or wheelchairs. Pets are allowed. It goes through residential areas. The bike has two 25km loops, one rated 1 and one rated 3. You have two distance options. Only one event credit regardless of the distance chosen. Bikers must sign waiver and should wear a helmet. These routes go through residential areas.

Corvallis - 10km Walk (YR1295) Jan **1-Dec 31**
Credit Only Event
Sponsoring Club: AVA-499, Corvallis Cruisers
POC: Clark Elwell, 541-753-6744. 1208 Grant, Corvallis, OR 97330

Start Point: The Book Bin, 228 SW Third (between Madison & Jefferson). I-5 exit 228/Hwy 34 West to Corvallis. Cross Willamette Bridge onto Harrison St. Turn left on 4th. Parking is available around

148

OREGON, cont.

4th & Jefferson. Street parking in downtown grid is restricted to two hours monitored Mon-Sat. Ask cashier for registration book.

Event Info: Mon-Sat, 8-5; Sun 8-4. Closed major holidays. Trail is rated 1 and is suitable for strollers but wheelchairs may have difficulty with uncut curbs. Pets are allowed. Route follows riverfront bike paths. You will go past the historical society and the Benton County Courthouse. Visit OSU's campus and city parks.

Dundee - 10m Walk (YR1017) **Jan 1-Dec 31**
Credit Only Event
Sponsoring Club: AVA-700, McMinnville Mac Trackers
POC: Margaret J. Forster, 503-864-3517. 5720 NE Duniway Rd, Dayton, OR 97114

Start Point: Dundee Grocery & Deli, 710 SW Hwy 99W. From I-5 take exit 294 and proceed west on Hwy 99W through Tigard and Newberg to Dundee. Start point is on the right, half way through town. From Salen take Wallace Rd to Dayton, then Hwy 18 east to Hwy 99 east to Dundee. From the coast take Hwy 18, by-pass McMinnville and Lafayette to Dundee.

Event Info: Daily, 6am-11pm. Closed Christmas. Trail is rated 3 and would be difficult for strollers and wheelchairs due to gravel and narrow road shoulders. Pets are not allowed in the grocery. It is recommend that you carry water. Route is on paved roads with approximately 3km of gravel road. It has gradual hills and goes into a shady wooded area that opens up to a beautiful view of Dundee and the valley below.

Eugene - Two 10km Walks (YR413 & YR677)   25km Bike (YR414) **Jan 6-Dec 31**
B Awards available
Sponsoring Club: AVA-455, Eugene-Springfield Mossback Volkssport Club
POC: Frank W. Ross, 541-726-7169/547-3949. 2398 N. 8th, Springfield OR 97477

Start Point: Run Pro, 525 High St; 541-343-1842. From I-5 exit 194B (West I-105), take first exit off I-105 with signs to City Center/Mall. Cross bridge and take exit to City Center/Hwy 99N. Stay in right lane, at bottom of ramp, turn right onto High Street. Start is approximately 1/2 block down. There is free parking a few blocks north. For YR677 you drive about 2 miles south to Amazon Park to start the walk.

Event Info: Mon-Fri 10-6; Sat 10-5; Sun 11-4. Sunday hours subject to change. Please call ahead. Closed New Years, Easter, Memorial Day, 4th of July, labor Day, Thanksgiving and Christmas. **YR413** is rated 1+ and is suitable for strollers and wheelchairs. Pets must be leashed. This route is on paved streets and bike paths with little elevation change. This route goes through downtown, the Unviersity of Oregon Campus and the rose garden. **YR677** is rated 3 suitable for strollers but wheelchairs will have some difficulty. Pets must be leashed. This trail is on paved bike paths & residential sidewalks. It has one long gradual hill and one short steep hill. Walk along Amazon Creek, through Amazon Park and in residential areas. **YR414**, the bike, is rated 1. Bikes & helmets can be rented at Pedal Power, located next to Run Pro. It is on highly acclaimed paved bike paths along the Willamette Rive and through several parks. Bikers must sign a waiver and should wear a helmet.

Florence - 10km Walk (YR349) 25km Bike (YR1023) **Jan 1-Dec 31**
Credit Only Events
Sponsoring Club: AVA-695, Yachats Coastal Gems
POC: Shirley's, 541-547-3292. PO Box 896, Yachats OR 97498

Start Point: Sportsman's Store, 249 Hwy 101. 541-997-3336. Florence is located midway between Coos Bay and Newport on US Hwy 101 along the central Oregon coast. The start is located about 2 blocks north of the only bridge in Florence on the west side of Hwy 101. Park on side streets, not in the Sportsman's lot.

Event Info: Mon-Sat 9-7; Sun 10-5. Closed major holidays. The walk is rated 1+, suitable for strollers and wheelchairs with some difficulty from curbs and a sawdust path. Leashed pets only. This event is on city streets, bike paths and some sawdust and gravel paths. you will have views of the city, Siuslaw River and a trip through historic "old-town". The bike is rated 2 and is on bike lanes and paths, one country road and some low traffic streets. Bikers must sign a waiver and should wear a helmet.

Gales Creek - 11km Walk (YR1297) **Jan 1-Dec 31**
Credit Only Event
Sponsoring Club: AVA-225, Webfoot Walkers
POC: Alan Pollock, 503-357-3393. 1733 Camino Dr, Forest Grover, OR 97116

Start Point: Gales Creek Country Store, 8995 NW Gales Creek Rd. From Hwy 26 take Bank's exit (Hwy 6) and proceed to intersection of Hwy 8 and turn left to Gales Creek (2 miles). Entering Forest Grove on Hwy 47 from the north, turn right on Hwy 8 (Pacific Avenue). Turn right and proceed 8.5 miles to Gales Creek. From the south, turn left on Hwy 8 and proceed to Gales Creek.

Event Info: Mon-Sat 7-5; Sun 12-5. Closed official holidays. Trail is rated 3+, suitable for strollers or wheelchairs. Pets must be leashed.

Gaston - 10/13km Walk (YR755) **Jan 1-Dec 31**
Credit Only Event
Sponsoring Club: AVA-225, Webfoot Walkers
POC: Allan Pollock, 503-357-3393. 1733 Camino Dr, Forest Grove, OR 97116

Start Point: Gaston Market, 222 Front Street. Located on Hwy 47 approximately 7 miles south of Forest Grove and approximately 19 miles north of McMinnville. From east or west on Hwy 26 (Sunset Hwy) take North Plains/Hillsboro exit. South to signal light at Zion Church Rd. Right on Zion Church Rd/Cornelius Schefflin Rd (approximately 3.5 miles) to "T" at Verboort Rd. Right on Verboort Rd (approximately .5 miles) to Martin Rd. Left on Martin Rd/Quince St. At signal cross Pacific Ave (Hwy 8)to Hwy 47 Bypass. Follow McMinnville signs to Gaston. From east or west on Hwy 99W just east of McMinnville, take Hwy 47 through Carlton and Yamhill to Gaston or take Hwy 8 (Tualatin Valley Hwy) through Hillsboro and Cornelius to Hwy 47 Bypass then left on Hwy 47 to Gaston.

Event Info: Mon-Sat 8-4:30; store closes at 8. Sun 9:30-3:30; store closes at 7. Closed Easter, Thanksgiving, Christmas & New Years. Only one event credit even if doing both trails. Trails are rated 2. Suitable for strollers but wheelchairs will need assistance. Dogs must be leashed. The 10km is in the town of Gaston, out and back on a tree shaded, gravelled road. The 13km takes you on old Hwy 47 to Patton Valley Rd, then onto gravelled road and back to Gaston.

Gervais - 10/15km Walk (YR794) **Jun 1-Nov 1**
Credit Only Event
Sponsoring Club: AVA-425, Silverton Walk Abouts
POC: Dell Duda, 503-393-0937. PO Box 33, Silverton, OR 97381

Start Point: Willamette Mission State Park, 503-393-1172. 10991 Wheatland Rd, NE. From I-5, take exit 263 and follow the park signs approximately 5 miles to the park.

Event Info: Daily, dawn to dusk. Trail is rated 1 and is suitable for strollers and wheelchairs. Pets must be leashed. Event starts at the wildlife viewing station on the right, just passed th toll booth. There is a $3.00 per day park fee. Flooding can be a problem. Call ahead in rainy weather. Trail is on paved and natural paths. See the world's largest Cottonwood and the Wheatland Ferry.

Gold Beach - 10km Walk (YR846) **Feb 1-Nov 30**
Credit Only Event
Sponsoring Club: AVA-507, South Coast Wavewalkers
POC: Ann Inman, 541-756-7828. PO Box 284, Coos Bay, OR 97420

Start Point: McKay's Market, Hwy 101. From I-5 take Oregon Hwy 38 or 42 to Hwy 101. Travel south on Hwy 101 to Gold Beach. McKay's is on the west side of the street in the middle of town.

Event Info: Daily, 8-dusk. Trail is rated 1+ and is suitable for strollers and wheelchairs with some problems with curbs. Pets are allowed. Trail cr0sses the Rogue River and you may walk the beach at low tide. Also enjoy the great coastal town of Gold Beach.

Government Camp (Mt Hood) - 10km Walk (YR433) **May 3-Sept 28**
B Awards available
Sponsoring Club: AVA-600, Tough Trail Trompers
POC: Wendy Bumgardner; 503-692-3994. PO Box 1651, Tualatin, OR 97062-1651

Start Point: Mt. Hood Inn, 87450 E Government Camp Rd. From I-5 or I-205, take I-84 east. Take I-84 exit 16A (Wood Village) and proceed south on 238th St for 3 miles. Turn left on Burnside which joins Hwy 26 heading east. Proceed 42 miles. Turn left at the Ski Bowl East/Government Camp sign onto Government Camp Loop Rd. The Inn is on the right.

Event Info: Daily dawn to dusk. Trail is rated 3, no strollers or wheelchairs. Pets are allowed. Please carry water and hiking boots and bug repellant are recommended. For trail conditions call, 503-666-0771 and ask for Pioneer Bridle Trail #795. Altitude is 4000 ft. Snowpack varies. This is an alpine multi-use trail to Enid Lake with postcard view of Mt Hood. Native rhododendrons bloom along the forested trail. One hill at start then easy terrain on good surface.

Grants Pass - Four 10km Walks (YR419, YR633, YR1204 & YR1256) 25km Bike (YR991) **Jan 1-Dec 31**
B Awards available
Sponsoring Club: AVA-498, Rogue Valley Walkers
POC: Shirley O'Hare, 541-479-7989. 199 Gordon Way S, Grants Pass OR 97527

Start Point: Three Rivers Hospital & Health Center, 1505 NW Washington Blvd. Exit I-5 at #58. Proceed south on 6th St to Midland (Pizza Hut on corner). Turn right on Midland, go two blocks and turn right again onto NW Washington. Register in the Emergency Room Admitting Entrance behind the volunteer station.

Event Info: Daily, dawn to dusk. **YR419:** (Grants Pass Historical Walk) is rated 2, not suitable for strollers or wheelchairs. Pets are allowed. This walk will take you by many of the historic homes and buildings in Grants Pass. They are detailed in a separate trail guide. The route goes through the business areas, Riverside Park, Croxton Memorial Park where old tombstones are displayed on a carousel-type monument. **YR633:** (Name that Park Walk) is rated 2, no strollers or wheelchairs. Pets are allowed. This walk highlights some of the interesting points in Grants Pass and takes you by seven parks. The route goes through the business district, a newly developing All Sports Park and past some historic homes. **YR1204:** (Rogue River Trail) is rated 4. No stroller or wheelchairs. Pets are allowed. Please carry water on this route. Trail is along the "wild river" section of the Rogue River. Many rafters run this section of the Rogue and may be observed. The trail is steep and rocky in spots and is on the sunny side of the river. Early morning or late afternoon when temperatures are low are the best times to walk. **YR1256:** (NW Hills) is rated 3+. No strollers or wheelchairs. Pets are allowed. This walk has one long, steep uphill climb (Starlite Dr) that gives you a panoramic view of Grants Pass and the surrounding mountains. Other parts of the walk take you through wooded hills of the NW section of town. Return to start/finish through historic downtown and residential areas. Several historic points of interest are noted on the walk. **YR991:** (Grants Pass Bike) is rated 3. Bikers must sign waiver and must wear helmets. This bike goes on marked bike routes on city streets then out into the rolling hills and farmlands of the Rogue Valley, returning along the river and back into town. The road along the river is an old country road with little or no shoulder but it is not heavily traveled.

151

Gresham - 10km Walk (YR519) **Jan 1-Dec 31**
A Award available
Sponsoring Club: AVA-552, East County Windwalkers
POC: Ida Lieb, 503-663-9222. 13025 SE Orient Dr #41, Boring, OR 97009

Start Point: Pony Soldier Inn, 1060 NE Cleveland. From west & east by I-84 take exit 16A, Wood Village and proceed south on 242nd Ave. Turn right on NE Division to Cleveland. Turn right onto Cleveland. The Inn is on the corner. From MAX light rail system, get off in Gresham at Cleveland/8th, the last stop and walk north to the Inn.

Event Info: Daily, dawn-dusk. Trail is rated 2 and is suitable for strollers and wheelchairs. Pets must be leashed. Tour new housing developments in Gresham and travel down a long section of the springwater corridor.

Gresham - Two 10km Walks (YR612 & YR687) **Jan 1-Dec 31**
A Awards available
Sponsoring Club: AVA-552, East County Windwalkers
POC: Ida/Norm Lieb, 503-663-9222. 13025 SE Orient Dr #41, Boring, OR 97009.

Start Point: Mount Hood Medical Center, 24800 SE Stark St. From I-84 east or west, exit Wood Village/Gresham (16A). Go south on 238th Dr (away from the Columbia River) and stay on 238th Dr as it curves and becomes 242nd. Turn left on Stark St which is the fourth stop light past the freeway. Turn right into the hospital entrance and park in an outlying spot. Start box is in the entrance area.

Event Info: Daily dawn to dusk. **YR612** is rated 2 and is suitable for strollers and wheelchairs. Pets are allowed. Quiet neighborhoods, gorgeous parks and parts of downtown Gresham highlight this trail. **YR687** is rated 1+ and is not suitable for strollers or wheelchairs. Pets are not allowed on campus. This route provides scenic views of Mt Hood and the campus of Mt Hood Community College. You will aslo meander through several Gresham neighborhoods.

Hillsboro - 10km Walk (YR098) **Jan 1-Dec 31**
Credit Only Event
Sponsoring Club: AVA-745, Tualatin Valley Volks
POC: Sheila Day, 503-324-6191. 41320 NW Lodge Rd, Banks OR 97106

Start Point: Hillsboro Tuality Hospital, 335 SE 8th Ave. Take Hwy 26 west (toward coast). Exit at Hillsboro/Cornelius Pass exit. Follow directional signs to Hillsboro, passing the airport. Continue into town on Cornell which turns into 10th Ave. At Baseline turn right. Proceed to 8th Ave and the start. Parking on the right side.

Event Info: Daily 8-dusk. Trail is rated 1 and is suitable for strollers and wheelchairs but some curbs are not cut. Pets must be leashed. Route goes through the downtown area, through parks with historic homes & buildings.

Junction City - 10km Walk (YR1024) **Jan 4-Dec 31**
B Awards available
Sponsoring Club: AVA-455, Eugene-Springfield Mossback
POC: Frank W. Ross, 541-726-7169/547-3949. 2398 N 8th St, Springfield, OR 97477

Start Point: Guest House Motel, 541-998-6524. 1335 Ivy St (Hwy 99). I-5 southbound, exit 209. I-5 northbound, exit 195, Beltline West. Southbound follow sign to Harrisburg and south from Harrisburg on 99E to Junction City. Northbound follow signs to 99E Airport-Junction City and north on 99E to Junction City. Parking on 14th St. Please do not park in motel parking.

Event Info: Daily dawn to dusk. Trail is rated 1, strollers with difficulty and not suitable for wheelchairs. Strollers must use caution on the country roads. Pets must be leashed. Route is on city streets and along country roads. It takes you through the Scandinavian Festival Grounds. The Festival is held four days in mid-August.

Lake Oswego - Four 10km Walks (YR347, YR405, YR406 & YR611) **Jan 1-Dec 31**
Credit Only Events
Sponsoring Club: AVA-242, Columbia River Volkssport Club
POC: Julia Ferreira, 503-636-5520. 2161 Crest Dr, Lake Oswego OR 97034

Start Point: Finish Line Sports, 333 S. State St. Located 8 miles S of Portland & 6 miles N of West Linn on State Hwy 43 (I-205 exit 8 for West Linn or I-5 exit 299 for Macadam Ave). Free parking in Lake Place Center in the perimete spaces. Please do not park directly in front of the stores.

Event Info: Mon-Fri 10-7; Sat 10-6 & Sun 11-5. Closed major holidays. **YR347:** (Tryon Creek Loop) is rated 2, not suitable for strollers or wheelchairs. Pets are allowed. Visit the water sports center along the Willamette River. Then enter Tryon Creek State Park following the Iron Mountain Hiking Trail. View the bottom of Oswego Lake's golf course and return along the north shore of Oswego Lake. **YR405:** (Skylands Loop) is rated 3, no wheelchairs or strollers. Pets are allowed. Walk along Oswego Creek and ascend into Hallinan Heights area. Climb again to the Skylands area with its million dollar views and homes. Return through Freepons Park and George Rogers park. **YR406:** (Iron Mountain Loop) is rated 3 and is not suitable for strollers or wheelchairs. Pets are allowed. This walk goes along the lake front by the cabanas. Then ascend Iron Mountain via the old railbed to the iron mines. Top out in the uplands area for a view from the top of Oswego Lake's golf course. Return through Springbrook Park and the Iron Mountain Trail to the North Shore of Oswego Lake. Historic Trail brochure available to accompany this route. **YR611:** (Marylhurst Loop) is rated 2. It is not suitable for strollers or wheelchairs. Pets must be leashed. Walk through historic Old Town and George Rogers Park. Follow the Willamette River south to Robinwood. Circle back through the Marylhurst College Campus and along Old River Road. A Historic Homes brochure is available to accompany this route.

Lake Oswego - 10km Walk (YR793)   12km Walk (YR545) **Jan 1-Dec 31**
Credit Only Events
Sponsoring Club: AVA-752, Lake Oswego Puddle Jumpers
POC: Bob Parsons, 503-699-8820. PO Box 1853, Lake Oswego OR 97035

Start Point: Vienna Coffee Co, 406 "A" Avenue. From I-5 take exit 292. At the top of the ramp, turn left on Kruse Way to Lower Boones Ferry Rd (about 2k). Turn left on Boones Ferry to Country Club Rd. Turn right and follow Country Club until it becomes "A" Ave. Follow "A" to 4th. Start is on the corner.

Event Info: Daily 7-5. YR793 is rated 2, okay for strollers but difficult for wheelchairs. Pets are okay. This is a pleasant walk through the oldest part of town -- parks and river view and a small view of Lake Oswego. YR545 is rated 3, suitable for strollers but not recommended for wheelchairs. Pets are okay. Walk around the lake. You will be very close to the lake and have great views.

Lake Oswego - Two 10km Walks (YR578 & YR605) **Jan 1-Dec 31**
Credit Only Events
Sponsoring Club: AVA-752, Lake Oswego Puddle Jumpers
POC: Bob Parsons, 503-699-8820. PO Box 1853, Lake Oswego, OR 97035

Start Point: McDonald's, 16044 SW Lower Boones Ferry Rd. From I-5 North or South, take exit 292. At the top of the ramp, turn left on Kruse Way to Lower Boones Ferry Rd. Turn right on Lower Boones Ferry to start on left side approximately 1 mile. Park towards the back of the lot.

Event Info: Daily dawn to dusk. Both trails are rated 1+. YR605 because of one hill and YR578 because of stairs. The are suitable for strollers but not wheelchairs. Pets must be leashed. **YR605** goes over the highway & thru some woods. It is a pleasant walk through residential homes and a park then through a business park and by a water pond. **YR578** is a quiet walk through residential areas with some nature paths.

OREGON, cont. ―――――――――――――――――――

Lincoln City - Three 10km Walks (YR311, YR312 & YR313)   25km Bike (YR1027)   **Jan 1-Dec 31**
YR311 has an A Award available   All others are Credit Only Events
Sponsoring Club: AVA-727, Lincoln Fogchasers
POC: Raylene Erickson, 541-994-6705. PO Box 22, Neotsu, OR 97364

Start Point: Sea Gypsy Motel, 145 NW Inlet Ave. Go to D River Wayside off Hwy 101, middle of town at SW First St to park. Walk the river bridge to NW 2nd St, left to Sea Gypsy Motel. Self registration in the lobby. Please don't use Sea Gypsy parking.

Event Info: Daily, dawn to dusk. **YR311:** This trail is rated 2 and is suitable for strollers & wheelchairs if they take the pavement. Pets are allowed. Pass bakery, shops, Abraham Lincoln statue and historical Dorchester House. There is an option between pavement or sandy beach for return. **YR312:** Trail is rated 2 but is not suitable for strollers or wheelchairs. Pets are allowed. Check the tide tables before doing this event. Route is on sandy beach (sometimes rocky) from the D River to Road's End wayside and back. **YR313:** This event is rated 3 (2 at lowtide). It is not suitable for strollers or wheelchairs. Pets are okay. Trail follows a sandy & sometimes rocky beach from the D River to Siletz Bay and back. The Siletz Bay area is being preserved as a coastal wetlands wildlife refuge. **YR1027:** This bike event is rated 2+. Bikers must sign a waiver and wear a helmet. Register and pick up map and then drive south on Hwy 101 to the signal at 51st St and turn right to the Taft public parking area on the right about 1/2 block, near Siletz Bay across from the historical Museum. Water & restrooms are available at the start only. Route goes up Schooner Creek to Anderson Creek to Drift Creek, past Oregon's oldest covered bridge and the Elk's Wapiti Park.

McMinnville - 10km Walk (YR668) 10/15km Walk (YR571)   27km Bike (YR1018)   **Jan 1-Dec 31**
Credit Only Events
Sponsoring Club: AVA-700, McMinnville Mac Trackers
POC: Margaret J. Forster, 503-864-3517. 5720 NE Duniway Rd, Dayton, OR 97114

Start Point: Jane's Safari Restaurant, 325 N Hwy 99W. From I-5 north or south, take exit 294 and proceed west on Hwy 99W to McMinnville. Jane's Restaurant is next to Safari Motor Inn between Evan's and 19th St on Hwy 99W. Please park in the back lot away from hotel guest parking. The start/finish cabinet is behind the restaurant in the meeting rooms entrance.

Event Info: Daily dawn to dusk. Closed Christmas. **YR571:** Rated 1+, suitable for strollers; wheelchairs questionalble. There is an alternate route in the city park for wheelchairs to avoid stairs. Pets are okay. Trail goes through quiet residential areas, a city park and along a golf course. **YR668:** Rated 1, strollers and wheelchairs will have some difficulty due to natural wood-chip trail through the park. Pets must be leashed. This route takes you through residential areas to downtown with its shops, galleries, coffee houses and many restaurants. A portion is in a park and has a natural wood chip trail. **YR1018:** This bike trail is rated 1. Bikers must sign a waiver and helmets are required. This ride is relatively flat with some rolling hills. You will see all four sides of McMinnville and along the way you get to visit the countryside with a new section of a bike lane. See Linfield College, a beautiful view of Mt Hood (on a clear day), and some residential areas.

Medford - 10km Walk (YR1029) **Jan 1-Dec 31**
B Awards available
Sponsoring Club: AVA-498, Rogue Valley Walkers
POC: George/Pauline Minter, 541-772-8311. 2549 Samoan Way, Medford, OR 97504

Start Point: Ray's Food Place, 1990 N Pacific Hwy. Exit I-5 at #30. From the north: turn right and go to third stop light. Turn right. The start is on the right by Wendy's. From the south: turn left at the light and go to next light. Turn right and go up Hwy 62. Continue on Hwy 62 to the 4th stop light. Turn right. The store is on the right by Wendy's.

Event Info: Daily dawn to dusk. Trail is rated 1 and is not suitable for strollers and wheelchairs. Pets must be leashed. Route goes along a bike path and city streets, through a park and a historic district.

Millersburg - 10/12km Walk (YR666) 25/50km Bike (YR667) **Jan 1-Dec 31**
B Awards available
Sponsoring Club: AVA-474, Albany Fitwalkers Volkssport Club
POC: Chuck Boeder 541-967-9162. 2908 Millersburg Dr NE, Albany OR 97321

Start Point: Private Residence, 541-967-9162. 2908 Millersburg Dr, NE (about 1 mile off I-5). I-5 north or south bound exit 238, turn west at stop sign. Turn right at 1st side road (Morningstar). 1/10 mile turn left at Millersburg Dr. Start is the gray & white house 1/2 mile down on the left. Start box is by garage. Do not block the gate and do NOT let your dog loose in the yard.

Event Info: Daily dawn to dusk. No restrooms available at start. **YR666** is rated 1, suitable for strollers and wheelchairs. Restrooms may not be available. **YR667** is rated 1+. You will pass the Millersburg City Park, Store, City Hall, Rural Fire Department and you will enjoy the views of the area and the distant mountain ranges.

Mosier - 10km Walk (YR1229) **Jan 1-Dec 31**
Credit Only Event
Sponsoring Club: AVA-833, The Gorge Walkers
POC: Marilynn Shaw, 541-478-3772. 1460 Morgensen Rd, Mosier, OR 97040

Start Point: H & H Auto Service, 1202 First Ave. From I-84 east or west take exit #69. Follow road into town of Mosier. Start is the first business past the school.

Event Info: Mon-Fri, 7-7; Sat & Sun 8-5. Trail is rated 2+ and is suitable for strollers but not wheelchairs. Pets are allowed. This walk is an out (one continuous incline) and back with a turn around at one of the original viewpoints. Many spectacular river views. The wildflowers are especially beautiful in March-May. There are narrow shoulders. You will walk on the old Historic Columbia River Highway.

Newberg - Two 10km Walks (YR356 & YR357) **Jan 1-Dec 31**
Credit Only Events
Sponsoring Club: AVA-738, Y-B Normal Adventurers
POC: Cathie Bittler, 503-845-9499. 812 N Meridian, Newberg, OR 97132

Start Point: Private residence, 812 N. Meridian. Exit Newberg-Tygard exit #294 off I-5. Proceed west on 99W for about 18 miles. In Newberg, the highway will make a sharp right and become one way. Continue 3 blocks on one way and turn right on Meridian. Start point is on the right just before the railroad tracks approx 7 blocks down.

Event Info: Daily, dawn to dusk. Trails are both rated 2. They are suitable for strollers but not wheelchairs. Pets are allowed on both trails. **YR356** is a country route. It follows sidewalks and country roads with beautiful vistas. **YR357** is a city walk through the city of Newberg with a little country thrown in. It is mostly sidewalks and roadways.

Newport - Two 10km Walks (YR438 & YR665) **Jan 1-Dec 31**
Credit Only Events
Sponsoring Club: AVA-695, Yachats Coastal Gems
POC: Shirley's, 541-547-3292. 271 Hwy 101, Yachats, OR 97498

Start Point: Oregon State University/Hatfield Marine Science Center, 2030 Marine Science Dr. Starts near the Oregon Coast Aquarium. Take Hwy 101 to South Beach, south side of the Yaquina Bay bridge from Newport. Exit Hwy 101 following signs to the Science Center. Self start box is located outside to the right of the Center entrance. For walk 665, register and pick up map before driving to the Newport Elk's Club parking lot.

Event Info: Daily dawn to dusk. **YR438** is rated 2, not suitable for strollers or wheelchairs. This route is on a nature trail, the Yaquina Bay south jetty with views of the bay and ocean. Restrooms are available at the start when the center is open, otherwise available near checkpoint. Check tides before walking the beach route. 7 ft or more make the beach nearly impassable. **YR665** is rated 2+, not suitable for strollers or wheelchairs. It goes along the oceanfront to the Viet Nam Memorial, then by historical buildings in Newport. Check tide tables before walking the beach option. Tides in excess of 7.5 ft could make passage difficult.

North Bend - 10km Walk (YR495) **Feb 1-Nov 30**
Credit Only Event
Sponsoring Club: AVA-507, South Coast Wavewalkers
POC: Ann Inman, 541-756-7828. PO Box 284, Coos Bay, OR 97420

Start Point: McDonald's, corner of Newmark & Broadway. From I-5 take Oregon Hwy 38 or 42 to US Hwy 101 then to North Bend. Follow signs to Oregon Beaches, turning west on Virginia Street, past Pony Village Mall and turning south at Broadway.

Event Info: Daily, 8 to dusk. Trail is rated 1, suitable for strollers but difficult for wheelchairs. Pets are allowed. This walk is along city streets and Empire Lakes. You will have views of North Bend, Empire Lakes, Community College and the mall.

Oregon City - 10km Walk (YR273) **Jan 1-Dec 31**
Credit Only Event
Sponsoring Club: AVA-253, Valley Volkswalkers
POC: Pat Miller, 360-254-8009. 1609 SE 14th Court, Vancouver, WA 98684

Start Point: Willamette Falls Hospital, 1500 Division St. From I-205 take exit 9 (Oregon City). Go left on McLoughlin Blvd. Turn left on 14th Ave (by Union 76 station). At signal light turn left on Washington. Turn right on 15th and go up the hill until you see the hospital straight ahead at the flashing light. Please DO NOT park in the Hospital lot. Use street parking.

Event Info: Daily dawn to dusk. Rated 3, suitable for strollers or wheelchairs with alternate route. Pets must be leashed. This route takes you to the lower levels of Oregon City, along the Willamette River, up the municipal elevator, along the promenade, past the County Museum, historic homes (including the McLoughlin House) and back to the start.

Parkdale - 11km Walk (YR1296) **Jan 1-Dec 31**
Credit Only Event
Sponsoring Club: AVA-833, The Gorge Walkers
POC: Mary Parrott, 541-352-7418. 7845 Clear Creek Rd, Parkdale, OR 97041

Start Point: Parkdale Grange, 7375 Clear Creek Rd. Take I-84 to Hood River. Take exit 64. This is Hwy 35. From Hwy 35 take the Parkdale exit at the Mt. Hood Store. This will be Cooper Spur Rd. Where Cooper Spur meets Baseline is a blinking light. Turn right onto Baseline. Take a left on Clear Creek Rd. The Grange is the only white building on the left, at the end of the tracks. Start box is on the porch.

Event Info: Daily, dawn to dusk. Trail is rated 2+, suitable for strollers but not wheelchairs. Pets are allowed. Bring your cameras. You will have views of Mt Hood, Mt Adams and valleys. Orchards line the walk. See migratory songbirds, wild flowers and the Hutson Museum. Route is a mostly gradual grade. Two short areas of steeper grade. Road shoulders are good most of the way. A few areas where shoulders are not as good.

Portland - 10km Walk (YR989) **Jan 1-Dec 31**
Credit Only Event
Sponsoring Club: AVA-242, Columbia River Volkssport Club
POC: Ruth Pennington, 503-636-0629. 2121 Wembly Park Road, Lake Oswego, OR 97034

Start Point: Nature Center, Tryon Creek State Park. Between Portland & lake Oswego at 11321 SW Terwilliger Blvd. Located adjacent to Lewis 7 Clark Law School in SW Portland. From I-5 southbound, take Terwilliger exit 297; go right on Barbur Blvd; then right on Terwilliger Blvd for 2.5 miles. From I-5 northbound, take Terwilliger Blvd exit 297; go right on Terwilliger for 2.4 miles. Park entrance is one mile south of Lewis & Clark Law School entrance.

Event Info: Daily, dawn to dusk. Trail is rated 2+ and is not suitable for strollers or wheelchairs. Pets are okay. Walk on mostly natural trails with some asphalt.

Portland - 10km Walk (YR409) 11km Walk (YR033) **Jan 1-Dec 31**
B Awards available
Sponsoring Club: AVA-446, Rose City Roamers
POC: Carol Ottoson, 503-774-2072. 5960 SE Tibbetts, Portland OR 97206

Start Point: Providence Medical Center, 503-215-1111. 4805 NE Glisan. I-84 eastbound, exit 3, 58th Ave.. Right on Glisan to 49th. Right to parking. I-84 westbound to exit 2, 43rd Ave. Right at signal, Halsey St to 47th. Right to Glisan. Left on Glisan to 49th. Left to parking garage. Start box is adjacent to Securities desk in Providence Hall at the 49th Ave entry.

Event Info: Daily dawn to dusk. Trails are rated 1+, suitable for strollers and wheelchairs but all curbs are not cut. Pets must be leashed. **YR033** takes you past the shops and restaurants on Hawthorne Blvd, through the Laurelhurst & Ladd Addition residential areas. **YR409** goes through the Rose City Park neighborhoods.

Portland - 10km Walk (YR256) 10/14/24km Walk (YR410) 10/12km Walk (YR411) **Jan 1-Dec 31**
B Awards available
Sponsoring Club: AVA-446, Rose City Roamers
POC: Carol Ottoson, 503-774-2072. 5960 SE Tibbetts, Portland, OR 97206

Start Point: Good Samaritan Hospital, 503-229-7711. 1015 NW 22nd Ave. I-5 northbound to exit 299B to I-405. Exit 405 at Everett St, exit 2B onto NW 14th. Continue north on NW 14th two blocks to Glisan St (2nd signal). Left on Glisan to 21st. Right on 21st to Marshall (6 blocks, flashing light). Left on Marshall 1/2 block to parking bldg 2 or 3. I-5 southbound to exit 302B to I-405. Cross Fremont Bridge, take exit 3, NW Industrial area/Vaughn St ramp. Left at signal at NW 23rd to Northrup. Left on Northrup one block to 22nd. Right one block to Marshall. Left 1/2 block to parking bldg 2 or 3. Self-service start in switchboard area adjacent to main lobby Info desk.

Event Info: Daily dawn to dusk. **YR256** is rated 1+. Strollers can make it but wheelchairs will have difficulty because of steps. Portland State University is featured on this walk. **YR410** is rated 1+. Longer options are rated 2+. Only one event credit even if doing all routes. This trail is okay for strollers & wheelchairs but all curbs are not cut. Pets are allowed. The short route goes through town and along the waterfront. Longer routes also go along Terwilliger Blvd. **YR411** is rated 2+. Longer route is rated 3. Possible for large wheeled strollers but not wheelchairs. Pets are allowed. This trail features the Portland Heights area.

Portland - 10km Walk (YR675) 11km Walk (YR676) **Jan 1-Dec 31**
Credit Only Events
Sponsoring Club: AVA-549, Cedar Milers Volkssport Club
POC: Shirley Corey, 503-203-1222. 8404 NW Hawkins, Portland, OR 97229

Start Point: Sunset Athletic Club, 13939 NW Cornell Rd. From I-5 northbound take Hwy 217 to US26 west towards ocean beaches. Exit Murray Rd. Turn right on Murray to Cornell Rd. Turn left on Cornell Rd. The Athletic Club is on the right across from Sunset High School. From I-5 southbuond, take I-405 to US26 west. Go west on US 26 to Murray Rd. Continue as above. From I-84 west, follow Beaverton/US26 west signs. Exit on Murray and continue as above.

Event Info: Mon-Fri, 5:30am-10pm; Sat 7am-9pm; Sun, 8:30-7:30. Closed Christmas. Call for other holiday hours. You must be off the trail by dusk. **YR675** is rated 1+, suitable for strollers but no wheelchairs. This is a fairly level walk through neighborhoods and a golf course. **YR676** is rated 3, no strollers or wheelchairs. This is a challenging walk with several hills going through several beautiful residential areas. Pets are allowed on both routes but must be leashed.

Portland - 10km Walk (YR412) **Jan 1-Dec 31**
Credit Only Event
Sponsoring Club: AVA-242, Columbia River Volkssport Club
POC: Betty Macken, 503-667-6408. 419 SE 205th Place, Gresham, OR 97030

Start Point: Columbia Sportswear Outlet, 8128 SE 13th Ave. From Northbound on I-5, take Corbett St exit 298. Turn right on corbett to SW Nebraska (approximately 1 mile). Turn left to SW Macadam (approximately 3 blocks). Turn right onto Macadam to Sellwood Bridge. Turn left onto Sellwood Bridge to SE 13th and Tacoma. Turn right on 13th - 1/2 block to start. From I-5 Southbound, take exit 299A, Lake Oswego, Johns Landing, Macadam exit south to Macadam to Sellwood Bridge. Continue as above.

Event Info: Mon-Fri 9-6; Sat 9-5; Sun 12-5. Closed major holidays. Trail is rated 1, suitable for strollers & wheelchairs. Pets are allowed. There are no restrooms at the start. This route is on paved paths and sidewalks. It is a pretty stroll crossing the Sellwood bridge and then going along the Willamette River with downtown Portland and Mt Hood and St Helens in the background. Lots of quaint antique shops at the beginning, boutiques and restaurants galore in the Johns Landing area. There should be something for everyone.

Portland - 10km Walk (YR615) **Jan 1-Dec 31**
A Award available
Sponsoring Club: AVA-552, East County Windwalkers
POC: Ida Lieb, 503-663-9222. 13025 SE Orient Dr #41, Boring, OR 97009

Start Point: Portland Adventist Medical Hospital, 10323 NE Market. I-205 south take exit 21A, Glisan St. Stay in right lane through first light, turn left at third light (Washington St). Get into right lane and turn right at 99th Ave (this curves and becomes 96th). Turn left onto Main, the first street past Mall 205. Turn right at 100th Ave and turn left into hospital parking lot. From I-205 norht, take exit 20, Washington St. Turn right at first light (Washington St). Turn right at 99th Ave and continue as above. Start box is in the lobby.

Event Info: Daily dawn to dusk. Trail is rated 3. It is not suitable for strollers or wheelchairs. Pets are allowed. Trail goes up into the old Mt Tabor neighborhoods an up through the park itself. This is an extinct volcano that provides breathtaking views of Portland.

Portland - 10km Walk (YR427) 11km Walk (YR173) **Jan 1-Dec 31**
A Awards available
Sponsoring Club: AVA-552, East County Windwalkers
POC: Ida Lieb, 503-663-9222. 13025 SE Orient Dr #41, Boring, OR 97009

Start Point: Woodland Park Hospital, 10300 NE Hancock. From I-205 North take exit 21A, Glisan St. Turn right on Glisan and go to 102nd Ave. Turn left on 102nd for five or six blocks, past four stop lights to Hancock St. Turn right to the Hospital. From I-205 South, take exit 21A, Glisan St. Turn left on Glisan and go to 102nd Ave and continue as above. From the West, take I-84 to exit 7, Halsey/Gateway District. Continue to 102nd Ave, turn left and proceed to Hancock St. From the East, take I-84 to I-205 South and exit at Glisan St (Exit 21A) and follow directions above.

Event Info: Daily dawn to dusk. Both trails are rated 1+, suitable for strollers and wheelchairs if they use alternate routes that are available. Pets are allowed. **YR173** (Glendoveer) is on quiet streets,

Oregon, cont. ─────────────────────────────────────

sidewalks and paths through some older, well-taken-care-of neighborhoods and parks. You will walk through a portion of the Glendoveer Golf Course Trail. Pets must walk on the outside of the Glendoveer Trail. **YR427** (Rose City) goes through pleasant neighborhoods, parks and has scenic views of Rose City Golf Course and Mt Hood. It is on city streets and sidewalks and is mostly flat. It takes you by Multnomah Bible College.

Portland - 10km Walk (YR754) **Jan 1-Dec 31**
Credit Only Event
Sponsoring Club: AVA-738, Y-B Normal Adventurers
POC: Cathie Bittler, 503-845-9499. 812 N. Meridian, Newberg, OR 97132

Start Point: Red Lion Hotel, 503-283-4466. 909 N Hayden Island Dr. On I-5 take Jantzen Beach Exit #308 just south of the Interstate Bridge. Hotel is on the east side of bridge.

Event Info: Daily dawn to dusk. Rated 1+. Okay for strollers, no wheelchairs. Leashed pets. Route is mainly on paved surfaces and some natural trails. It is along the Columbia River and around Hayden and Tomahawk Islands.

Portland - 10km Walk (YR1021) **Jan 1-Dec 31**
Credit Only Event
Sponsoring Club: AVA-446, Rose City Roamers Volkssport Club
POC: Carol Ottoson, 503-774-2072. 5960 SE Tibbetts, Portland, OR 97206

Start Point: 7-11, 503-289-3158. 2815 N Killingsworth. I-5 north or south to exit 304, Portland Blvd. Turn west (left from the south, right from the north) to Greeley. Left to Killingsworth. Store is on the right. Please do not park in the 7-11 lot.

Event Info: Daily dawn to dusk. Trail is rated 1+, suitable for strollers but not wheelchairs. Pets are allowed. The route features the Overlook area with several nice viewpoints overlooking the Willamette River. It is almost all on pavement with some short natural trail sections.

Portland (Rooster Rock State Park) - 10km Walk (YR990) **Apr 1-Dec 31**
Credit Only Event
Sponsoring Club: AVA-242, Columbia River Volkssport Club
POC: Marge Lusby, 503-252-7605. 12532 NE Knott, Portland, OR 97230
Start Point: Rooster Rock State Park, Adjacent to exit 25 on I-84 east of Portland. Travel east from Portland on I-84 to exit #25.

Event Info: Summer: daily 6-4; Fall/Winter: daily 7-4. Trail is rated 2+ and is not suitable for strollers or wheelchairs. Pets are allowed but not on the beach. There is a $3.00 per car entrance fee to the park. Route is on natural trails and paved walkways. It circles the entire park and features views of waterfalls, the columbia River, boat basin, picnic areas and expanisve stretches of beach.

Rockaway Beach - Two 10km Walks (YR684 & 685) **Jan 1-Dec 31**
Credit Only Events
Sponsoring Club: AVA-738, Y.B. Normal Adventurers
POC: Cathie Bittler, 503-845-9499. 812 N. Meridian, Newberg OR 97132

Start Point: Silver Sands Motel, 503-355-2206. 215 Pacific St. For reservations, 1-800-457-8972. From Portland take Hwy 26 to Hwy 6 and Hwy 6 to Tillamook. In Tillamook follow Hwy 101 N to Rockaway Beach. Turn west on 2nd St and go two block to the Motel.

Event Info: Daily dawn to dusk. Trails are rated 1+ and would be very difficult for strollers and are not for wheelchairs. Pets are allowed. Both routes are along the beach. You will cross two streams. Check tide schedules before you walk. Water & restrooms are a block from the start/finish at the Wayside.

Roseburg - Two 10km Walks (YR084 & YR164) **Jan 2-Dec 31**
Credit Only Events
Sponsoring Club: AVA-472, Umpqua Valley Walkers
POC: Leola Beck, 541-672-8518. 888 W. Indianola, Roseburg OR 97470

Start: Columbia Douglas Hospital Emergency Room, 748 West Harvard Ave. From the north take I-5 south to exit 124. Hospital is across from the exit ramp on your left. From the south, take I-5 north to exit 124. Turn left on W Harvard Ave. Go one block to the stop light. Hospital is on your right. Parking is limited. There is additional parking behind the hospital and on side streets.

Event Info: Daily dawn to dusk. Trails are rated 2, suitable for strollers and wheelchairs with some caution. Pets are allowed. **YR084** is a new route with a combination of old & new. Residential & commercial, flat & hilly. You will cross the Umpqua River twice, pass Gaddis park (Little League), see a new development area, our new Library and some of our downtown commercial area. Enjoy the murals on the buildings. **YR164** goes thru the Veterans Facility, part of Stewart Park and on city streets thru a residential district in NW Roseburg. Some of this area is without sidewalks.

Salem - 10km Walk (YR1028) **Jan 1-Dec 31**
B Awards available
Sponsoring Club: AVA-362, Willamette Wanderers
POC: Mary Brillhart, 503-581-4385. 743 J David S, Salem, OR 97306

Start Point: Ramada Inn, 503-363-4123. 200 Commercial St. From Portland on I-5, take exit 253 and turn right onto Hwy 22, follow Mission St (Hwy 22) to Liberty St (about 3 miles). Turn right. Travel 5 blocks north on Liberty. The Inn will be on your left between Liberty and Ferry St.

Event Info: Daily dawn to dusk. Trail is rated 1+ and is suitable for strollers and wheelchairs. Pets must be leashed. This route follows city sidewalks and paved paths with one hill. It passes the capitol grounds, college campus, the Governor's Mansion and tree shaded parks.

Seaside - 10km Walk (YR300) **Jan 1-Dec 31**
Credit Only Event
Sponsoring Club: AVA-679, Turnaround Trekkers
POC: Pauline Vincent, 503-738-5960. PO Box 975, Seaside, OR 97138-0975

Start Point: Register at Providence Seaside Hospital, 725 S Wahanna Rd. Proceed to the Seaside Chamber of Commerce, 7 N. Roosevelt Dr. to start the walk. Stay on Hwy 101 to stoplight at junction of Hwy 101 (Roosevelt Dr) and Broadway. Turn E off Hwy 101 and then right on Wahanna Rd and left at Hospital entrance. Proceed to emergency room parking lot. Registration is just inside the main entrance. After returning to the Chamber to start your walk, please park away from the Chamber building (north of restroom building).

Event Info: Daily, 8 to dusk (early start box in windowsill of Chamber foyer has instructions/maps. Door to foyer is always unlocked, even when closed sign is showing). Trail is rated 1. It is not suitable for wheelchairs but strollers should be okay.

++Silverton - 10km Walk (YR171) **Apr 12-Nov 17**
Sponsoring Club: AVA-425, Silverton Walk Abouts
POC: Joan Rowe, 503-873-4907/Earl Coffey, 503-873-6638. PO Box 33, Silverton, OR 97381

Start Point: Roth Foodliner, 918 N 1st St. From I-5 take Woodburn exit 271. Follow signs east to Silverton on Hwy 214. Roth is on the north edge of town. After registering, follow the Silver Falls Loop Highway to the Park. You must drive 14 miles along the scenic Silver Falls Loop Hwy to the start at Silver Fall's State Park.

Event Info: Daily, 7-7. $3.00 per car entrance fee. This walk is rated 2+ and is not suitable for strollers or wheelchairs. Pets are permitted. Part of the route can be quite muddy. Good shoes are a must. Part of the trail is quite isolated. Walk with a partner. Trail is on paved paths and roads plus natural hiking and horse trails. Great fall foliage and spring wild flowers.

Silverton - Two 10km Walks (YR106 & YR1034) **Jan 1-Dec 31**
B Awards available
Sponsoring Club: AVA-425, Silverton Walk Abouts
POC: Earl Coffey, 503-873-6638/Larry Todd, 503-873-2353. PO Box 33, Silverton, OR 97381

Start Point: Silverton Thriftway Store, 301 Westfield St (just pass Payless). From north on I-5, take the Woodburn-Silverton exit 271. Follow signs along Hwy 214 to Silverton. Once in Silverton, turn right on "C" St and follow to second stop sign (4 way stop). Continue straight uphill past Payless Drug to Thriftways. From the south on I-5 take the Market St exit #256 in Salem. Follow the signs to Silverton on Hwy 213. As you enter Silverton there is a 4 way stop sign, turn right. Go past Payless Drug to Thriftways. Start desk is in the lobby.

Event Info: Daily dawn to dusk. Closed Christmas & Thanksgiving. Both walks are rated 1+, suitable for strollers and wheelchairs. Pets are allowed. **YR106** features the best of Silverton: Schools, churches, park, hospital and the downtown with its murals. **YR1034** is a country walk past Cooley's Iris Gardens and fields of grain. Best time is late May and early June when the iris are in bloom. Cooley's Gardens are open for free tours at this time. Route is on city streets and road shoulders.

Springfield - 10km Walk (YR800) 31km Bike (YR801) **Jan 4-Dec 31**
B Awards available
Sponsoring Club: AVA-455, Eugene-Springfield Mossback Volkssport Club
POC: Frank Ross, 541-726-7169/541-547-3949. 2398 North 8th, Springfield, OR 97477

Start Point: McKenzie Willamette Hospital, 1460 "G" St. From I-5, exit 194A (East I-105) Springfield east to second Springfield exit. Right on Mohawk Blvd to "I" St. Left on "I" St to street or hospital parking. Enter hospital at Emergency Room entrance on Mohawk Blvd. Turn right to elevator/stairway by soft drink machine. Registration materials in file cabinet to the left of soft drink machine. You will drive about 1.5 miles west of the hospital to Island Park to start the walk. Bike starts at the hospital.

Event Info: Daily, dawn to dusk. Walk is rated 2, suitable for strollers and wheelchairs if they can navigate curbs without cuts. Pets are allowed on a leash. The route is mostly on paved sidewalks and bike paths. The bike is rated 2 and is **NOT WALKABLE**. Bikers must sign a waiver and should wear helmets. No pets are allowed. This route is on city streets, country roads and bike paths. It features the beautiful Mohawk Valley and the McKenzie River.

St Paul - 10/17km Walk (YR218) **Jan 1-Dec 31**
Credit Only Event
Sponsoring Club: AVA-567, The Walking Connection
POC: Marge Bergeron, 503-636-1025. 5276 West Sunset Dr, Lake Oswego, OR 97035.

Start: Champoeg State Park Visitor's Center, 8239 Champoeg Rd, NE. I-5 from North or South, exit 278 (Donald/Aurora). Turn west (right if coming from north, left from south) on Ehlen Rd (becomes Vergen Rd) for 3.6 miles. turn right on Case Rd for 1.4 miles. Turn left on West Champoeg Rd for 1 mile to park entrance. Park fee or seasonal park pass required.

Event Info: Summer: Daily, 8-5; Winter: Daily, 9-4. Closed New Year's, Thanksgiving & Christmas. Trail is rated 1+ and is suitable for strollers but not wheelchairs. Pets must be leashed. This is a nice place to walk on hot days. A very safe area. It is a beautiful park walk along the Willamette River. Many natural trails with birds and some native animals. Overnight camping is available.

OREGON, cont. —————————————————————

Stayton - 11km Walk (YR090) **Jan 1-Dec 23**
A Award available
Sponsoring Club: AVA-479, Buffalo Quick Steppers
POC: Dale Goble, 503-769-6774. PO Box G, Stayton, OR 97383

Start Point: Buffalo Quick Print, 503-769-6774. 570 N 3rd Ave. 12 miles E of Salem. From I-5 north or south take the Hwy 22 (Stayton/Detroit Dam) exit and go east 12 miles to the Stayton/Sublimity exit. Turn right and go into town. After the 1st stop light you will be on 1st Ave. Go to the next light and turn left onto Washington. Go two blocks to Third Ave and turn right. Go two blocks to Buffalo Quick Print.

Event Info: Mon-Fri 9-2. Finish by 5. Closed weekends and major holidays. Call ahead if there is a question about hours or days available. Trail is rated 1+ and is suitable for strollers and wheelchairs. Pets are allowed. Route is on small town city streets. It is flat with one short (one block) hill.

Tigard - 10km Walk (YR056) **Jan 1-Dec 31**
Credit Only Event
Sponsoring Club: AVA-253, Valley Volkswalkers
POC: Lee Byington, 503-643-4772. 5992 SW Heights Lane, Beaverton, OR 97007

Start Point: McDonald's of Tigard III, 12388 SW Scholl's Ferry Rd. From I-5 Northbound, follow signs to US 26 via I-405 (toward the Oregon Coast). Turn south on Hwy 217 to Scholl's Ferry Rd exit. Right onto Scholl's Ferry approximately 1 miles to N Dakota St (at the light). Left on N Dakota and left again on McDonald's access road. From I-5 Southbound, take exit 292. Go North on Hwy 217 (signs say Tigard/Beaverton) to Scholl's Ferry exit. Turn left onto Scholl's Ferry, corssing over Hwy 217. See above directions to McDonald's. From the west on Hwy 26 from the Oregon Coast, take Hwy 217 exit (to Tigard/Salem). Take Scholls Ferry Rd exit and turn right on Scholls Ferry.

Event Info: Daily 7-dusk. Trail is rated 1+ and is suitable for strollers and wheelchairs. Pets must be leashed. Route is on city sidewalks and paved park paths.

Tigard - Two 10km Walks (YR534 & YR542) **Jan 1-Dec 31**
Credit Only Events
Sponsoring Club: AVA-700, Mac Trackers Walking Club
POC: Barbara Burns, 503-538-3509. 16162 NE Kings Grade Rd, Newberg, OR 97132

Start Point: McDonald's Restaurant, 16200 Pacific Hwy (Hwy 99W). From I-5 take 99W (Pacific Hwy) to Durham Rd. McDonald's is located at the corner of Hwy 99W and Durham Rd in Tigard.

Event Info: Mon-Sat, 6-dusk; Sun 7-dusk. Closed Christmas. **YR534** is rated 1+ and is suitable for strollers but not wheelchairs. It is on paved sidewalks, bike and walking paths with some bark paths in Cook Park. It goes through beautiful residential areas. Pets are allowed. **YR542** is rated 2+. It is suitable for strollers but not wheelchairs. Pets are allowed. It winds through the Summerfield and other residential areas of beautiful homes and yards.

Troutdale - 10km Walk (YR196) **Jan 1-Dec 31**
A Award available
Sponsoring Club: AVA-552, East County Windwalkers
POC: Ida Lieb, 503-663-9222. 13025 SE Orient Dr #41, Boring, OR 97009

Start Point: Burger King, 366 SW Frontage Rd. Westbound on I-84, take exit 17, Troutdale. Turn left at the stop sign. Turn right at 2nd stop sign. Burger King is immediately on your left. Eastbound on I-84, take exit 17, Troutdale to Frontage Rd. Burger King is about 1/2 mile down on the right. Start box is near the water fountain.

Event Info: Daily dawn to dusk. Closed Thanksgiving and Christmas. Trail is rated 1+, suitable for strollers and wheelchairs. Note, however, that some sidewalks are very high. Pets are not allowed. Route goes through historic Troutdale and along the Columbia Gorge Hwy. Tour the grounds of McMinimans Edgefield Manor.

Tualatin - 10km Walk (YR798) **Jan 1-Dec 31**
B Awards available
Sponsoring Club: AVA-600, Tough Trail Trompers
POC: Wendy Bumgardner, 503-692-3994. PO Box 1651, Tualatin, OR 97062

Start Point: Legacy Meridian park Hospital, 19300 SW 65th. I-5 exit 289 (Tualatin). If southbound, turn left. If northbound turn right on Nyberg Rd. Nyberg curves to the right becoming 65th. Turn left at the entrance to the hospital. Park near the main entrance. Start box is in the lobby.

Event Info: Daily, 5am-9pm. Trail is rated 3 and is not suitable for strollers or wheelchairs. Pets are allowed. Walk in rolling terrain. Includes mile long barkdust jogging trail, newer suburbs, duck pond and Atfalati Park nature trail. Some moderate hills.

Waldport - 10km Walk (YR348) **Jan 1-Dec 31**
Credit Only Event
Sponsoring Club: AVA-695, Yachats Coastal Gems
POC: Shirley's, 541-547-3292. 271 Hwy 101, Yachats OR 97498

Start Point: Ray's Food Place, 580 NE Broadway. Waldport is located 16 miles south of Newport and 8 miles north of Yachats on US Hwy 101. Ray's is located about six blocks east of Hwy 101 on US Hwy 34 on the corner of Hwy 34 and Broadway.

Event Info: Daily 7:30am-8pm. Reduced hours on major holidays. Trail is rated 2 and is not recommended for strollers or wheelchairs. Pets must be leashed. Route is on sidewalks, quiet streets, with a short section of forest trail and briefly along Hwy 101. Views of ocean, bay, bridge and town. One hill fairly easy up and fairly steep down.

Warrenton/Hammond - 10km Walk (YR174) 25km Bike (YR435) **Jan 1-Dec 31**
Credit Only Events
Sponsoring Club: AVA-679, Turnaround Trekkers
POC: Donna Byes, 503-738-0139 (weekdays 8-4:25 503-861-2589). PO Box 975, Seaside, OR 97138-0975

Start Point: KOA Campground, 1100 Ridge Rd. Traveling north from Seaside, or south from Astoria, follow the signs to Fort Stevens State Park. The KOA Campground is on Ridge Rd across from the main entrance to the park. Register here & drive to start point for the walk. Bike starts at KOA Campground. Please park away from KOA building as far as possible.

Event Info: Daily dawn-dusk. Walk is rated 2 and is not suitable for strollers or wheelchairs. Pets are allowed. It is recommended that you carry water. This trail is mostly along paved park trails with approx 1.5 km on forest trails. The bike is rated 1+. Bikers must wear a helmet and sign a release form. Recommended that you carry water. The bike is all on paved roads or trails.

West Linn - Two 10km Walks (YR1254 & YR1255) **Jan 1-Dec 31**
Credit Only Events
Sponsoring Club: AVA-253, Valley Volkswalkers
POC: Rachel Spanks, 503-655-5268. 4962 Prospect, West Linn, OR 97068

Start Point: Willamette Thriftway, 2000 SW 8th Ave. From I-205 north or south, exit #6 (to 10th St). Right to 8th. Right to parking. Please park in outer perimeter.

Event Info: Daily, dawn to dusk. Closed Christmas. **YR1254**, Barrington Heights Challenge, is rated 4, not suitable for strollers or wheelchairs because of steep hills and narrow shoulders. Pets must be leashed. Carry water in heat. This is a steep climb. Restrooms are only at the start/finish. Trail has beautiful view of the valley and magnificent estates. A bonus is Mt. Hood. **YR1255**, Historic Willamette District, is rated 2+ and is suitable for strollers and wheelchairs except some curbs may not be cut. Pets must be leashed. This trail meanders through the historic district of Willamette with descriptions of historic buildings and areas. Very picturesque.

Winchester Bay - 10km Walk (YR494) **Feb 1-Nov 30**
Credit Only Event
Sponsoring Club: AVA-507, South Coast Wavewalkers
POC: Ann Inman, 541-756-7828. PO Box 284, Coos Bay, OR 97420

Start Point: Beck's Market, 8th & Hwy 101. From I-5 take Oregon Hwy 38 to US Hwy 101 at Reedsport. Then south on Hwy 101 to Winchester Bay. From Coos Bay/North Bend, take Hwy 101 north to Winchester Bay. Turn west on 8th.

Event Info: Daily, 8 to dusk. Trail is rated 1+. It is okay for strollers but not wheelchairs. Pets are allowed. This walk is along the waterfront, up a hill to the Umpqua Lighthouse and on to Lake Marie. This is on the forest floor with spectacular views.

Yachats - Two 10km Walks (YR276 & YR752) **Jan 1-Dec 31**
Credit Only Events
Sponsoring Club: AVA-695, Yachats Coastal Gems
POC: Shirley's, 541-547-3292. PO Box 896, Yachats OR 97498

Start Point: Shirley's, 541-547-3292. 271 Hwy 101, downtown. On US Hwy 101 midway between Florence and Newport along the central Oregon Coast. Shirley's is located next to the bakery in the only shopping complex in the center of Yachats. Don't park in the main parking lot. Please use side streets.

Event Info: Shirley's is open daily 9:30-5. Closed major holidays. Pets are allowed on all routes if leashed. Check the listing at Shirley's to see what discounts volkssporters qualify for. **YR276:** Rated 1 and is suitable for strollers and wheelchairs. It is along city streets, near the ocean, thru residential areas and along the historic 804 trail near the beach. **YR752:** Rated 2+ and is not suitable for strollers or wheelchairs. This walk is on city streets, sidewalks, sand/grass and gravel paths. It is along the ocean, river and historic 804 Trail. There is one significant hill.

Yachats/Cape Perpetua - 10/14km Walk (YR275) **Jan 1-Dec 31**
Credit Only Event
Sponsoring Club: AVA-695, Yachats Coastal Gems
POC: Shirley's, 541-547-3292. PO Box 896, Yachats, OR 97498

Registration Point: Shirley's, 271 Hwy 101. On US Hwy 101 midway between Florence & Newport. Shirley's is located next to the bakery in the only shopping complex in the center of Yachats. It is open daily from 9:30-5 except for major holidays.

Start Point/Alternate Registration Point: Cape Perpetua Visitor Center, 3 miles south of Yachats on Hwy 101. The Visitor's Center is open on weekends only from Oct 1-May 1 from 10-4 and daily from May 1-Oct 1 from 9-5. Closed major holidays.

Event Info: The trail is rated 3 but the 4km option makes it a 4 due to an 800 ft climb. Pets must be leashed. Strollers and wheelchairs should not attempt. This trail is on paved and forest trails along the ocean and into an old-growth forest area. Restrooms and water are available near the start and along the trail in the summer.

Yachats/Carl G. Washburne State Park - 10km Walk (YR664) **Mar 1-Nov 1**
Credit Only Event
Sponsoring Club: AVA-695, Yachats Coastal Gems
POC: Shirley's, 541-547-3292. 271 Hwy 101, Yachats, OR 97498

Start Point: Carl Washburne Park is mid-way between Yachats & Florence. You may register, get walk map & directions and stamp your books in either town and drive to the park to walk. From the South: Register at Sportsman's Store in Florence. From the North: Register at Shirley's in Yachats. See listings for Yachats & Florence for directions to registration points.

Event Info: Daily, dawn to dusk. Closed major holidays. Trail is rated 2 and is not suitable for strollers or wheelchairs due to sandy beaches. This walk is on a sandy beach, forest trails and bike paths through old growth forest and through a campground.

PENNSYLVANIA ▬▬▬▬▬▬▬▬▬▬▬▬▬▬▬▬▬

Bellefonte - 10km Walk (YR971) **Jan 1-Dec 31**
B Awards Available
Sponsoring Club: AVA-726, Nittany Nomads
POC: Linda Trimpey, 814-353-9364. 751 Halfmoon St, Bellefonte, PA 16823

Start Point: Boscaino's Variety Store, 325 W High St. From north, east, or west via I-80 take exit 23, then Rt 150 south to Bellefonte. At first traffic light turn right onto High St. Start is on the right adjacent to Talleyrand Park. From South take Rt 322. Before Boalsburg, take 322 bypass, then Rt 26 North, then Rt 150 North to Bellefonte. At 6th light (at bridge) turn left onto High St. Boscaino's is on the right, immediately after Talleyrand Park, which is on the left.

Event Info: Mon-Sat 5:30 a.m. to 8 p.m; Sun 5:30 a.m. to 1 p.m. Closed Christmas. Other holidays 8am-1pm. Trail is rated 2+; not suitable for strollers or wheelchairs. Pets are allowed. The majority of the walk is on sidewalks with some roadside walking. There are two steep hills.

Chambersburg - 10km Walk (YR127) **Jan 2-Dec 30**
Credit Only Event
Sponsoring Club: AVA-171, Cumberland Valley Lead Foot Club
POC: Frances Humelsine, 717-263-8633. 257 East King St., Chambersburg, PA 17201-1808

Start Point: Olympia Ice Cream Parlor, 717-263-8597. 43 South Main. 1/2 block south and west of the intersection of US-11 South and US-30 West.

Event Info: Mon-Sat 11-2 hrs before dusk; Sun noon-2 hrs before dusk. Closed Easter, Memorial Day, July 4th, Labor Day, Thanksgiving, Christmas Eve and Christmas. Trail is rated 1+, suitable for strollers and wheelchairs with some difficulty from uncut curbs. Pets must be leashed and clean up is required. Hardee's is the checkpoint and they offer volkssporters a 10% discount. The trail is basically on sidewalks with no significant obstacles.

Doylestown - 10km Walk (YR1187) **Jan 1-Dec 31**
A Award Available
Sponsoring Club: AVA-238, Liberty Bell Wanderers
POC: Carol Taubenberger, 215-343-2580. 1565 Stuckert Road, Warrington, PA 18976

Start Point: Doylestown Inn, 215-345-6610. 18 West State Street. From Penna Turnpike, Exit 27 (Willow Grove Interchange). Go North on Rt. 611 for 8.8 miles and take right fork at Doylestown sign onto S. Main St. Turn left onto West State St. Doylestown Inn is #18 on the left. Free parking is 1 ½ blocks past State St. on N. Main St. at sign "Bucks County Parking Garage."

PENNSYLVANIA, cont.

Event Info: Daily, 8 a.m. to dusk. Trail is rated 1+ along mostly shaded sidewalks with no significant hills. It is suitable for strollers but not recommended for wheelchairs because not all corners have curb cuts. Pets must be leashed and clean up is enforced. Walk past Victorian homes with beautiful flower gardens. See James Michener Art Museum and Mercer's two concrete castles and tile works.

Harrisburg - 10km Walk (YR1041) 11km Walk (YR745) **Jan 1-Dec 31**
B Awards Available
Sponsoring Club: AVA-328, Susquehanna Rovers
POC: Pat Nagle, 717-657-1781. 5602 Devonshire Road, Harrisburg, PA 17112.

Start Point: Holiday Inn Express - Riverfront, 525 South Front St. Located off I-83, Exit 23 (Second St.)

Event Info: Daily, dawn to dusk. Both trails are rated 1+ and are suitable for strollers and wheelchairs but some curbs lack cuts. Pets must be leashed. Volksmarchers will receive 10% off the regular room rate at the Holiday Inn Express. **YR1041** follows a portion of the Capital Area Greenbelt, circles Italian Lake, passes "Peace Gardens" along the Susquehanna River, the Governor's Mansion and other outstanding buildings. **YR745** follows a portion of the Capital Area Greenbelt, passing houses dating from the 1700's to the present, including the Governor's Mansion, the Capitol complex and the John Harris Home.

Johnstown - 10km Walk (YR1040) **Jan 1-Dec 31**
B Awards Available
Sponsoring Club: AVA-408, Altoona-Johnstown Summit Striders
POC: Phoebe Reighard, 814-539-2090. 601 Indiana St., Johnstown, PA 15905.

Start Point: Holiday Inn Downtown, 814-535-7777. 250 Market St. Follow Rt 56 into Johnstown. Exit Rt 56 at Walnut St. Turn right onto Lincoln St. Turn right on Market St. Go one block to start.

Event Info: Daily, dawn to dusk. Trail is rated 1, suitable for strollers and wheelchairs. It encompasses sites and points of interest primarily related to the Great 1889 Flood. It is on flat city sidewalks.

Kleinfeltersville - 10km Walk (YR484) 28km Bike (YR483) **Mar 1-Oct 20**
10km Walk (YR1277) **Mar 1-Sept 15**
Credit Only Events
Sponsoring Club: AVA-579, Penn Dutch Pacers Volksmarch Club, Inc.
POC: Pat Boyer, 717-665-4976. 28 S. Penn St., Manheim, PA 17545

Start Point: Visitors Center at Middle Creek Wildlife Management Area, 717-733-1512. Take PA 501 north from Lancaster to Schaefferstown, then right on PA 897 for 2.5 miles to Kleinfeltersville, Or take PA 501 south from US 422 at Myerstown to Schaefferstown, then left on PA 897 to Kleinfeltersville. In Kleinfeltersville, turn right (south) on Hopeland Rd., 2.5 miles to the Middle Creek Visitor Center.

Event Info: Tues-Sat 8-4 Sun noon-4. Closed Mondays and all holidays. **YR484** is rated 1+, suitable for strollers & wheelchairs. Pets must be leashed. It is called the Woods and Meadows Trail, on paved and forest roads within the Wildlife Management Area, with gently rolling hills. Water and restrooms available at all Middle Creek picnic areas along the route. **YR1277** is rated 1+ and is suitable for strollers and wheelchairs. It is called Lakeview Trail and is on paved and forest roads around the lake within the Wildlife Management Area. **YR 483** is a bike event rated 2+ on paved and forest roads within the Wildlife Management Area and surrounding countryside with rolling hills.

Lancaster - 10km Walk (YR137) 11 km Walk (YR1276) 25km Bike (YR488) **Jan 1-Dec 31**
Credit Only Events
Sponsoring Club: AVA-579, Penn Dutch Pacers Volksmarch Club, Inc.
POC: Pat Boyer, 717-665-4976. 28 S. Penn St., Manheim, PA 17545.

166

Register: Your Place Country Inn, 717-393-3413. 2133 Lincoln Hwy E. Bike starts here. You must drive into Lancaster for the start of the walk trails. Your Place Country Inn is on US 30 just east of Lancaster, approximately 5 miles, to the end of the limited access highway. Continue past the traffic light at East Town Mall for 2/10 miles. Your Place Country Inn is on the left (north side of the highway). Area is congested. Please use caution.

Event Info: Daily 8 to dusk. Closed Christmas. Walks are rated 1+, suitable for strollers and wheelchairs. Pets must be leashed. Your Place Country Inn will give volkssporters $10.00 off the regular room rate. **YR137** called the "Bars, Breweries, and Bawdy Houses" walk is a lighthearted stroll through Lancaster, including some historical buildings and areas not generally mentioned in your history books. **YR1276** is callled the "Trail of Myths and Legends" and is a walk through the history of Lancaster with little known stories of the people who were present at the founding of our country. **YR488**, the bike, is rated 1+. Bikers must sign waiver. Please do not take facial photos of our Amish neighbors. The bike is on paved country roads with gently rolling hills through the Pennsylvania Dutch farm area just east of the city.

Lebanon - 10km Walk (YR1172) **Jan 1-Dec 31**
B Awards Available
Sponsoring Club: AVA-096, Baloney Stompers Volksmarch Club, Inc.
POC: Charles Baeckert, Jr. 717-272-0655. 421 Weidman St, Lebanon, PA 17046

Start Point: Lebanon Plaza Mall - Horn & Horn Restaurant, Rt 72, Quentin Rd. From east and west take PA Turnpike exit 20, north on PA Rt 72 for 6.5 miles. North on I-Rt 81, Lebanon exit (Rt 72) south on Rt 72.

Event Info: Daily, 7am-8pm. Closed Easter, Thanksgiving & Christmas. Trail is rated 1+, suitable for strollers but may be difficult for wheelchairs as not all streets have curb cuts. Pet are allowed but not in the Plaza. This trail will go through residential areas and the business district of Lebanon. Various historical buildings are along the route.

Lititz - 10km Walk (YR1283) **Jan 1-Dec 31**
Credit Only Event
Sponsoring Club: AVA-579, Penn Dutch Pacers Volksmarch Club, Inc.
POC: Pat Boyer, 717-665-4976. 28 S Penn St, Manheim, PA 17545

Start Point: General Sutter Inn, 717-626-2115. 14 East Main St. Take PA 501 north from Lancaster six miles to Lititz. Enter Lititz on South Broad St and continue to the Town Square. The Inn is located on the corner of Broad St & Main St.

Event Info: Daily, dawn to dusk. Trail is rated 1 and is suitable for strollers and wheelchairs. Pets are allowed on the walk but not at the Inn. This trail takes you on a tour of historic downtown Lititz, past the Moravian Church and cemetery where General Sutter is buried. Past Linden Hall, the first all girls boarding school, Sturgis Pretzel factory and Wilbur Chocolate factory. You travel through residential communities, school grounds and Lititz Springs park. The trail utilizes paved paths, sidewalks, and roads.

Monroeville - 10km Walk (YR1168) **Jan 1-Dec 31**
A Award available
Sponsoring Club: AVA-748, West Penn Walkers
POC: Rich Narushoff, 412-373-4388. 214 Fairlawn Dr, Monroeville, PA 15146

Start Point: Crossroads Food Mart, 412-372-6955. Beatty Rd & Old William Penn Hwy. PA Turnpike (I-76), exit 6 to US 22E or I-376/Parkway East to exit 17, US 22 east. Left onto Old William Penn Hwy one mile from exit. Hills/Giant on corner of turn. Crossroads Food Mart is on the right at the first stop sign. After registering, pick up directions to the walk site which is Boyce Park.

Event Info: Daily, 8am-dusk. Trail is rated 2+, not suitable for strollers or wheelchairs. Pets are allowed on a leash. The trail winds through mostly wooded scenery, following the cross-country ski trail. It includes the nature center, Indian relic grounds and a clear-day view of Pittsburgh skyline. Be prepared for changing weather, ground conditions and insects.

Newport - 10km Walk (YR110) **Jan 1-Dec 31**
B Awards available
Sponsoring Club: AVA-328, Susquehanna Rovers Volksmarch Club
POC: Louise A. Clouser, 717-567-9537. RD4, Box 461, Newport PA 17074

Register: Sharar's Grocery Store and Deli, 19 South 2nd St. Access from Routes 322 and 34. Sharar's is just off the Square. Drive to Start Point, Little Buffalo State Park, approximately three miles from Sharar's.

Event Info: Mon-Sat 8-10; Sun 9-9. Closed Christmas. Trail is rated 3, not suitable for strollers or wheelchairs. Pets are allowed on a leash. A walking stick is recommended in wet weather. This is a scenic trail that passes through woods, grassy areas and by a lake. Trail is marked both forward and reverse.

Ohiopyle State Park - 10km Walk (YR471)   25/34/37km Bike (YR470) **Apr 1-Oct 25**
Sponsoring Club: AVA-408, Altoona-Johnstown Summit Striders
POC: Phoebe Reighard, 814-539-2090. 601 Indiana St, Johnstown, PA 15905

Start Point: Laurel Highlands Outdoor Ctr. behind Falls City Baptist Church, 800-472-3846. North of Rt 40 on PA 381.

Event Info: Daily, 9-4. Closed Easter. Walk is rated 3, not suitable for strollers or wheelchairs. Pets are allowed. Overcrowded conditions may occur during summer weekends. Guided raft trips and white water excursions are available at the start/finish. The route covers some of the 18,700 acres of Ohiopyle State Park, gateway to the Laurel Mountains. The trail includes Ferncliff Peninsula, a National Landmark. The bike is rated 1. Only one event credit regardles of the distances chosen for the bike. Bikes can be rented from Laurel Highlands Outdoor Ctr. The trail is a smooth, hard surfaced trail converted from an abandoned railroad that parallels the Youghiogheny River. Excellent area to see many species of wildlife.

Philadelphia - 10km Walk (YR482) 11km Walk (YR1278) **Jan 1-Dec 31**
Sponsoring Club: AVA-238, Liberty Bell Wanderers
POC: (YR482) Joan Lampart, 215-722-3095. 513 E. Alcott St, Philadelphia, PA 19120
(YR1278) Gene Maier, 215-663-1328. 228 Leona Ave, Huntingdon Valley, PA 19006
OR Bill Simpson, 215-725-5991. 1219 Standwood St, Philadelphia, PA 19111

Start Point: Holiday Inn, 4th & Arch St. PA Turnpike, exit 24. Route 76E to 676 E. Exit to 8th St Independence Mall exit. Off ramp to right to first light at Race St. Left four blocks to 4th St. Right 1 1/2 blocks to hotel entrance on right. Parking garage on left side of bldg. From NJ Turnpike, exit 4, Rt 73N to 38W. 38W to 30W to Benjamin Franklin Bridge. Cross the bridge, take first right and follow around sharp "U" turn down to 4th St. Go right on 4th for 2 1/2 blocks to hotel entrance on right. Parking in garage on left. From I-95, exit 17. Follow signs for historical area. At bottom of ramp, right onto Callowhill St, then left four blocks to hotel on right. There is a charge for parking. Free parking is available on the street on Sundays only. At Registration desk, ask for "Volksmarch Box." Please be patient & courteous to other hotel guests. DO NOT CALL THE HOTEL FOR EVENT INFORMATION.

Event Info: Daily 8-dusk. Both trails are rated 1, suitable for strollers and wheelchairs. Pets must be leashed. The hotel offers a special rate to volkssporters. Call 1-800 THEBELL for information. **YR482** goes past the grave of Benjamin Franklin, the Liberty Bell, Independence Hall (where the Declaration of Independence was signed), City Hall, various museums and the steps of the Art Museum which the movie Rocky made famous. Run up the steps if you can (this is not part of the walk!)

YR1278 goes past the Betsy Ross House, the waterfront with the USS Olympia (Dewey's Flagship), submarine "Becuna" and the Port Museum. You will also pass the Vietnam Memorial, Italian market, Independence Hall and the Chinese Gate.

Prospect - Two 10km Walks (YR1169 & YR1170) **Apr 1-Nov 1**
B Awards available
Sponsoring Club: AVA-748, West Penn Walkers
POC: Rich Narushoff, 412-373-4388. 214 Fairlawn Dr, Monroeville, PA 15146

Start Point: Fairgrounds Market, 412-865-9523. 1138 New Castle Road. Drive to actual walk site at Slippery Rock, PA after registering. PA Turnpike (I-76), exit 3 to I-79 North, exit 29, US 422 east toward Butler. Go past Moraine State Park entrance and PA 528 for approximately 1/2 mile. As you come to the Butler County Fairgrounds on the left, the start is on the right.

Event Info: The Market is open 6am-11pm daily. The Park is open daylight hours only. The trails are rated 2+, not suitable for strollers or wheelchairs. Pets are allowed on a leash. Be prepared for changing weather, ground conditions and insects. **YR1169** is mostly wooded with stretches of pine forest, some hills and lake-side routing. **YR1170** is all wooded with a prairie area, winding pathways, a bubbling stream and an old mill site.

Reading - 11km Walk (YR1284) **Jan 2-Dec 31**
A Award available
Sponsoring Club: AVA-096, Baloney Stompers
POC: Delores Waldman, 610-372-1841. 2510 Ventnor Ave, Reading PA 19605-9616

Start Point: Bagels, Beans and Beignets, 1208 Rockland St. From 422 West, take the 422 Bypass East. At the Rt 222 split, take 222 north to 11th St. (You will see a sign for Albright College). Go to the traffic light, turn left. Go to start located at the end of the strip mall (Giant Food is at one end Bagels at the other.)

Event Info: Mon-Fri, 6:30-4; Sat & Sun, 7:30-2 (except during May-Aug when Sunday hours are 7:30-12:30). Closed all holidays. Trail is rated 3+ and is not suitable for strollers or wheelchairs. Pets are allowed. If snowy, the trail will be difficult through the woods to the Pagoda. The trail will be on city sidewalks, natural trails to the Pagoda with a beautiful view of the city.

State College - Two 10km Walks (YR744 & YR1197) **Jan 1-Dec 31**
B Awards available
Sponsoring Club: AVA-726, Nittany Nomads
POC: Jule McGinty, 814-234-9670. 1957 Highland Dr, State College, PA 16803

Start Point: Best Western State College Inn, 814-237-8005. 1663 S. Atherton St. From I-80 take exit 24. Route 26 South to Business Rt 322. Turn left and go two miles east to start on the left. From Pittsburgh, Rt 22 East to Rt 220 North to Rt 322 East, then Business Rt 322 to start on left. From Harrisburg, Rt 322 West to Business Rt 322 to start on the right. Plenty of parking behind the Best Western.

Event Info: Daily dawn to dusk. Rated 2, suitable for strollers. Pets must be leashed with clean up. Best Western State College Inn offers a special rate. Phone 1-800-635-1177 and say "I'm a volksmarcher." Special rates not available on holidays or special events. **YR744** is on paved sidewalks thru neighborhoods and downtown area of State College. **YR1197** is on paved walkways and bike paths through the village of Boalsburg. (This route will be closed after heavy snows. Call ahead if in doubt). For list of festivals/activities in the area, send a SASE to the POC.

St. Marys - 10km Walk (YR952) **Jun 1-Nov 1**
B Awards available
Sponsoring Club: AVA-726, Nittany Nomads
POC: Terry & Patti McClain, 814-781-3849. 972 Vine Rd, St Marys, PA 15857

Start Point: Towne House Inn, 814-781-1556. 138 Center St. From I-80 east exit 18 route 153 to Penfield. At Penfield, turn right on 255 north to downtown St Marys. After the light by the movie theatre, turn left before the red block building into the back entrance of the Towne House. From I-80 west, exit 17, Rt 255 North to downtown St Marys. After the light by the movie theatre, turn left before the red block building into the back entrance of the Towne House.

Event Info: Trail is rated 3. There are four hills and the walk is not suitable for strollers or wheelchairs. Pets must be leashed.

Valley Forge - 11km Walk (YR288) **Jan 1-Dec 31**
A Award available
Sponsoring Club: AVA-641, Valley Forge Troopers
POC: June Hankins, 610-948-5872. 38 Roboda Blvd, Royersford, PA 19468

Start Point: Valley Forge National Historical Park, Visitors Center at the Book Store. From the south: I-95 North to 476 North to north on Rt 76. Leave 76 at exit 26B and follow signs to **422 W to valley Forge Rt 23 West exit. Right on 23 West, cross the intersection into Valley Forge National Park, straight ahead to Visitors' Center. From the North: (Rt 9 NE ext of Turnpike) east and west, exit #24. Rt 202 South exit 26A to 422 West (.3 miles), then follow above directions from **.

Event Info: Daily 9-4. Closed Christmas. Trail is rated 1+, suitable for strollers & wheelchairs. Pets must be leashed. Route is mostly on blacktop multi-use trails and in rolling countryside in the most historical section of the park.

RHODE ISLAND ━━━━━━━━━━━━━━━━━━━━━━

Bristol - 10km Walk (YR365) **Apr 1-Nov 30**
A Award available
Sponsoring Club: AVA-410, Empire State Capital Volkssporters
POC: Beryl Wolf, 518-383-2880. 605-B Clifton Park Center Rd, Clifton Park, NY 12065. Emily Koch, 518-374-3588. 2061 Lexington Pkwy, Schenectady, NY 12309

Start Point: Blithewold Mansion & Gardens, 101 Ferry Rd (Rte 114); 401-253-2707. From Providence, take Exit 2 off Rte 195 in Mass. Follow Rte 136S for 8.5 miles. Turn right onto Griswold Ave, follow to the end & take left onto Ferry Road. Start is on right. From Boston, take Rte 24. Take Mt. Hope Bridge exit, cross the bridge, bear left at fork onto Ferry Road (Rte 114). Start is on the left. From Newport, take Rte 114N. Cross the Mt. Hope Bridge, bear left at fork onto Ferry Road. Start is on left.

Event Info: Daily, 10-4. May be closed some holidays. Please call to verify if in doubt. Trail is rated 1, suitable for strollers & wheelchairs with help. There is an entrance fee to Blithewold Gardens which is part of the walk. Volksmarchers receive $1.00 off. A guided tour of the mansion & grounds is available. No pets are allowed. This trail follows paths through the gardens overlooking Narragansett Bay, then sidewalks in the lovely seaside village of Bristol. Famed for its 4th of July parade which follows red, white & blue stripe painted streets. The trail passes by Linden Place, the 1810 mansion featured in the movie, "The Great Gatsby".

++Newport - 11km Walk (YR729) **Apr 15-Nov 1**
A Award available
Sponsoring Club: AVA-269, Walk 'n Mass Volkssport Club
POC: John Woodhouse, 401-847-1502. 3 Haymaker Rd, Middletown, RI 02842

Start Point: Cliff Walk Manor, 82 Memorial Blvd; 401-847-1300. Rt 24 South beyond Fall River, MA to Rt 138 (Middletown). Right at bottom of ramp. After several miles, turn left onto Rte 138A toward Newport Beaches. Left at 2nd light (T-intersection). This road becomes Memorial Blvd. Start is on the left after Newport Beach.

Event Info: Memorial Day to Columbus Day: 8am-dusk. Before Memorial Day & After Columbus Day, please call to check hours of opening. Trail is rated 3.5 (an alternate course rated 2 is available). Main course is not suitable for strollers or wheelchairs. Alternate is suitable for strollers only. Pets must be leashed. There is free parking at Cliff Walk Manor. The trail traverses famous Cliff Walk, passes multiple mansions & includes the International Tennis Hall of Fame & downtown Newport. Only one event credit even if doing both trails.

Providence - 10km Walk (YR1092) **Apr 15-Nov 1**
A Award available
Sponsoring Club: AVA-269, Walk 'n Mass Volkssport Club
POC: Betty Foley, 508-443-4857. 807 Boston Post Rd, Sudbury, MA 01776

Start Point: Roger Williams National Memorial, 401-521-7266. 282 North Main St. From Rt 95 south take exit 23, Charles St. Go right at stop. Take first left around onto Ashburton St. At next light turn right onto Charles St which becomes Canal St (one way). Stay to left. Parking on left on Canal St. From 95 north, take exit 24 (Branch Ave). Go right onto North Main St. At light, go right onto Randall St. Turn left on Charles St which becomes Canal St. Parking on the left after the 2nd light.

Event Info: Daily, 9-4. Trail is rated 2 & is suitable for strollers but not wheelchairs. Pets are allowed if leashed. This is a paved, somewhat hilly route. Areas of interest include restored historic homes, the impressive State House, Roger Williams Park & a revitalized downtown. Pick up the color-coded map from the start. It high-lights areas of interest as well as restaurants.

SOUTH CAROLINA ━━━━━━━━━━━━━━━━━━━━━━━━━━━━━━

Cleveland - 10km Walk (YR1321) Jan 1-Dec 31
Credit Only Event
Sponsoring Club: AVA-848, South Carolina State Parks
POC: Bill Morrell, 864-836-6115. 8155 Greer Hwy, Cleveland, SC 29635

Start Point: Caesors Head State Park Office, 8155 Greer Hwy. Located 30 miles NW of Greenville on US 276 near the SC/NC border.

Event Info: Apr-Sept 9-9; Oct-Mar 9-6. Office hours year round are 9-5. Trail is rated 2 but is not suitable for strollers or wheelchairs. Pets must be leashed. Carry water and bring a snack. Raven Cliff Falls is an easy to moderate path on a wide, well marked trail over a short gravel road and through a forest area of old hickory trees. 3 1/2 miles into the trail takes walkers to the swinging bridge and the turn around point. This bridge sits atop a 400' waterfall and the view is extraordinary.

Pickens - 10km Walk (YR1323) **Jan 1-Dec 31**
Credit Only Event
Sponsoring Club: AVA-848, South Carolina State Parks
POC: Scott Stegenga, 864-878-9813/864-878-7381. 246 Table Rock Park Rd, Pickens, SC 29671

Start Point: Table Rock State Park, 246 Table Rock Park Rd. Park is located 12 miles north of Pickens on SC 11. Follow signs to the park.

Event Info: Park hours are 7-dark daily. Office hours are 9-5 weekdays; Sat 11-noon; Sun 4-5. If office is closed on weekends, check the Nature Center or find the Park Ranger. The Nature Center is on the opposite end of the parking lot from the office, across the road. Trail is rated 4-5. It is not suitable for strollers or wheelchairs. Pets must be leashed. Bring water and a snack. Change in elevation can lead to unexpected cooler temperatures at the top so come prepared with an extra layer of clothing. $2.00 per car entrance fee required. Table Rock Trail was constructed in the mid 1930's by the Civil Conservation Corp. It is a strenuous climb experiencing a 2,000 foot change in elevation. The trail widens through boulder fields and a rock outcropping. There are nice overlooks from the top.

Rock Hill - 10km Walk (YR1216) **Jan 1-Dec 31**
Credit Only Event
Sponsoring Club: AVA-830, Rock Hill Trailblazers
POC: Kendra Gloster, 803-329-5672. PO Box 11706, Rock Hill SC 29731

Start Point: Cherry Park Tower, 803-329-5672. 1466 Cherry Rd. Located in the middle of the softball complex. From I-77 take exit 82B. Park is located on Bus Hwy 21 S (Cherry Rd) 2 miles from exit on the left. From I-85 take exit 102. Turn right on Hwy 198. At first intersection take a left on Hwy 5 South. Follow to Rock Hill. Take a left on Hwy 322 (Cherry Rd). Park is 2 miles on the right. From Hwy 72, take a left onto Hwy 5 North. At intersection with Hwy 322 (Cherry Rd) take a right. Park is 2 miles on right.

Event Info: Daily, 7:30-5. Office is closed on major holidays but the trail is open year round. Trail is rated 1 and is suitable for strollers & wheelchairs. Pets are allowed.

Rock Hill - 10km Walk (YR1215) **Jan 1-Dec 31**
Credit Only Event
Sponsoring Club: AVA-830, Rockhill Trailblazers
POC: Brenda Brown, 803-329-5200. YCCVB, 201 E Main St, Rock Hill, SC 29730

Start Point: York County Convention & Visitors Bureau, 201 East Main St. From I-77 take exit 79 (SC 122, Dave Lyle Blvd) following signs to downtown Rock Hill and the YCCVB. Go approximately 3.2 miles & take a left onto White St. Take the next right at Caldwell St. YCCVB is located on the left at next corner (Main St. From I-85 Take exit 102. Turn right on SC Hwy 198. At first intersection, take a left onto SC Hwy 5 South. Follow to Rock Hill. Take a left onto Hampton St, just past City Hall. Take a right on Main St. YCCVB is located on the left at corner of Caldwell & Main. From SC Hwy 72, Follow Hwy 72 Bus into downtown Rock Hill. Cross Hwy 5/Hwy 21 (Black St). At next intersection take a left onto Main St. In block after first stoplight, YCCVB is on the right.

Event Info: Mon-Fri, 9-5; Sat, 10-4; Sun, 1-4. Closed major holidays. Trail is rated 1 and is suitable for strollers & wheelchairs but there are some steps. Pets are not recommended.

Santee - 10km Walk (YR1322) **Jan 1-Dec 31**
Credit Only Event
Sponsoring Club: AVA-848, South Carolina State Parks
POC: David Green or Mike Spivey, 803-854-2408. 251 State Park Rd, Santee, SC 29142

Start Point: Santee State Park Office, 803-854-2408. 251 State Park Rd. Located off SC6, three miles NW of Santee and I-95 (exit 98). Follow signs to park. From I-26 take exit 154 (301 North) for 6 miles to Hwy 47. Left on 47 and follow signs to park.

Event Info: Office hours: Spring/Summer, 8am-10pm; Fall/Winter, 8am-6pm. Trail is rated 2 but is not suitable for strollers or wheelchairs. Pets must be leashed. After completing the Limestone Nature trail loop, you may either cross over the road and return to the start point via the bike trail or you may follow the road. The bike trail runs parallel to Lake Marion and passes through different natural habitats. It is relatively flat with a few inclines on grass with some sand. From the bike trail cross over the road to the Limestone Nature Trail which is rolling terrain circling a portion of the park pond. Cross a narrow bridge about 60 feet long.

SOUTH DAKOTA

Brookings - 10km Walk (YR018) **Apr 1 - June 30** 10km Walk (YR506) **July 1-Sept 30** 25km Bike (YR503) **Apr 1-Sept 30**
B Awards available
Sponsoring Club: AVA-160, Prairie Wanderers
POC: Gwen Pickett, 605-692-5495. 415 11th Ave, Brookings SD 57006

Start Point: Brookings Hospital, 300 22nd Ave. From I-29 take exit 132 west onto Hwy 14 (6th St) to 22nd Ave. Turn south 3 blocks to hospital on left side of 22nd Ave at 3rd St. Coming rom the West, stay on Hwy 14 going east to 22nd Ave. Then 3 blocks to the start.

Event Info: Daily 7am-9pm. All events are rated 1. The walks are suitable for strollers and wheelchairs. Pets are allowed on a leash. Both walks are on city sidewalks and the bike is on city sidewalks, city streets and a walk/bike path.

Custer State Park - 10km Walk (YR101) **May 17-Oct 31**
B Awards available
Sponsoring Club: AVA-417, South Dakota Parks & Recreation Volkssport Assoc.
POC: Sally Svenson or Brian Madetzke, 605-255-4515. HC 83, Box 70, Custer SD 57730

Start Point: Peter Norbeck Visitor Center. Located on Hwy 16A near the State Game Lodge. From Rapid City take Hwy 79 south to Hwy 36. Turn right and go to the intersection with Hwy 16A then 3 miles to Peter Norbeck Visitor Center.

Event Info: May 17-Sep 4, 8am-6pm. Finish by 8pm. Sep 5-Oct 31, 9am-3pm. Finish by 5pm. A Vehicle entrance fee is required. Trail is rated 3, not suitable for strollers or wheelchairs. Pets on a leash only. This trail contains several long hills and follows mowed paths and dirt trails. Carry water on this route.

Dell Rapids - 10km Walk (YR502) **Apr 1-Sept 30**
B Awards available
Sponsoring Club: AVA-160, Prairie Wanderers
POC: Eunice McGee, 605-446-3484. 25174-467th Ave, Colton SD 57018

Start Point: The Rose Stone Inn, 605-428-3698. 504 East 4th St. From I-29 take exit 98, east 3 miles to Hwy 115 and continue 5 blocks to the Inn on the left.

Event Info: Daily, 7 to dusk. Rated 1+, not suitable for strollers or wheelchairs. Pets on a leash. This walk takes you through this picturesque town and by the rapids and dells on the Big Sioux River from which the city (pop 2,484) got its name. There is a historic main street.

Hot Springs - 10km Walk (YR764) **Apr 1-Sept 30**
B Awards available
Sponsoring Club: AVA-274, Black Hills Volkssport Assn.
POC: Reta Ringer, 605-745-5587. HCR 52, Box 168A, Hot Springs, SD 57747

Start Point: Mammoth Site, 605-745-6017. Hwy 18 truck by-pass within city limits.

Event Info: Apr 1-May 14, 9-2 finish by 5. May 15-Aug 31, 8-5 finish by 8. Sept 1-Sept 30, 9-2 finish by 5. Trail is rated 2, suitable for strollers but not wheelchairs as it has some hills. Pets must be leashed. Guided tours are available at the Mammoth Site. The trail follows paved streets through historical downtown area. Walk on the Freedom Trail.

Mitchell - 10km Walk (YR186) **Apr 1-Sept 30**
B Awards available
Sponsoring Club: AVA-160, Prairie Wanderers
POC: Shirley Luther, 605-692-5159. 1511 - 8th St South, Brookings, SD 57006

173

Start Point: Queen of Peace Hospital, 605-996-2000; 5th & Foster. Mitchell is located in south central South Dakota on I-90 and S.D. Hwys 37 & 38. From I-90 exit 332 north on Burr St to 5th Ave. Right to Foster. From Hwy 37 N or S, go east on 5th Ave to Foster. From East or West on Hwy 38, go north on Burr to 5th Ave then east to Foster.

Event Info: Daily, dawn-dusk. Trail is rated 1, suitable for strollers but not wheelchairs. Pets on a leash only. Trail is on city streets and past the world's only Corn Palace. If hospital personnel are busy, please wait until they can serve you.

Pierre - 10km Walk (YR768) **Jan 1-Dec 31**
A Award available
Sponsoring Club: AVA-858, Capitol City River Ramblers
POC: Pierre Area Chamber of Commerce, 800-962-2034. 800 West Dakota Ave, Pierre, SD 57501

Start Point: Pierre Area Chamber of Commerce, 800-962-2034. 800 West Dakota.

Alternate Start Point: (Evenings & Weekends) RamKota Inn, 920 W. Sioux (Hwy 14/34) at the MO River Bridge.

Event Info: Daily, dawn to dusk. Closed Christmas. Must be at second checkpoint by 7pm. Trail is rated 1+, suitable for strollers and wheelchairs. Pets are allowed on a leash. Use caution during inclement weather, sidewalks may be icy. Trail winds along the river through scenic areas of Pierre passing the Capitol Building and several parks.

Rapid City - Four 10km Walks (YR045) **Jan 1-Mar 31** (YR492) **Apr 1-Jun 30** (YR493) **Jul 1-Sep 30** (YR529) **Oct 1-Dec 31**
A Awards available
Sponsoring Club: AVA-274, Black Hills Volkssport Association
POC: Douglas Kapaun, 605-348-5191. 3020 Sunny Hill Cir, Rapid City SD 57702

Start Point: Hotel Alex Johnson, 523 6th St; 605-342-1210. from I-90 east or westbound exit 57 on I-190 southbound. You will be on West Blvd. Left on St Joseph to 6th St and Hotel Alex Johnson. Easily accessible on Loop 90, Hwy 79 or Hwy 16 taking Omaha, Main or St. Joseph to 6th St downtown. Register at the front desk.

Event Info: Daily, dawn to dusk. Closed Christmas. This is one trail broken down to four seasonal events. Trail is rated 1+, suitable for strollers and wheelchairs. Pets must be leashed. Parking permits are available at registration. This trail is easy walking on city sidewalks and bicycle paths.

Rapid City - 25km Bike (YR646) **Apr 1-Dec 31**
B Awards available
Sponsoring Club: AVA-497, Bandit Hikers
POC: Don Donatiello, 605-341-6235. 2702 Ivy Ave, Rapid City, SD 57701

Start Point: Two Wheeler Dealer Cycle & Fitness, 100 East Blvd. N; 605-343-0524. From I-90 exit 58. Drive S on Haines Ave. Left onto Omaha St. Left onto East Blvd. Start is on right.

Event Info: Mon-Fri 9-8 (After Labor Day the store closes at 5:30); Sat 9-5; Sun 9-4. Trail is rated 1. You must sign a waiver and you should wear a helmet. The route consists of city streets and the city bike path. It takes you by Rapid Creek and through many parks.

Rapid City - 10km Walk (YR964) **Apr 1-Dec 31**
A Award available
Sponsoring Club: AVA-497, Bandit Hikers Volkssport Club
POC: Beth Hendricks, 605-393-0888. 3401 Colvin St, Rapid City, SD 57701

SOUTH DAKOTA, cont.

Start Point: Lake Park Motel, 605-343-0234. Hwy 44 and Chapel Lane. From I-90 take exit 57 and drive south on I-190. Right onto West Main then left onto Mountain View Rd. Right onto Jackson Blvd (Hwy 44). Chapel Lane is on the left just past Canyon Lake Park. The motel is on the left side of Chapel Lane.

Event Info: Summer Hours (June-Aug): Daily 7-7. Winter Hours: Mon-Sat, 7-7; Sun, 12-7. Trail is rated 1, suitable for strollers and wheelchairs. Pets are allowed. The trail winds over city sidewalks and the bike path around Canyon Lake. There will be some residential and historical places along this scenic route.

Rapid City - 10km Walk (YR1290) **Jan 1-Dec 31**
Credit Only Event
Sponsoring Club: AVA-274, Black Hills Volkssport Assn.
POC: Sharlene Mitchell, 605-343-8891/Cam Cross, 605-348-1102. 1813 Copperdale Dr, Rapid City, SD 57701

Start Point: Gas Plus, 1903 N Maple Ave.

Event Info: THIS IS A MALL WALK. Go from Gas Plus north 2 blocks on North Maple and park & walk into Rushmore Mall. Walk inside 9 times around or outside 6 times around the mall. Mon-Fri, 7am-9pm; Sat, 7-7; Sun, 11:30-5:30. Closed Christmas & Thanksgiving. Trail is rated 1 suitable for strollers & wheelchairs. Pets are not allowed. Everyone MUST sign a release agreement form for the Rushmore Mall. Fill out in full. Only required once per year. No more than five walkers per group.

Sioux Falls - 10km Walk (YR505)   25km Bike (YR501) **Apr 1-Sept 30**
B Awards available
Sponsoring Club: AVA-160, Prairie Wanderers
POC: Sharon Hofstad, 605-338-9100; 1437 North Dr, Sioux Falls SD 57104

Start Point: Omer's Market, 1401 North Main Ave. From I-29 take exit 81, east on Russell St to Main Ave. Omer's Market is on the NW corner of Russell and Main.

Event Info: Daily 7am-9pm. Trail is rated 1+, suitable for strollers and wheelchairs. Pets must be leashed. The route is on city sidewalks and blacktop bicycle trails. The trail winds along the Big Sioux River and through several city parks. The bike is rated 1+. Bikers must sign a waiver and should wear a helmet.

Spearfish - 10km Walk (YR035) **Jan 2-Dec 31**
A Award available
Sponsoring Club: AVA-274, Black Hills Volkssport Association
POC: Darlene Matthesen, 605-642-3058. 921 Pinedale, Spearfish, SD 57783

Start Point: Big D Texaco Station, 305 W Jackson Blvd; 605-642-5151. From I-90 exit #12 onto Jackson Blvd. Continue on Jackson to start (on the left hand side of street) which is two blocks past the traffic light.

Event Info: Daily dawn to dusk. Closed Christmas and New Years. Trail is rated 1, suitable for strollers and wheelchairs. Pets are allowed. The trail is easy walking on city sidewalks and bicycle paths.

Sturgis - 11km Walk (YR610) **May 1-Oct 31**
A Award available
Sponsoring Club: AVA-028, Sturgis Ft. Meade Walkfest Association
POC: Ernest Miller, 605-347-3354. PO Box 504 S Junction Ave, Sturgis SD 57785

Start Point: Star-Lite Motel, 605-347-2506. S Junction 57785 near I-90 Exit 32.

Event Info: Daily dawn to dusk. Closed Aug 1-15. Trail is rated 2+, not suitable for strollers or wheelchairs. Pets on a leash only. Route is on sidewalks, streets and gravel roads. Many scenic views, Pony Express grave, Ft Meade Museum, Old Post Cemetery (1878-1943), 4th Cavalry Troop Buildings and stables.

Sturgis - 10km Walk (YR532) **May 1-Sep 1**
A Award available
Sponsoring Club: AVA-417, South Dakota Parks & Recreation Volkssport Assn.
POC: Tony Gullett, 605-347-5240. Box 688, Sturgis SD 57785

Start Point: Bear Butte State Park Visitor's Center; 605-347-5240. Follow Hwy 34 thru Sturgis from I-90. Turn left on SD79. Turn right into Bear Butte State Park, proceed to the A-framed Visitor Center.

Event Info: May 1-May 31 & Aug 31-Sep 1, 9-4; Jun 1-Aug 30, 8-7. Trail is rated 3+ unless you take the summit route which is rated 4+. It is not suitable for strollers or wheelchairs. Pets must be leashed. This mountain is sacred to the Lakota & Cheyenne. Please follow the etiquette guidelines as posted. There is a park entrance fee. This trail is a combination of mowed paths, existing hiking trails and asphalt roads. It is somewhat flat with moderate hills. the alternate route to the summit is strenuous but the view is worth it. **NOTE:** Due to Aug 1996 fire, all repairs to trails may not be finished. If so, routes may be changed. Please check at start point for details.

Watertown - 10km Walk (YR184) **Apr 1-Sept 30**
B Awards available
Sponsoring Club: AVA-160, Prairie Wanderers
POC: Eunice Solem, 605-874-2437. 711 3rd Ave South, Box 523, Clear Lake SD 57226

Start Point: Prairie Lakes West Hospital, 400 10th Ave. NW. From I-29, exit 177 west 3.7 miles to SD 20. Turn right (north) and go 1.5 miles to 10th Ave NW, then turn right again to hospital.

Event Info: Daily 8-dusk. Trail is rated 1+, suitable for strollers and wheelchairs. Pets must be leashed. The trail mostly consists of hard surface city streets. There is one steep hill. Allow time to see Bramble Park Zoo and Mellette House, home of the last Territorial Governor and the first State Governor.

Yankton - 10km Walk (YR185)   25km Bike (YR648) **Apr 1-Sept 30**
B Awards available
Sponsoring Club: AVA-160, Prairie Wanderers
POC: Helen Bechtold, 605-692-2902. 618 13th Avenue, Brookings SD 57006

Start Point: Rick's Conoco. West Hwy 52. From Yankton, go west on SD 52 about three miles to start. Rick's is on the right side of the road. From I-29, west on SD 50 to Yankton, west on SD 52 to start.

Event Info: Daily 7-dusk. Finish by dark. Both the walk and the bike are rated 1. The walk is suitable for strollers and wheelchairs. Pets must be leashed. Both routes follow an asphalt bike trail. Bikers must sign waiver and should wear a helmet.

TENNESSEE

Clarksville - 10km Walk (YR727) **Jan 1-Dec 31**
B Awards available
Sponsoring Club: AVA-020, Tuck-A-See Wanderers
POC: Vernon Hessey, 502-439-3716. PO Box 956, Oak Grove, KY 42262

Register: Clarksville/Montgomery County Tourist Information Center, 615-648-0001. 180 Holiday Road. Exit 4 off I-24. Go south 500 yards and turn left on Holiday Rd (next to Holiday Inn). After picking up your start card, you drive to Dunbar Cave to complete the walk (5 miles). Preregistration is available by contacting the POC at PO Box listed.

Event Info: Center is open 8-5 during daylight savings time. The remainder of the year it is open Mon-Fri 8-4; Sat & Sun 9-4. Please call for schedule during Christmas holidays. Trail is rated 2+. Pets must be leashed. It is not suitable for strollers or wheelchairs. The trail is on paved roads, gravel paths and woodland trails with two moderately steep hills. Avoid the smog and exhaust fumes of the big city streets on this walk.

Gatlinburg - 10km Walk (YR1224) **Jan 1-Dec 31**
B Awards available
Sponsoring Club: AVA-742, Gatlinburg Hiking Club
POC: Tom Brosch, 423-436-6000. 905 River Road, Gatlinburg, TN 37738

Start Point: The Happy Hiker, 905 River Rd. Follow I-75 to Knoxville. Take I-40 East to exit 407. Follow Hwy 66 throughSevierville to Hwy 441 North towards Gatlinburg. Follow the Parkway in Gatlinburg to traffic light #6. Take a right on River Rd and follow through traffic light #10. The start is on the left in the Burning Bush Plaza.

Event Info: Daily, 9-5. Trail is rated 1+. It is not suitable for strollers or wheelchairs. No pets allowed. Volkssporters will receive a 10% discount on purchases at the Happy Hiker. Walk down River Rd to the entrance of the Great Smoky Mountains National Park. There you will follow a 2 mile trail along the west prong of the Little Pigeon River leading to the Sugarlands Visitors Center. At Sugarlands you will follow a self-guided nature trail. Loop back to Little Pigeon Trail and then follow to Cataract Falls. Back track to Little Pigeon and then back to start/finish.

Mountain City - 10km Walk (YR1136) **Jan 1-Dec 31**
Credit Only Event
Sponsoring Club: AVA-NC, Tarheel State Walkers
POC: Karen Procter, 910-945-5506. PO Box 844, Lewisville, NC 27023-0844 or Mary Lois Leith, 901-765-6668.

Start Point: Mountain Empire Motel, 615-727-7777. 1615 S Shady St (US 421). Follow US 421 to Mountain City where it turns into Shady St.

Event Info: Daily dawn to dusk. Trail is rated 2, difficult for strollers and wheelchairs. Pets must be leashed.

TEXAS

Abilene - Two 11km Walks (YR193 & YR393) **Jan 2-Dec 31**
B Awards available
Sponsoring Club: AVA-757, Shoeleather Express
POC: The Scotts, 915-698-5616/698-1313. 3117 Meander St, Abilene TX 79602-6624

Start Point: The Quality Inn Downtown, 915-676-0222. 505 Pine St. Downtown. From I-20, exit 286A. Stay on Pine St as N Treadaway will vear off to the left. You will go about 23 blocks to 5th and Pine.

Event Info: Daily dawn-dusk. Box is available 24 hrs a day, 365 days a year. The Quality Inn offers volkssporters the corporate rate with a full breakfast. Pets are allowed on trails if leashed. Walks are rated 1+, but are not suitable for strollers or wheelchairs. On **YR193** you will go thru ACU and downtown Abilene and see several turn-of-the century (1890-1936) homes and buildings. **YR393** takes you past several historical churches, McMurry University, Oscar Rose Park, Safety City and quaint craft shops.

Austin - Two 10km Walks (YR068 & YR069) 25km Bike (YR082) **Jan 1-Dec 31**
B Awards available
Sponsoring Club: AVA-077, Colorado River Walkers
POC: Richard Kersch, 512-282-5790. 3003 Six Gun Trail, Austin, TX 78748

Start Point: Austin Hyatt Regency Hotel, 208 Barton Springs Rd; 512-477-1234. Take the Riverside exit off of IH-35. Go west on Riverside to Barton Springs Rd. Turn right and the Hyatt is on the left. OR From Loop 1 (MOPAC) take Zilker Park exit. Go past Zilker Park to Barton Springs Rd. Hyatt is on the left after Riverside.

Event Info: Daily dawn-dusk. All walks are rated 1 and are suitable for strollers but wheelchairs may need assistance due to curbs & stairs. **YR068** is a historical walk through downtown Austin, past the Capitol Bldg, LBJ Presidential Library and the University of Texas Campus. **YR069** is the Town Lake Walk and is on a granite/gravel hike and bike trail along the lake. **YR082** is the bike. It is not rated. Bikers must sign a waiver and should wear helmets. Leashed pets are allowed on all events. The bike is on a hike and bike trail along Town Lake.

Bastrop - 10km Walk (YR1143) **Jan 1-Dec 31**
B Awards available
Sponsoring Club: AVA-844, Texas State Parks Volkssporting Assoc
POC: Brent Leisure, 512-321-1673. PO Box 518, Bastrop, TX 78602

Start Point: Bastrop State Park, 512-321-2101. PO Box 518. From Hwy 71 in Bastrop, take Hwy 21 east from Bastrop 1/2 mile to the State Park Hqs.

Event Info: Memorial Day-Labor Day: Wed-Mon 8-7; Tue 8-5. All other times of the year: 8-5. Trail is rated 2+ and is not suitable for strollers or wheelchairs. Pets are allowed on a leash only. The trail follows park road 1A and the Lost Pines Hiking Trail. Heavily wooded in a Loblolly Pine/Oak forest, the trail traverses rolling terrain with moderate challenges.

Boerne - 10km Walk (YR220) 11km Walk (YR234) 26km Bike (YR379) **Jan 1-Dec 31**
A Awards available
Sponsoring Club: AVA-652, Hill Country Hikers
POC: Barbara Hill 210-816-1718 or 210-537-4172. 115 S Hilltop Dr, Boerne TX 78006

Start Point: Key to the Hills Motel, 1228 S. Main; 800-690-5763/210-249-3562. Take Hwy 46 (exit 540) off IH 10 West and turn east . Go to next intersection (US Hwy 87 known as Main St) and turn left at traffic light by Wendy's to start point on the left next door to Family Korner Restaurant. Park at the back of the parking lot.

Event Info: The Motel has offered lower rates for volkssporters. Identify yourself at time of registration as a participant of this AVA event. Daily dawn-dusk. **YR220** is rated 1 but is not suitable for strollers or wheelchairs. It is over paved roads and sidewalks through Benedictine Convent, neighborhoods and downtown. **YR234** is rated 1 and is suitable for strollers. There is no restroom and some hills on this route which is over paved roads and out in the country. You will have to drive about three miles from the Motel to the start of this event. **YR379,** the bike, is rated 1. Bikers must sign a waiver and should wear a helmet. This route is over paved roads and has some hills. Pets are allowed but must be on a leash at all times.

Carrollton - 12km Walk (YR1234) **Jan 1-Dec 31**
A Award available
Sponsoring Club: AVA-034, Dallas Trekkers
POC: Jo Trautmann, 972-492-5830. 3116 Luallen Dr, Carrollton, TX 75007

Start Point: Whataburger Restaurant, NE Corner of intersection of Josey & Frankford. From Dallas: I-35 north to Trinity Mills, east to Josey, north to Frankford. From Garland/NE Dallas: I-635 west to Josey, north to Frankford. From Irving: I-35 north to Trinity Mills (same as 1 above). From Plano: West on Plano Pkwy which becomes Hebron Pkwy, to Josey Lane. South on Josey to Frankford.

Event Info: Daily, dawn to dusk. Trail is rated 1+ and is suitable for strollers and wheelchairs. Pets are allowed. Route is on gently rolling terrain, around a lake, through residential streets to Greenbelt, through and along greenbelts, residential streets, pass a historic cemetary and return.

Corpus Christi - 11km Walk (YR709) **Jan 1-Dec 31**
B Awards available
Sponsoring Club: AVA-179, Sparkling City Strollers
POC: Joyce Penny, 512-855-7482/512-902-4998. 4318 Vestal, Corpus Christi, TX 78416

Start Point: Best Western Sandy Shores, 800-242-5814/512-883-7456. 3200 Surfside. Located on the beach by the Aquarium, next to the USS Lexington. North side of High Bridge 3 blocks to beach.

Event Info: Daily, 6-6. Trail is rated 2 and is not suitable for strollers or wheelchairs. Pets are not allowed. Come join us for Corpus Christi's Founder's Walk. Exciting. Educational. Entertaining. Mile long bridge, historical homes; experience the art & culture. Fun for everyone.

Corpus Christi - 10km Walk (YR057) **Jan 1-Dec 31**
A Award available
Sponsoring Club: AVA-179, Sparkling City Strollers
POC: Marjorie Louise Hays, 512-991-2383/fax 512-991-6870. 1014 Ronald Dr, Corpus Christi TX 78412-3548

Start Point: Ramada Hotel Bayfront, 601 North Water St. From I-37 downtown, turn right at Water St 1 block before shoreline.

Event Info: Daily dawn-dusk. Trail is rated 1 and is suitable for strollers and wheelchairs. Pets must be leashed. Tour the downtown historical district. Pass Watergarden and walk the shoreline by the water. See the sailboats.

Dallas - 10km Walk (YR085) **Jan 1-Dec 31**
B Awards available
Sponsoring Club: AVA-034, Dallas Trekkers
POC: Earl Anderson, 214-341-8654. 8209 Lullwater, Dallas, TX 75218

Start Point: Union Station, Downtown. 400 S Houston St. Located in downtown Dallas. Start box is located at the Union Station lobby. See security guard if you do not see the box. Parking is available at nearby Reunion Arena for $2.00 per day or you can park on the city streets.

Event Info: Daily, 9-2. Must finish by 5. Closed Thanksgiving & Christmas. Trail is rated 1 but is not suitable for strollers or wheelchairs. No pets allowed. This walk is near the John F. Kennedy Exhibit, 411 Elm St, which is open daily. An entrance fee is charged.

Dallas - 15km Walk (YR141) 25km Bike (YR142) **Jan 1-Dec 31**
B Awards available
Sponsoring Club: AVA-034, Dallas Trekkers
POC: Jim Ross, 972-681-0045. 5229 Springlake Dr, Garland, TX 75043

Start Point: Jack Johnston Bicycle Shop (White Rock Lake), 9005 Garland Rd at Emerald Isle St. White Rock Lake is located NE of downtown Dallas. Take I-30 east to East Grand Ave. Turn northeast on East Grand which becomes Garland Rd.

Event Info: Daily 9-3 hours before dark. Bike shop closes at 7 pm. Closed Christmas. Both trails are rated 1 and the walk is suitable for strollers and wheelchairs. This trail circles the lake on well marked paved hike and bike trails. Pets are allowed. Bikers must sign a waiver and should wear a helmet. Bikes are available for rent. The bike also circles the lake then continues north on a loop along the White Rock Greenbelt.

Denison - 10km Walk (YR629) **Jan 1-Dec 31**
Sponsoring Club: AVA-767, Texoma Amblers
POC: Bill Jones, 903-893-6801. 401 Iowa, Sherman TX 75090 or Pat Taylor, 903-465-7170. 2621 Brookhollow, Denison, TX 75020

Start Point: Central Fire Station, 700 West Chestnut. From the south on Hwy 75, take Spur 503 (exit 66) north to Chestnut St. Turn left and go six blocks to Fire Station. From thenorth on Hwy 75 take Denison/Sherman exit south to downtown. Turn right on Chestnut St and go six blocks to the Station.

Event Info: Daily dawn-dusk. Trail is rated 1, suitable for strollers and wheelchairs. Pets must be leashed.

DeSoto - 10km Walk (YR201) **Jan 1-Dec 31**
B Awards available
Sponsoring Club: AVA-034, The Dallas Trekkers
POC: Layne/Mary Harper, 972-224-3740. 1311 Holt Ave, DeSoto, TX 75115

Start Point: Albertsons Supermarket, 901 Polk St at Pleasant Run Rd. DeSoto is 14 miles south of Dallas on I-35. Exit to 415 (Pleasant Run Rd) and go west for one mile to Polk St.

Event Info: Daily dawn-dusk. Trail is rated 1 and is suitable for strollers and wheelchairs. Pets are allowed. Pick up volkssport box at Customer Service Module. During summer months an early start is best. This is a sunny walk.

El Paso - 11km Walk (YR702) **Jan 1-Dec 31**
A Award available
Sponsoring Club: AVA-769, Amigo Amblers
POC: Bill Hollis, 915-833-7048. 305 Sundown Place, El Paso, TX 79912

Start Point: Southwest Grocers, 5300 Doniphan Dr. I-10 exit 11 Mesa. Go west to Mesa St for .6 miles (towards McDonald's). Turn right on Doniphan and go .7 miles. Jordan's is on the right. Park between street & parking lot light poles. Do not park close to the market.

Event Info: Daily 7-11. Closed Thanksgiving and Christmas. Trail is rated 1+ and is suitable for strollers with large wheels but not wheelchairs. Carry water in the summer months. This walk is along canals and levees of the Rio Grande Valley. Trail parallels Rio Grande for a stretch.

El Paso - 10km Walk (YR900) **Jan 1-Dec 31**
A Award available
Sponsoring Club: AVA-769, Amigo Amblers
POC: Charlie Hollis, 915-833-7048. 305 Sundown Place, El paso, TX 79912

Start Point: Columbia Life Care Center, 3333 North Mesa. Coming from New Mexico on I-10, exit at Downtown/Convention Center, exit 19. Travel 4 short blocks to Mesa and turn left. Coming from Texas on I-10, exit at Mesa, exit 19A. Turn right on Mesa. Start is about 1.6 miles ahead on the left. Start box is at the desk in the fitness center.

TEXAS, cont.

Event Info: Mon-Fri, 5:30am-8:30pm; Sat, 6-2. Closed on Sunday. Trail is rated 2+ and is suitable for strollers & wheelchairs if the use care. No pets are allowed. Carry water during hot weather. This walk goes through some lovely older neighborhoods of El Paso and through the UTEP Campus.

El Paso/Ft Bliss - 10km Walk (YR439) **Jan 1-Dec 31**
A Award available
Sponsoring Club: AVA-769, Amigo Amblers
POC: Mary Seagrove, 915-595-2291. 2024 Pier Lane, El Pase, TX 79936

Start Point: Ft Bliss Inn, 1744 Victory Ave. From I-10 exit onto US Hwy 54 towards Alamogordo. Take Fred Wilson exit, turn right on Fred Wilson. Turn right at first signal, Marshall Rd and enter Ft Bliss. Turn left at first street. Inn is ahead on left.

Event Info: Daily dawn-3 hours before dark. Trail is rated 1 and is suitable for strollers and wheelchairs. Pets are allowed. Carry water during hot weather. Route is mostly on sidewalks and paved roads. Tour Ft Bliss Museums and older sections of Ft Bliss.

Fredericksburg - Three 10km Walks (YR001, YR107 & YR108) 26km Bike (YR448) **Jan 1-Dec 31**
A Awards available
Sponsoring Club: AVA-001, Volkssportverein Friedrichsburg
POC: Elizabeth Crenwelge, 210-997-2533. 326 West Glenmoor, Fredericksburg, TX 78624 or D.C. Breland, 210-997-9323 or Bob Deming, 210-997-6251

Start Point: Comfort Inn, 908 S. Adams. Hwy 16 South. Instructions for registering and detailed maps & start cards can be found in the Volkssport Box in Motel Lobby. For motel reservations call, 210-997-9811.

Event Info: Daily dawn to dusk. **YR001** is rated 1 and is suitable for strollers or wheelchairs. Pets are allowed. This is the historical walk and it is a self guided tour of Fredericksburg's Historical District. It is totally within the city limits on paved roads. **YR107** is rated 1 and is suitable for strollers and wheelchairs. Pets are allowed. This route (The Cemetery Walk) passes the two historical cemeteries of Fredericksburg: Der Stadt Friedhof (Garden of Peace) which was established in 1846, and the Catholic Cemetery, established in 1850 It is on paved roads. **YR108** is rated 1+ and is suitable for strollers or wheelchairs. Pets are also allowed on this route. This is a shortened version of the previous 11km route with scenic overlooks of Fredericksburg. **YR448**, the bike, is rated 2 dut to long hills. Bikers must sign a waiver and should wear helmets. This is a town and country ride with breathtaking views.

Ft Worth - 10km Walk (YR044) **Jan 2-Dec 31**
A Award available
Sponsoring Club: AVA-019, Tarrant County Walkers, Inc.
POC: Sue Layton, 817-924-8450. 516 East Drew, Ft. Worth, TX 76110

Start Point: Hardwicke Interpretive Nature Ctr, Fort Worth Nature & Refuge Center, 817-237-1111. 9601 Fossil Ridge Rd. Take Hwy 199 west of Fort Worth and west of Lake Worth to the Nature Center sign. Follow signs to start point.

Event Info: Daily, 9:30-1:30. Must be off trail by 4:30. Closed Mondays and some holidays. Trail is rated 3 with some uphill and sandy areas. It is not suitable for strollers or wheelchairs and no pets are allowed in buildings. This trail is through wooded areas as well as grasslands. See the Bison herd along with other wildlife and birds.

Ft Worth - 10km Walk (YR363) **Jan 1-Dec 31**
A Award available
Sponsoring Club: AVA-019, Tarrant County Walkers, Inc.
POC: Ernest LaCroix, 817-451-1291. 4920 Emerald Lake Drive, Ft. Worth, TX 76103

━━━━━━━━━━━━━━━━━━━━━━━━━━━━━━━━━━━

Start Point: Ramada Inn, 1700 Commerce St, 817-335-7000. From I-30 exit Commerce St to Ramada Inn. From I-35 exit to I-30 to Commerce.

Event Info: Daily 1 hour after dawn-3 hours before dusk. Trail is rated 1 and is not suitable for strollers or wheelchairs. Pets are allowed on a leash. Route is along city streets and on park trails.

Ft Worth - 10km Walk (YR630) **Jan 2-Dec 31**
A Award available
Sponsoring Club: AVA-019, Tarrant County Walkers, Inc.
POC: Mac Mackechnie, 817-926-4477. PO Box 100193, Ft. Worth TX 76185-0193

Start Point: Buster's Mini-Mart Phillips Station. From I-20 take exit 434A, go north to the corner of Trail Lake and Grandbury Rd. From I-30 take exit 12A, go south on University to corner of Trail Lake & Granbury Rd.

Event Info: Daily 7-3 hours before dark. Closed Thanksgiving, Christmas and New Years. Trail is rated 1 but may be difficult for strollers and wheelchairs. Pets are allowed on a leash. The route is in park areas and along city streets.

Galveston Island - Three 10km Walks (YR088, YR562 & YR756) **Jan 1-Dec 31**
B Awards available
Sponsoring Club: AVA-251, Friendswood Fun Walkers
POC: Alice Gillespie, 713-482-7947. 112 Royal Ct, Friendswood, TX 77546 or Jan Phillips 713-332-3063.

Start Point: Galveston Island Visitor's Bureau (Moody Center) 2106 Seawall Blvd; 1-800-351-4237 or 409-763-4311. I-45 from Houston to Galveston. Right on 61st St and left on Seawall Blvd. To 21st St OR right on 21st St to Seawall.

Event Info: Mon-Sat 9-5; Sun 9-5 summer & 12-5 winter. Closed Christmas. Check with Visitor's Center for changes in operating hours. Trails are rated 1, wheelchairs & strollers may have difficulty with high curbs. Pets must be leashed. In the summer, carry your own water. Visitor's Center will send you an info packet with discount information on local activities. **YR088** goes through the Historic Area, along the Strand and to the Tallship Elyssa. **YR562** follows Seawall to University of Texas Medical Center and through the silk stocking district. **YR756** is an up and back along the seawall with an option to walk on the beach.

Garland - 10km Walk (YR324) **Jan 1-Dec 31**
B Awards available
Sponsoring Club: AVA-034, The Dallas Trekkers
POC: Marilyn Boyd, 972-270-3598. 1415 Butterfield Dr, Mesquite, TX 75150-6002

Start Point: Express Way Convenience Store, 3925 Broadway. Northeast of Dallas on I-30. Turn north on Belt Line/Broadway and go two miles to Apache St. Ask store clerk for Volkssport box and follow instructions in the box. Please park on the north side of the parking lot adjacent to the street.

Event Info: Daily one hour after daylight to one hour before dark. Closed some holidays. Trail is rated 1 and is suitable for strollers and wheelchairs. Pets are allowed. Route is along paved bike paths and some city streets. Go thru Audubon Park and Duck Creek Greenbelt.

Granbury - 10km Walk (YR382) **Jan 1-Dec 31**
· B Awards available
Sponsoring Club: AVA-718, Hood County Hummers
POC: Ardyce Pfanstiel, 817-326-2164. 3621 Fairway DCBE, Granbury TX 76049-5228

Start Point: Lodge of Granbury, 400 E Pearl St. From the north or east: From Loop 820 (I 20) in Ft Worth go southwest on Hwy 377 approximately 30 miles to Granbury. Take the Historic District exit to the Lodge located on the left. From the south or west: From the intersection of Hwy 377 and Hwy 144 turn north on 144 (Morgan St) and proceed to Pearl St. Take a right to the Lodge.

Event Info: Daily 8-3 hours before dark. Trail is rated 1+ and strollers and wheelchairs will encounter difficulty on parts of the trail. Pets must be leashed. There is heavy traffic at intersections. Please use the stop lights and pedestrian control devices. This route includes historical landmarks, boutiques and restaurants. Additional information is available at the Convention and Visitors Bureau on Granbury's Historic Square.

Hondo - 10km Walk (YR428) 27km Bike (YR652) **Jan 1-Dec 31**
Credit Only Events
Sponsoring Club: AVA-099 SAM Ramblers
POC: Harry C. Long, phone/fax: 210-696-8440. 11808 Mill Pond St, San Antonio, TX 78230-2112

Start Point: Hondo Texaco, 210-426-4902. Ave M & Hwy 90. From east or west on Hwy 90 proceed to Ave M. Texaco is located on the SW corner of Hwy 90 and Ave M.

Event Info: Daily, 7am-11pm. The walk is rated 1 and is suitable for strollers & wheelchairs. Pets must be leashed. Please pay by check made payable to SAM RAMBLERS. Use SASE envelopes provided in Start Box. This trail goes through historic, business & residential districts of Hondo. The bike is also rated 1 and goes through the countryside surrounding Hondo.

Houston - 10km Walk (YR143) 11km Walk (YR071) **Jan 1-Dec 31**
B Awards available
Sponsoring Club: AVA-015, Houston Happy Hikers
POC: Connie Bath, 713-665-2663. 2502 Watts, Houston TX 77030

Start Point: Holiday Inn Medical Ctr, 6701 S Main St (Between Main & Fannin). From 610 South loop, take Main St north to the Holiday Inn. From US 59 take Greenbriar south to University, then left on University to Fannin and right on Fannin to the Holiday Inn.

Event Info: Special rates available to walkers. Daily dawn to dusk. All trails are rated 1 and are suitable for strollers and wheelchairs. Pets must be leashed. **YR071** is an intersting and varied course. It goes past Rice Village shops and restaurants, thru Rice University, past museums, fountains and scenic residential areas. **YR143** passes through Hermann Park, past the Children's Museum and the Museumof Natural History, along the Bayou and by the newly created Japanese Garden in the park.

Irving - 10km Walk (YR316) **Jan 1-Dec 31**
B Awards available
Sponsoring Club: AVA-681, Star Trekkers
POC: Gunhilt Money, 972-986-5086. 2828 Game Lake, Irving, TX 75060

Start Point: McDonald's Restaurant, 302 W. Irving Blvd. From North (I-35, LBJ635) take Loop 12 (Walton Walker Blvd) to Irving Blvd (Hwy 356) Turn right and continue to McDonald's on your left side before O'Conner St. From the South (I-20) take Spur 408 to Loop 12, continue to Irving Blvd., turn left and follow until you reach start (past Main St.)

Event Info: Daily 7-3 hours before dusk. Closed Thanksgiving & Christmas. Pets must be leashed. Trail is rated 1+ and would be okay for strollers with some difficulty. Not suitable for wheelchairs. Route is on city sidewalks, including some park area. Contains original homes of early settlers. It is fairly level with lots of shade.

Irving (Las Colinas) - 10km Walk (YR202) **Jan 1-Dec 31**
A Award available
Sponsoring Club: AVA-681, Star Trekkers
POC: Carol Talpey, 972-717-3988. 3916 Acapulco, Irving, TX 75062

TEXAS, cont.

Start Point: Tom Thumb Store, 4010 N. MacArthur Blvd. If coming from the south (from 183) take Macarthur exit and go north to Northgate Dr. If coming from the north (LBJ ext 635 or 114) take Macarthur exit and go south to Intersection with Northgate Dr. Ask at cashier's office for walkers' box.

Event Info: Daily 8 until 3 hours before dusk. Trail is rated 1+ and is suitable for strollers but not wheelchairs. Pets must be leashed. This is a lovely walk through a master-planned development, passes by residential, business, parks and points of interest such as the famous mustangs, the horticultural clock, the canals and others.

Irving - 10km Walk (YR671) **Jan 1-Dec 31**
A award available
Sponsoring Club: AVA-681, Star Trekkers
POC: Allan Ortiz, 972-255-7648. 1518 McHam Street, Irving TX 75062

Start Point: 7-11 Food Store, 9400 N. MacArthur Blvd. In the Village Shopping Center (Valley Ranch). From the north, go south on I-35 to Hwy 635. Turn right and take Mac Arthur exit. Go north on Mac Arthur to the Village Shopping Center to 7-11. From the south, go north on I-35 to Hwy 635. Turn left and take Mac Arthur exit. Go north on Mac Arthur to the Village Shopping Center.

Event Info: Daily 7 to 3 hours before dusk. Trail is rated 2 and is suitable for strollers but not wheelchairs. Pets must be leashed. Route is in residential area along a beautifully landscaped path in the green belt. It passes the Dallas Cowboys Training facilities and the Dallas Stars Ice Hockey training facility.

Kerrville - Two 10km Walks (YR026 & YR027) 26km Bike (YR1142) **Jan 1-Dec 31**
A Awards available
Sponsoring Club: AVA-106, Kerrville Trailblazers
POC: Barbara K. Cox, 210-895-4382. PO Box 2097, Kerrville, TX 78029-2097

Start Point: Inn of the Hills, 210-895-5000. 1001 Junction Hwy. From I-10 exit 505. South on Harper Rd to Junction of Hwy 27. Turn left (signal light). Inn of the Hills is on the right, on Junction Hwy and can be seen from the intersection.

Event Info: Daily dawn to dusk. Both walks are rated 1+ and are suitable for strollers but not wheelchairs. Leashed pets only. **YR026** follows the Guadalupe River and historic, renovated Water St. Also goes into Louise Hayes Park and around Tranquility Island. **YR027** is the residential route and goes into the west side of Kerrville and includes a small park. **YR1142** (bike) is rated 1+. It is along rolling country roads west of Kerrville. There are no steep hills. Bikers must sign a waiver and should wear a helmet.

Lake Somerville (Birch Creek Park) - 10km Walk (YR1188) **Jan 1-Dec 31**
Credit Only Event
Sponsoring Club: AVA-844, Texas State Parks Volkssporting Assn.
POC: Todd Dickenson, 409-535-7763. Rt 1, Box 499, Somerville, TX 77879

Start Point: Ranger Station, Birch Creek Unit, Lake Somerville State Recreation Area, 409-535-7763. Rt 1, Box 499. From US 290 at Brenham, take TX 36 N to FM60. turn south (left) and follow to Park Rd 57. Turn left and follow to ranger station.

Event Info: Daily, 8-5. Trail is rated 2 but is not suitable for strollers and wheelchairs due to sandy trails. Pets are allowed if leashed. There is a $2.00 per person entrance fee for persons not having a Texas Parkland Passport or Conservation Pass. This trail follows slightly hilly terrain through nature areas. Beautiful wildflowers are seen in the springtime. There are two separate 10km events on Lake Somerville. One originates at Birch Creek State Park and another at Nails Creek State Park.

184

Lake Somerville (Nails Creek Park) - 12km Walk (YR1189) **Jan 1-Dec 31**
Credit Only Event
Sponsoring Club: AVA-844, Texas State Parks Volkssporting Assn
POC: Glen Korth, 409-289-2392. Rt 1, Box 61-C, Ledbetter, TX 78946

Start Point: Ranger Station, Lake Somerville State Rec Area, Nails Creek Unit, 409-289-2392. From Brenham, go west on Hwy 290 13 miles to Burton. Turn right (north) to FM 180. Turn right and follow FM 180 3 miles to park entrance. From Caldwell, take TX 21 west to FM60. Turn left to Park Rd 57 and follow to park entrance or take TX 36 to Park Rd 57. Turn right and follow to park entrance.

Event Info: Daily 8-5. Trail is rated 2 and is not suitable for strollers and wheelchairs due to sandy trails. Pets must be leashed. A $3.00 entrance fee per car is charged unless you have a Texas Parklands Passport or a Conservation Pass. This trail is on natural surfaces and meanders over a few small hills through post oak savannah and numerous wildflower meadows.

Lampasas - 10km Walk (YR371) **Jan 1-Dec 31**
Credit Only Event
Sponsoring Club: AVA-205, Trotting Texas Turtles
POC: Karl/Beverly Kittinger, 817-547-1403 (evenings only) 712 Ridge St, Copperas Cove, TX 76522-3137

Start Point: Country Inn at the Park, 512-556-5615. Hwy 281S at Hwy 190. Adjacent to Hancock Park.

Event Info: Daily, 8-dusk. Trail is rated 1+ and is passable for strollers but not suitable for wheelchairs. Pets must be leashed. Route includes the historical downtown area, older residential homes and a paved/gravel trail along Sulphur Creek.

McKinney - 10km Walk (YR229) **Jan 1-Dec 31**
A Award available
Sponsoring Club: AVA-124, Plano Plodders Walking Club, Inc.
POC: Maggie Cole, 214-612-8129. 4221 Whistler Dr, Plano, TX 75093 or Jerry Slayton, 972-424-6485.

Start Point: Holiday Inn, Central Expressway at White Ave. Exit 40B from Hwy 75 (Central Expressway) at White Ave. Holiday Inn is at the SE corner of 75 and White Ave.

Event Info: Daily 1 hour after dawn to 3 hrs before dusk. Trail is rated 1+ and would be okay for strollers but not wheelchairs. Pets must be leashed. The route will take you along the nostalgic streets of McKinney, graced by Victorian homes and distinctive late 19th and early 20th century buildings that earned the city a listing in the National Register of Historic Places.

Midlothian - 10km Walk (YR036) **Jan 1-Dec 31**
B Awards available
Sponsoring Club: AVA-034, The Dallas Trekkers
POC: Randy/Marilyn Tarin, 972-723-6536. 515 N 6th St, Midlothian, TX 76065

Start Point: Midlothian Police Dept, 101 E Ave F. At the junction of Hwy 287 and 67, approximately 25 miles SW of Dallas and 25 miles SE of Ft Worth. Proceed east from Highway junction on Hwy 287 to town center to start. Park in the city park parking lot. Please do not park in front of the Police Station. Follow instructions in the box located in the Police Station Lobby.

Event Info: Daily 8-3 hours before dark. Trail is rated 1+ and has one steep hill. It is not suitable for strollers or wheelchairs. Pets are allowed.

New Braunfels - 11km Walk (YR614) **Jan 1-Dec 31**
B Awards available
Sponsoring Club: AVA-036, New Braunfels Marsch-und Wandergruppe
POC: Don Flick, 210-625-0742. 407 Windsor Lane, New Braunfels TX 78132

Start Point: Hotel Faust, 240 S Seguin Ave. Take I-35 to exit 187 to South Sequin.

Event Info: Daily dawn to dusk. Trail is rated 1. Strollers okay but may have to be carried short distances. Not suitable for wheelchairs. Pets must be leashed. Route is through historical residential areas, Landa Park and the Comal River.

Ottine - 10km Walk (YR703) **Jan 1-Dec 31**
A Award available
Sponsoring Club: AVA-844, Texas State Parks Volkssport Assn.
POC: Mark Abolafia-Rosenzweig, 210-672-3266. Palmetto State Park, Rt 5, Box 201, Gonzales, TX 78629.

Start Point: Palmetto State Park, Park Hqs. From I-10 take the Hwy 183 exit south toward Gonzales. Turn right at Park Rd 11 and follow the road to the Park Hqs. located two miles ahead on the right side of the road in Ottine. From Gonzales, take US Hwy 183 north. Turn left on FM 1586 to Ottine. In Ottine, turn left on Park Road 11. Hqs is just ahead on the right.

Event Info: Daily 8-5. The park is closed if the San Marcos River is flooding. Trail is rated 1+ and is suitable for strollers but not wheelchairs. Pets must be leashed. The trail follows nature trails and park roads through the park and the surrounding community of Ottine. The trails are relatively flat, improved but not paved.

Pflugerville - 10km Walk (YR478) 300m Swim (YR477) 28km Bike (YR516) **Jan 1-Dec 31**
B Awards available
Sponsoring Club: AVA-077, Colorado River Walkers
POC: Richard Kersch, 512-282-5790. 3003 Six Gun Trail, Austin, TX 78748

Start Point: Police Station, 100 East Main. FM1825 Pflugerville exit from I-35 north of Austin. Go east about three miles to light at Railroad Ave. Go left one block then turn left and police station is on the right.

Event Info: Pool hours vary by season. Call ahead 512-251-5082. It is closed Mondays and some holidays. Swimmers must sign a waiver. The Police Station is open daily dawn to dusk. The walk is rated 1, suitable for strollers and wheelchairs. Pets are allowed. It follows a hike and bike trail along Billeland Creek, through downtown and nearby neighborhoods. Bikers must sign a waiver and should wear a helmet. Route is mainly on country roads with some gentle hills.

Plano - 10km Walk (YR151) **Jan 1-Dec 31**
A Award available
Sponsoring Club: AVA-124, Plano Plodders Walking Club, Inc.
POC: Maggie Cole, 972-612-8129. 4221 Whistler Dr, Plano, TX 75093 or Jerry Slayton, 972-424-6485.

Start Point: Brookshire's Food Store, 2060 Spring Creek Pkwy. From Hwy 75 (Central Expressway), take exit 31 (Spring Creek Pkwy) west to Custer Rd. Brookshires is at the SE corner of the intersection.

Event Info: Daily 1hr after dawn to 3 hrs before dusk. Trail is rated 1+, suitable for strollers but not wheelchairs. Pets must be leashed. The Chisholm hike and bike trail is an 8ft wide concrete trail beside a creek that flows through a greenbelt area. You will be walking along the creek for most of the walk.

Port Aransas - 11km Walk (YR710) **Jan 1-Dec 31**
A Award available
Sponsoring Club: AVA-179, Sparkling City Strollers
POC: Carol Woodfin, 512-749-5434 (5pm-10pm). PO Box 492, Port Aransas, TX 78373

Start Point: Tarpon Inn, 512-749-5555. 200 E Cotter. Take Hwy 361 from Aransas pass to Port Aransas and a free ferry ride (2 minutes) across the ship channel onto Cotter St. OR South Padre Island drive from Corpus Christi to #361 to Port Aransas and Cotter.

Event Info: Daily, 7-dusk. Trail is rated 1+. It is suitable for strollers but not wheelchairs. Pets must be leashed. Wear a hat, use sunscreen and carry water. Cameras and binoculars are recommended for bird watchers or naturalists. Route goes from Cotter to Roberts Point Park on the ship channel. There is a birding center with a resident alligator and herds of turtles. Also see "Main St" and the beach.

Salado - 11km Walk (YR450) **Jan 1-Dec 31**
Credit Only Event
Sponsoring Club: AVA-205, Trotting Texas Turtles
POC: Karl/Beverly Kittinger, 817-547-1403 (evenings only). 712 Ridge St, Copperas Cove TX 76522-3137

Start Point: Stagecoach Inn, IH 35; 817-947-5111. From IH-35 North, exit 284. Cross over 35 and continue to Main Street. Turn right on Main, cross Salado Creek, take first right onto Stagecoach Inn property. Continue until reaching parking area by main entrance. From south on IH-35, exit 284. At Exxon Station turn right and go one block to Main. Follow directions above.

Event Info: Daily dawn to dusk. Walk is rated 1 and is suitable for strollers but is not recommended for wheelchairs. Pets must be leashed. This route includes historical areas, quaint shops and a residential area.

San Antonio -10km Walk (YR261) **Jan 1-Dec 31**
A Award available
Sponsoring Club: AVA-006, Texas Wanderers
POC: Lyn Ward, 210-651-6536. 9355 Blazing Star Trail, San Antonio, TX 78266-2311

Start Point: Ft. Sam Houston, Bldg T300, Stanley Rd. From I-35, exit 159A. Go North on N. New Braunfels to Stanley Road. Go right on Stanley (opposite the base flag pole). Start box is located in the entrance way.

Event Info: Daily dawn to dusk. Trail is rated 1 and is suitable for strollers and wheelchairs. Pets must be leashed and are not allowed in the Quadrangle. This route goes through the Quadrangle where deer, fowl and rabbits run free, past the Gift Chapel, the 1916 and 1941 quarters of the Eisenhowers, Ft Sam Houston and US Army Medical Museums.

San Antonio - 11km Walk (YR462) 12km Walk (YR461)) 30km Bike (YR463) **Jan 2-Dec 31**
A Award available
Sponsoring Club: AVA-088, Selma Pathfinders
POC: Phyllis Eagan, 210-496-1402. 17314 Springhill, San Antonio TX 78232

Start Point: San Antonio Missions National Historical Park Visitors Center. Roosevelt at Mission Pkwy. From US 281 South, exit Southwest Military Dr and go west past Brooks Air Force Base to Roosevelt (3 miles). Turn right (north) and on the right (east) side of the street, a National Parks sign will direct you to the Visitors Center.

Event Info: Standard time 8-5; Daylight Savings time 9-6. Closed Christmas and New Years. **YR461** is rated 1 but is not suitable for strollers or wheelchairs. This route is along a hike-bike path that follows the San Antonio River and Mission Rd. The return trip follows same route. There is very little shade. **YR462** is also rated 1 but it is suitable for strollers and wheelchairs. This route is on a hike-bike trail and along a rural road leading from Mission San Jose to Missian San Juan. Return trip follows the same route and there is no shade. Pets must be leashed on both routes and are not allowed in the mission grounds. **YR463,** the bike, is rated 1. The route follows the hike-bike trail and a short distance along a street. Four missions built along the San Antonio River in the 1700's are visited along this route. Bikers must sign a waiver and should wear a helmet.

++San Antonio - 11km Walk (YR055) **Jan 1-Dec 31**
A Award available
Sponsoring Club: AVA-006, Texas Wanderers
POC: Lyn Ward, 210-651-6536. 9355 Blazing Star Trail, San Antonio, TX 78266

Start Point: Riverwalk North, (effective February 1997, name changes to Four Points by Sheraton) 110 Lexington Ave; 210-223-9461. Start box is located at the Bell Captain's Station. From I-35, exit 157B. Go south on McCullough toward downtown, to St. Mary's. Go right to Lexington and then turn left.

Event Info: Daily dawn-dusk. Trail is rated 1 but is not suitable for strollers or wheelchairs due to stairways to and from the Riverwalk. Pets are not appropriate but must be leashed if brought. This route meanders along Paseo del Rio or "Riverwalk", through the King William District, La Villiata, Hemisfair Park and through Mission San Antonio De Valero, better known as the Alamo.

San Marcos - 10km Walk (YR481) **Jan 1-Dec 31**
A Award available
Sponsoring Club: AVA-411, San Marcos River Walkers
POC: Barbara Piersol, 512-396-4463. 100 E Laurel Ln, San Marcos TX 78666

Start Point: Aquarena Springs Inn, 1 Aquarena Springs Dr; 512-396-8901. NOTE: Start is at the Inn and not the Park. Buildings are located in the same area. I-35, exit 206, Aquarena Springs Dr. Go west to entrance just beyond railroad tracks.

Event Info: Daily dawn-dusk. Trail is rated 2. Some areas not suitable for strollers or wheelchairs. Pets must be leashed and owners must pick up after them. The trail is through Southwest Texas State University Campus, historic San Marcos neighborhoods and along the San Marcos River. It is on city streets and sidewalks with some hills and steps on the campus.

Shiner - Two 10km Walks (YR221 & YR228) **Jan 1-Dec 31**
A Awards available
Sponsoring Club: AVA-460, Shiner Half Moon Walkers
POC: Virginia Helweg, 512-594-3304. 321 East 11th St, Shiner TX 77984

Start Point: Howard's Diamond Shamrock, 1701 North Avenue E. 512-594-4200. Located just outside of Shiner on Hwy 90A West towards Gonzales.

Event Info: Daily 7am-10pm. **YR221** is rated 1+ and strollers and wheelchairs may encounter some difficulty on the gravel roads and pasture area. **YR228** is rated 1 and is suitable for strollers and wheelchairs. This route is through residential areas, downtown Shiner and includes several historical markers. It is entirely on pavement. Pets are allowed on both routes.

Universal City - 10km Walk (YR510) 11km Walk (YR156)   26/27km Bike (YR147) **Jan 1-Dec 31**
Credit Only Events
Sponsoring Club: AVA-044, Randolph Roadrunners
POC: Iris V. Greene, 210-658-6536. 111 Forrest Trail, Universal City TX 78148

Start Point: The Comfort Inn, 210-659-5851; 200 Palisades Dr. From IH-35 exit at the 171/172 mile marker (Pat Booker/Randolph AFB exit). On Pat Booker Road, follow signs to the Comfort Inn. Palisades Drive is on the right. Blockbuster Video is on the corner. From Loop 1604 south, take Kitty Hawk exit turn-around and come back north 1/2 mile to Palisades Dr.

Event Info: Daily dawn-dusk. **YR156** is rated 1. It goes through residential areas, a city park, an undeveloped commercial park and on Universal City's main street past AVA Hqs. **YR510** is rated 1 and is mostly on residential roads through Olympia Hills and Coronado Village. Both routes are suitable for strollers or wheelchairs and pets are allowed. **YR147,** the bike, is rated 1+. The primary route follows city and country roads and the IH-35 access road out to Garden Ridge, returning past Retama Race Track. The alternate route stays east of IH-35 travelling through rolling hills of Selma, Schertz and Universal City. Bikers must sign a waiver and should wear a helmet. Only one event credit for the bike, even if doing both routes.

Vanderpool - 10km Walk (YR460) **Jan 1-Dec 31**
A Award available
Sponsoring Club: AVA-088, Selma Pathfinders
POC: Phyllis Eagan, 210-496-1402. 17314 Springhill, San Antonio TX 78232

Start Point: Lost Maples State Natural Area, Ranger Station. From San Antonio go north on Hwy 16 through Bandera and Medina, then west on FM337 to FM187. Turn right and go five miles to park. From Kerrville, take Hwy 27 to Ingram then Hwy 39 through Hunt. West of Hunt, turn left onto FM187 and follow it to the park.

Event Info: Park is closed on weekdays the first three weeks of December and the month of January but is open weekends. Remainder of year, daily 8-5. Trail is rated 2+ with an optional trail rated 4+. Neither is suitable for strollers or wheelchairs. Only one event credit even if doing both trails. Pets must be leashed. Please carry water and bring a walking stick. There will be a charge of $3.00 per car to enter the park except during Oct & Nov when the charge is $4. The trail follows park roads and nature trails that are somewhat rocky but have little change in grade. Optional trail is over primitive trails and hilly terrain with significant grade changes.

Waco - 11km Walk (YR626) **Jan 1-Dec 31**
B Awards available
Sponsoring Club: AVA-791, Chisholm Trail Blazers
POC: Jamina Ford, 817-776-1643. 6007 Haden Dr, Waco, TX 76710

Start Point: Hilton Hotel, 113 S. University Parks Dr. I-35 to University Parks exit (335B). Go West on University Parks Dr approximately 1/2 mile to the corner of University Parks and Franklin Ave to Hilton Hotel.

Event Info: Daily dawn to 3hrs before dusk. Trail is rated 1 and is suitable for strollers but not wheelchairs. Pets must be leashed. Walk crosses the Brazos River on the Suspension Bridge. It goes by museums, historic homes, McLennan County Court House, through Baylor University campus and along the River Walk.

Wichita Falls - Two 10km Walks (YR109 & YR203) **Jan 1-Dec 31**
B Awards available
Sponsoring Club: AVA-182, Buffalo Chipkickers Volksmarch Club, Inc.
POC: Chuck Samus, 817-691-0584 (eves). PO Box 8523, Wichita Falls TX 76307

Start Point: Econo Lodge, 1700 5th St; 817-761-1889. From the north or west on 281/287 take the Abilene exit and the Econo Lodge is on your right. From 281/287 south or east, take the Abilene exit. At the third light, turn left on 5th St. The Econo Lodge will be on your right.

Event Info: Daily dawn-dusk. **YR109** is rated 1+. Strollers and wheelchairs may have difficulty with curbs and a suspended bridge. The trail follows city sidewalks past historic buildings to a park trail leading to a suspended foot bridge across the Wichita River and on to the falls. **YR203** is rated 1 and is suitable for strollers and wheelchairs. You will register at the Econolodge and drive three miles to the start point for this walk. Do the walk and return to the Econolodge for your stamp. The trail follows sidewalks through Midwestern University and the Country Club section. There are many old homes and trees along this route. Pets are allowed on both trails but must be leashed.

UTAH ━━━━━━━━━━━━━━━━━━━━━━━━━━━━━

Murray - 10/11km Walk (YR1302) **Jan 1 -Dec 31**
Credit Only Event
Sponsoring Club: Footloose Volkssport Club
POC: Carolyn Lai, 801-250-2755/560-9286. 2936 S. Buccaneer Dr., Magna, UT 84044-1217.

Start Point: Walking Company, Fashion Place Mall, 801-264-9870. I-15 to I-215 East, Exit State St. At light, turn left and Fashion Place Mall is on the right. Route 2 registers here but you must drive to Winchester Park, 1100 West & 6400 South, two miles from the mall to start the walk.

Event Info: Walking Company M- Sat, 10-9; Sun 12-5; Fashion Place Mall - M-Sat 7 a.m. -10 p.m. Closed major holidays. This event has two routes. Only one event credit allowed even if doing both routes. Route 1 is rated 1 and is on city streets and inside mall. Suitable for strollers and wheelchairs. Pets are allowed. Route 2 is along the Jordan River Parkway, a paved trail, boardwalk over wetlands or visit the Gardner Historic Mill filled with quaint shops and restaurants. Do not walk alone. This route would be okay for strollers but difficult for wheelchairs.

Ogden - Two 10km Walks (YR062 & YR198) **Jan 1-Dec 31** 25km Bike (YR112) **Apr 1-Sept 30**
A Awards available
Sponsoring Club: AVA-436, Golden Spike Striders
POC: Joy Jeffs, 801-782-4070. 1036 East 2750 North, Ogden, UT 84414

Start Point: Travelodge Motel, 801-394-4563. 2110 Washington Blvd. Exit I-15 at 25 street (#346) near the Flying J. Plaza. Turn east towards the mountains and go approx 2 miles. The start is on the corner of 21st St & Washington Blvd across the street from the Ogden LDS Temple.

Event Info: Daily, dawn to dusk. **YR062** is rated 1+ and is suitable for strollers & wheelchairs but some older sidewalks are uneven and may be difficult to negotiate. Pets must be leashed. Route takes you past historic 25th Street, Union Station and through the historical residential area of this former railroad town. **YR198** is rated 1 and is suitable for strollers & wheelchairs. Pets must be leashed. Path may have snow and/or ice during winter months. The walk is on a scenic trail that follows the Ogden River from the city's main street to the Ogden Canyon Entrance. Walkers get a back door look at the dinasour park (fee area) and beautiful gardens. **YR112** is not rated. Bikers must sign a waiver and should wear a helmet. This route provides great scenic views of the city. There are some hills. Bike rental information is available at the starting point.

Orem - 10km Walk (YR326) **Jan 1-Dec 31**
A Award available
Sponsoring Club: AVA-731, Gadabout
POC: Myra Tams, 801-782-8580. 3897 N 1050 W, Ogden, UT 84414

Start Point: Canyon Chevron, 801-221-1576. 1565 East 800 North. Exit I-15 at #275 at Orem 8th north and drive toward Sundance. Station is on the left near the canyon entrance, 1565 East 800 North.

Event Info: Daily, 6am-11pm. Trail is rated 1 and follows a level, paved bike path. It is suitable for strollers and wheelchairs. Pets are allowed on a leash. Be prepared for cold, icy conditions in winter months. This event provides beautiful canyon scenery on a path to Bridal Veil Falls Resort. It follows the Provo River.

Provo - 10km Walk (YR327) **Jan 1-Dec 31**
A Award available
Sponsoring Club: AVA-731, Gadabouts
POC: Myra Tams, 801-782-8580. 3897 N 1050 W, Ogden, UT 84414

Start Point: Utah Travel Council, Historic County Courthouse, 801-370-8390. 51 S University Ave. I-15 exit 268 at Center St and drive to University Ave. The Utah Travel Council is located in the Historic County Courthouse Building. Parking is at the rear of the building. Enter at the south side of the building.

Event Info: Regular Hours: Mon-Fri 8-5; Sat/Sun 10-6. Summer Hours (Memorial Day to Labor Day): Mon-Fri 8-8; Sat/Sun 10-6. Closed all Federal and State Holidays. Trail is rated 1, suitable for strollers and wheelchairs. Pets are allowed on a leash. Prepare for warm summer days and cold, icy conditions in winter. This is an easy walk on paved roads and sidewalks with no hills. It goes around historic sites in Provo and Brigham Young University.

Salt Lake City - 10km Walk (YR075) **Jan 1-Dec 31**
B Awards available
Sponsoring Club: AVA-356, Footloose
POC: Carolyn Lai, 801-250-2755/560-9286. 2936 S Buccaneer Dr, Magna, UT 84044

Start Point: Shilo Inn, 801-521-9500. 206 S West Temple St. I-15 exit 310 - 600 South - City Center. At light drive up one block to West Temple St. Turn left. The Inn is 3 1/2 blocks up ahead on the left.

Event Info: Daily dawn to dusk. Route 1: rated 1, flat city streets. See Temple Sq., Historic Salt Lake, Trolley Sq. & D.T. shopping. Route 2: Trail is rated 2+, not suitable for strollers or wheelchairs. Pets are allowed. Elevation is 4000+ ft. Inn gives volkssporters $10.00 off on room rates. The route follows city streets and has steep hills. See the State Capitol, Pioneer Museum, Memory Grove and downtown shopping areas.

VERMONT ━━━━━━━━━━━━━━━━

Barton - 10km Walk (YR1289) **May 1-Oct 31**
A Award Available
Sponsoring Club: AVA-846, Kingdom Kickers
POC: Joyce V. Hanson, 802-525-4548. PO Box 403, Barton, VT 05822.

Start Point: Country Lovelies Craft and Gift Mini Mart, 802-525-3619. Main St. , Barton. The village of Barton in Vermont's beautiful Northeast Kingdom is a short distance from I-91. Take exit 25 turn north on Route 16 to Main St. and Country Lovelies Craft and Gift Mini Mart.

Event Info: Mon-Sat, 6:30 a.m. to 10 p.m.; Sun - 8 a.m. to 9 p.m. Closed Thanksgiving and Christmas. Trail is rated 2 and is suitable for strollers and wheelchairs. Pets OK on leash. Walk is on paved and some unpaved roads, rolling hills with some shady areas. The "Candle Pin" restaurant which welcomes families is midway on the route. A waterfall is just beyond this rest stop. Then proceed back to the village.

Burlington - 10km Walk (YR1333) 25km Bike (YR1332) **May 1-Nov 30**
A Awards available
Sponsoring Club: AVA-341, Twin State Volkssport Assn.
POC: Charlotte Phillips, 802-462-2019. PO Box 907, Middlebury, VT 05753

Start Point: Radisson Hotel, 60 Battery St. From I-89, take Exit 14 (US Rt 2) and follow Main St., toward Lake Champlain, where it ends. Turn right on Battery St. The Radisson is one block on the right.   Coming from the south on US Rt 7, continue to the downtown area and turn left on Main. From the Ferry, turn left on Battery St. There is three-hour metered parking on Cherry St. just past the hotel. Nearby parking lots are along the lake at the end of Main. NOTE: AVA box is locataed at the front desk.

Event Info: Daily, dawn to dusk. **YR1333** is rated 1+ and is suitable for strollers and wheelchairs. Pets are allowed.   Trail is along Lake Champlain on a paved bike path and through park, downtown and residential areas. **YR1332** is rated 1+ and is along Lake Champlain on a paved bike path. Rental bikes are available at 81 Main St.

East Burke - 10km Walk (YR1180) **May 1-Oct 31**
A Award Available
Sponsoring Club: AVA-846, Kingdom Kickers
POC: Karl/Merrily Wieland, 802-626-5230. PO Box 17, East Burke, VT 05832

Start Point: Bailey's Country Store, 802-626-3666. Rt 114. The village of East Burke is located in Vermont's Northeast Kingdom, 8 miles from I-91. Take exit 23 off I-91 in Lyndonville. Head north through the town to intersection of Rt 114. Follow Rt 114 for 6 miles to the Village of East Burke.

Event Info: Daily, 7am-8pm. This walk is rated 2, suitable for strollers but not wheelchairs. The trail follows country roads both paved and unpaved, with rolling hills and scenic vistas. Pets OK on leash.

Middlebury - 10/11km Walk (YR707) **Apr 1-Nov 30**
A Award Available
Sponsoring Club: AVA-341, Twin State Volkssport Association
POC: Charlotte Phillips, 802-462-2019. PO Box 907, Middlebury VT 05753

Start Point: Middlebury Inn, 802-388-4961. 14 Courthouse Square, Middleburry. US Rte 7 to town center, across from Village Green.

Event Info: Daily, dawn to dusk.   Trail is rated 1+. Not suitable for wheelchairs due to stairs. Strollers will need assistance. Trail goes through the village with small shops, places to eat, museums, beautiful Middlebury College with vistas of both Green and Adirondack Mountains. Pets OK on leash. Note: parking is available at the Info Center across Courthouse Square.

Montpelier - 10km Walk (YR978) **Apr 1-Nov 30**
A Award Available
Sponsoring Club: AVA-341, Twin State Volkssport Assn.
POC: Charlotte Phillips, 802-462-2019. PO Box 907, Middlebury, VT 05753

Start Point: Capital Plaza Hotel, 100 State St. From I-89 take exit 8, go toward Montpelier, head for the Capitol, cross Winooski River at Bailey St (first main street to the left), turn right on State St. Hotel is on the right just beyond the Capitol.

Event Info: Daily dawn to dusk. Trail is rated 3 and has two long hills. An alternate more level route is available. Strollers can do the alternate route but no wheelchairs. The trail passes the Capitol and homes of interesting architectural style. Pets OK on leash. Note: paid parking available behind the hotel. Get two coupons for more than two hours parking.

White River Junction - 11km Walk (YR094) **Apr 1-Nov 30**
A Award Available
Sponsoring Club: AVA-341, Twin State Volkssport Association
POC: Pat Stark, 802-296-2192 (eves) 295-9353 X32 (days). PO Box 184, Wilder VT 05088

Start Point: Hotel Coolidge, (near the Amtrak Station) 800-622-1124. 17 S. Main St. From I-91, take exit 11 (White River Jct.) and continue on Rt 5 North approximately 1 mile to the second stop light. Continue straight three blocks. Park in Town Lot across from Hotel Collidge.

Event Info: Daily, dawn to dusk. Rated 2+. Suitable for strollers but wheelchairs will have difficulty. Trail goes through town and residential areas with one long hill and several small ones. Route includes historic buildings, mill site and old railroad yards.

VIRGINIA ━━━

Abingdon - 10km Walk (YR587) **Jan 1-Dec 31**
Credit Only Event
Sponsoring Club: AVA-VA, Virginia Volkssport Assn.
POC: Jim Geith, 757-851-1829. 104 River Walk Court, Hampton, VA 23669-1246

Start Point: Abingdon Visitors Center, 335 Cummings St. From I-81 north: Take exit 17. Turn left at the bottom of the ramp. The start point is approximately 1/2 mile on the left. Sign in front says "Tourist Information". It is the first house (white) past the Taco Bell and Wendy's and is across from the Heilig-Meyers Furniture Store. From I-81 south: Take exit 17. Turn right and follow above directions.

Alternate Start Point: Super 8 Motel, 298 Town Centre Dr. Exit from I-81 as above and turn towards the Visitor's Center. Turn left at the second street (at the light) by Taco Bell and just past Wendy's. Turn left at the first street. The parking lot is on your left after one block.

Event Info: The Visitors Center is open daily, 9-5 and is closed Memorial Day to Labor Day. Open Mon-Sun Labor Day to Oct 31 and Open Mon-Sat Nov 1 to Memorial Day. The Super 8 is open daily dawn to dusk. The trail is rated 1+ and is suitable for strollers and wheelchairs. Pets must be leashed. Route is along a former railroad bed and is flat. It follows part of the Virginia Creeper Trail.

Alexandria - 10km Walk (YR061) **Jan 2-Dec 31**
A Award available
Sponsoring Club: AVA-151, Northern Virginia Volksmarchers
POC: Charlene Agne-Traub, 703-250-4008. 10260 Quiet Pond Terrace, Burke VA 22015

Start Point: King Henry Corner Deli, 703-684-5922. 1028 King St. Take I-95 to exit 1B, Rt 1 north. Go 8 blocks to Cameron St, turn left (one-way street with free 2hr parking). If no street parking is available, turn left onto Henry St (Rt 1 south) and go 1 1/2 blocks just pass the Deli and use the paid parking lot behind the Deli. Free parking on Sunday. Rest of the week $1.50/hour, $4.75 max all day.

Event Info: Mon-Sat 8am-9pm; Sun, 10-4. Closed New Years, Easter, 4th of July, Thanksgiving and Christmas. Call on other holidays in case hours are shortened. Trail is rated 1+, and is suitable for strollers but not recommended for wheelchairs. Pets must be leashed. The trail explores the historic Old Town section of Alexandria along city sidewalks and through city parks along the Potomac River. A town rich in history of the 17th and 18th centuries.

Alexandria - 10km Walk (YR1285) **Jan 2-Dec 31**
A Award available
Sponsoring Club: AVA-082, Pentagon Pacesetters, Inc.
POC: Ron Hamner, 703-922-1885. 5505 Helmsdale Lane, Alexandria, VA 22315

Start Point: Hayfield Exxon, 703-768-7700. 6948 South Kings Highway. From Washington Beltway in VA, take I-95 north or south to exit 2 for Telegraph Rd, South. Follow Telegraph Rd to the 6th traffic light and the start on your left (approx 3.3 miles). If start is closed, call the POC and he will come to the start within 10 minutes.

Event Info: Daily, 8-6. Closed Thanksgiving, Christmas and New Year's. Trail is rated 2 and is not suitable for strollers or wheelchairs. Pets are not allowed. Groups or participants wishing to walk the event on closed holidays should contact the POC in advance. This is a lovely 10km trail on natural surfaces and boardwalk in one of Americas top rated wetland parks. A superb bird watching park with over 200 documented species.

Bristol - 10km Walk (YR588) **Jan 1-Dec 31**
B Awards available
Sponsoring Club: AVA-VA, Virginia Volkssport Association
POC: Jim Geith, 757-851-1829. 104 River Walk Court, Hampton VA 23669-1829

Start Point: Bristol Convention & Visitors Bureau, 20 Volunteer Pkwy. From I-81 north, take exit 1 (Virginia). Follow US 421 (Gate City Hwy) south towards Bristol. At the 5th traffic light, the road becomes State Street (just past Walmart). The Convention and Visitors Bureau is on the right just after the train tracks. From I-81 south, take exit 3 (Virginia). Follow I-381 to its end and continue on Commonwealth Ave. The start is on the right just past State St.

Alternate Start Point: Holiday Inn Medical Center, US 11 W & I-81 (Exit 74B in Tennessee). From I-81 north or south, take exit 74B (Tennessee). You will see the Holiday Inn on your right. After you complete your registration, proceed by car to the Bristol Convention and Visitors Bureau.

Event Info: The Bureau is open Mon-Fri 8:30-5. Closed Sat, Sun and major holidays. Trail is rated 2 and is suitable for strollers & wheelchairs (there is a short section that has to be by-passed). Pets must be leashed. The trail takes you along major streets through the downtown area and residential areas. You walk on sidewalks as well as road shoulders. There are two steep hills. Part of the trail is in Tennessee.

Charlottesville - Two 10/11km Walks (YR742 & YR743) **Jan 2-Dec 31**
Credit Only Events
Sponsoring Club: AVA-VA, Virginia Volkssport Association
POC: Fred Lopez or Nancy Stenger, 703-631-8512. 14402 William Carr Lane, Centreville, VA 20120-2813

Start Point: Charlottesville/Albemarle Convention & Visitors Bureau, 804-977-1783. From I-64, take exit 121, Rt 20 south and follow signs to the Visitor Center.

Event Info: Mar-Oct daily 9-5. Nov-Feb daily 9-4:30. Closed major holidays. Both trails are rated 1+ and are suitable for strollers and wheelchairs. Pets must be leashed. **YR742** begins in the historic district and goes through the University of Virginia campus. **YR743** starts at a parking lot along the Rivanna River. The trail follows the river and returns to the parking lot then goes to the historic business district of charlottesville.

Chesapeake - 10km Walk (YR1334) **Jan 1-Dec 31**
A Award available
Sponsoring Club: AVA-013, Gator Volksmarch Club
POC: Dan or Dayle Horne, 757-523-1614. 1910 Shepherd's Gate, Chesapeake, VA 23320

Start Point: Greenbrier Food Mart, 757-547-1211. 1025-A Eden Way North. Take I-64 to exit 289, take Greenbrier Pkwy east past Greenbrier Mall; turn left at Eden Way; turn right on River Birch Run; turn into shopping center (mini) to Greenbrier Food Mart.

Event Info: Daily, dawn to dusk. Trail is rated 1 and is suitable for strollers & wheelchairs. Pets are allowed. Trail is entirely on sidewalks except for fifty yards on a dirt path.

VIRGINIA, cont.

Chesterfield County - 10km Walk (YR1281) **Jan 1-Dec 31**
Credit Only Event
Sponsoring Club: AVA-027, Lee Lepus Volksverband
POC: Bob Taylor, 804-790-1052. 12400 Bundle Rd, Chesterfield, VA 23832

Start Point: Powhatan Trail Parking Lot, Pocahontas State Park, Beach Rd. From I-95 take exit 62 for Rt 288. Rt 288 to State Rt 10 (Ironbridge Rd). East on Rt 10 to Beach Rd. West on Beach Rd to park entrance.

Alternate Start Point: During the off-season on weekends & holidays: Spencers Store, Beach & Bundle Rd, Chesterfield Cty. 1 3/4 miles west of park entrance.

Event Info: Daily, 8-4. Trail is rated 2+ and is not suitable for strollers and wheelchairs. Pets must be leashed. There may be an entrance fee to the park. The trail is on natural surfaces all within Pocahontas State Park.

Fairfax - 10km Walk (YR1166) **Jan 2-Dec 31**
A Award available
Sponsoring Club: AVA-151, Northern Virginia Volksmarchers
POC: Barry/Karen Plott, 703-352-5135. 3704 Mason St, Fairfax, VA 22030

Start Point: Fairfax Museum and Visitors Center, 703-385-8414. 10209 Main St. From the Washington Beltway, exit 6, Rt 236W (Little River Turnpike which becomes Main St) toward Fairfax. Proceed 4.3 miles to Museum parking lot on the left.

Event Info: Daily 9-5. Closed Easter, Thanksgiving Eve and Day, Christmas Eve and Day and school snow days. Trail is rated 1+ and is suitable for strollers and wheelchairs. Pets are allowed on a leash. Call ahead in wintry weather since the museum will be closed if county schools close. Follows paved and gravel surfaces in historic old town Fairfax, two wooded parks and some residential areas.

Fredericksburg - 10km Walk (YR115) **Jan 1-Dec 31**
A Award available
Sponsoring Club: AVA-610, Germanna Volkssport Association
POC: Leona Cravotta, 804-448-2461. 2317 Valentine Dr, Bumpass, VA 23024 OR Justin Hughes, 540-891-2968. 3 Dapple Gray Court, Fredericksburg, VA 22407

Start Point: Fredericksburg Visitor Center, 540-373-1776. 706 Caroline St. Exit 130 east from I-95 north or south. Follow Rt 3 east (William St) to Princess Anne St. Turn right on Princess Anne to Charlotte St. Go left for one block to Visitor's Center. Register in Center and get parking pass which permits parking in city lots and streets for longer than the two hours stated on the signs.

Event Info: Daily 9-5. Closed Thanksgiving, Christmas and New Years. Trail is rated 1+ and is suitable for strollers & wheelchairs. Pets are allowed. Walk along the Rappahannock River and through the historic district of Fredericksburg. Includes such sites as Mary Washington College, Fredericksburg Battlefield, Mary Washington's Home and The James Monroe Museum.

Gloucester - 10km Walk (YR875) **Jan 1-Dec 31**
B Awards available
Sponsoring Club: AVA-365, Explorer Post 49
POC: Sam Tollett, 757-766-3065. 3 Delmont Court, Hampton, VA 23666

Start Point: Beaverdam Park Ranger's Station, Roaring Springs Rd. Follow your favorite route to US 17 South. Turn left at the traffic light on South Business 17 into Gloucester. Do not go off at the other South Business 17 into Saluda or any other town. Go one block and turn left on Route 616 (Roaring Springs Rd). Follow Rt 616 approximately 2.4 miles. Road will dead end in the park. From US 17 North, cross the York River Bridge. Approximately 14 miles from bridge, turn right at traffic light on S. Business 17. Follow directions from North to Route 616 and park.

Event Info: Daily 8-dusk. Closed Christmas. Trail is rated 2 and is not suitable for strollers or wheelchairs. Pets must be leashed. No water is available on the trail. Route is along natural paths on an exercise, nature, and hiking trail in the park.

Hampton (Ft Monroe) - 10km Walk (YR874) **Jan 1-Dec 31**
A Award available
Sponsoring Club: AVA-142, Peninsula Pathfinders of Virginia
POC: Shirley Boyd, 757-722-5637. 11 Berkley Dr, Hampton, VA 23666

Start Point: Chamberlin Hotel, Registration Desk. Take I-64 to Hampton. Exit at 268, Phoebus. Turn left at stop light onto Mallory St. Go approximately 2/10 mile. Turn right on E. Mellen St (SR East 143). Follow signs to Fort Monroe. Turn right on McNair Dr. Follow signs to Hotel.

Event Info: Daily dawn to dusk. Trail is rated 1+ and is suitable for strollers or wheelchairs if they bypass portion that goes along top of the old fort. Pets must be leashed. Route is along roads on the Fort. Part of the trail goes through the old Fort and includes a section along the top of the Fort walls.

Kilmarnock - 10km Walk (YR872) **Jul 1-Sept 30**
Credit Only Event
Sponsoring Club: AVA-365, Explorer Post 49
POC: Sam Tollett, 757-766-3065. 3 Delmont Court, Hampton, VA 23666

Start Point: Get & Zip Convenience Store, Rt 3. From the north, take your favorite route to US 17 at Tappahannock. Turn on US 360 east. Follow US 360 approximately 7 miles to Rt 3 East. Go approximately 35 miles to Kilmarnock. The Get and Zip (Amoco Station) is on your left shortly before McDonald's. From Hampton/Newport News, follow US 17 north approximately 12 miles north of York River Bridge. Turn right at traffic light. Follow Rt 3 west approximately 32 miles to Kilmarnock. Start is on the right just past McDonald's.

Event Info: Daily dawn to dusk. Trail is rated 1 and is suitable for strollers & wheelchairs. Pets must be leashed. This trail is along sidewalks and the shoulders of roads in town.

Lexington - 10km Walk (YR589) 11km Walk (YR901) **Jan 2-Dec 31**
Credit Only Events
Sponsoring Club: AVA-VA, Virginia Volkssport Association
POC: Fred Lopez or Nancy Stenger, 703-631-8512. 14402 William Carr Lane, Centreville, VA 22020-2813

Start Point: Lexington Visitor Center, 540-463-3777. 102 E Washington St. Exit 188 West off I-81 or Exit 55 South off I-64. Follow signs to Visitor Center.

Event Info: Daily 9-5. Closed major holidays. **YR589** is rated 2+ and is suitable for strollers and wheelchairs. This trail covers the historic business and residental district of Lexington and VMI and W & L College campuses and also takes a 2 mile natural surface, Woods Creek Trail. **YR901** is rated 1+ and is not suitable for strollers or wheelchairs. Pets must be leashed. It is on natural surface on the Chessie Rails-to-Trails along the scenic Maury River.

Manassas - Two 10km Walks (YR340 & YR739) **Jan 2-Dec 30**
Credit Only Events
Sponsoring Club: AVA-306, Wood & Dale Wanderers
POC: Elaine Garcia, 703-680-7282 or Larry Morris 703-221-3588. PO Box 2422, Woodbridge VA 22193-2422

Start Point: Manassas Visitors Center, 703-361-6599. 9025 Center St. From I-95 take Rt 234 (exit 152) west towards Manassas. Rt 234 turns into Grant Ave. Take Grant Ave to Center St. Turn right onto Center St. Continue on Center to Visitors Center. From I-66, take exit for Rt 28 (Centreville Rd) towards Manassas. (You will take a right turn at the top of the exit ramp onto Rt 28 and cross over

I-66). Go several miles on Centreville Rd. It will change to Church St in Manassas and become one-way. Stay on Church St. Turn left on West St. Turn left on Center St. The Visitors Center will be on your right across from the Old Towne Hotel. Street parking may be limited during the week.

Event Info: Mon-Fri 9-5; Sat 10-4. Occasionally open Sundays. Call Manassas Visitor Center to check. Closed all major holidays. Trails are rated 1 and are suitable for strollers and wheelchairs. Pets must be leashed. Payment by check is preferred. Both events are easy walks on paved roads and sidewalks through historic and residential areas of Manassas.

Matthews - 10km Walk (YR868) **Jan 1-Mar 31**
Credit Only Event
Sponsoring Club: AVA-365, Explorer Post 49
POC: Sam Tollett, 757-766-3065. 3 Delmont Court, Hampton, VA 23666

Start Point: Hardees, Route 14. From the north, take your favorite route to US 17 south. Turn left on Rt 198 east shortly after you enter Gloucester County. Continue on Rt 198 after it joins with Rt 14 East. Start is on your right at the first stop sign (where Rt 14 turns right). From Hampton/Newport News, follow US 17 north approximately 12 miles north of the York River Bridge. Turn right at traffic light to 14 East. Follow 14 East approximately 17 miles to start.

Event Info: Daily 8-dusk. Trail is rated 1 and is suitable for strollers and wheelchairs. Pets must be leashed. Route is along sidewalks and shoulders of country roads.

Norfolk - 10km Walk (YR469) **Jan 2-Dec 31**
A Award available
Sponsoring Club: AVA-013, Gator Volksmarsch Club
POC: Tom Hornsby, 757-436-0446. 602 Fernwood Farms Rd, Chesapeake, VA 23320

Start Point: MacArthur Memorial Theater Bldg, 804-441-2965. Bank St & City Hall Ave. From I-64 to Norfolk, exit 284A to I-264 (downtown Norfolk). Exit 10 (City Hall Ave) to MacArthur Memorial City Hall Ave & Bank St.

Event Info: Mon-Sat 10-4:30; Sun 11-4:30. Finish by 4:30 each day. Closed New Year's, Thanksgiving & Christmas. Trail is rated 1, suitable for strollers and wheelchairs. Pets must be leashed. Route is entirely on city sidewalks.

Paris - 10km Walk (YR1154) **Jan 1-Dec 31**
B Awards available
Sponsoring Club: AVA-803, Mid-Atlantic Walking Assn
POC: Diane H. Evans, 703-354-1735. 5605 Asbury Ct, Alexandria, VA 22312-6302

Start Point: Sky Meadows State Park Ranger Office (Visitors Center), 540-592-3556. Rt 710 (Edmonds Lane). From I-66: Take I-66 to exit 23, Rt 17. Follow to Rt 710 (Edmonds Lane). Go left on Rt 710 at Sky Meadows Park Sign. Follow road to park entrance & contact station. From I-81: Take I-81 to exit 313, Rt 17/50East. At split of Rt 50 & Rt 17, turn right on Rt 17 to Rt 710 (Edmonds Lane). Turn right on Rt 710 at Sky Meadows Park sign. Follow road to park entrance & contact station. Ranger's office located upstairs in Mount Bleak House at parking area. Stairs located at rear of house.

Event Info: Daily, 9-4. Park entrance fee of $2.00 per card on weekends ($1.00 during week)/$8.00 per bus. Trail is rated 3+ and is not suitable for strollers or wheelchairs. Pets must be leashed at all times. Alternate trail segments available for those who do not wish to climb to the higher elevations or walk the rocky hiking segment. This event is on natural surface trails, rocky hiking trails and through adjacent pastures. Inclement weather will increase trail rating. Elevation change of 600 ft. Recommend walking sticks, hiking boots and walking with a buddy.

Richmond - Two 11km Walks (YR591 & YR592) 12km Walk (YR1282) **Jan 1-Dec 31**
YR591 & YR1282 have B Awards available   YR592 has an A Award
Sponsoring Club: AVA-027, Lee Lepus Volksverband
POC: Dee Schrum, 804-768-0055. 9301 Hickory Hollow Road, Chesterfield, VA 23838

Start Point: Virginia Historical Society, 804-358-4901. 428 N Blvd. From I-95, exit 78. Follow signs to Historical Society. Corner of North Blvd. & Kensington Ave. Parking is available in the rear of the building.

Event Info: Mon-Sat 10-5; Sun 1-5. Closed all Federal holidays. **YR591** is rated 1 and is suitable for strollers and wheelchairs. Leashed pets are allowed. It is along city & residential streets and parks. There are many historical buildings, shops and restaurants along the route. **YR592** is rated 1 but one set of stone steps would make it impossible for wheelchairs. Strollers would be possible. Pets are not allowed in the park under any circumstances. Please carry additional water. This event is also along city and residential streets and parks. **YR1282** is rated 3. It is suitable for strollers & wheelchairs. Leashed pets only. Please carry water. This trail is along city & residential streets and natural dirt roads.

Roanoke - 10km Walk (YR911) **Jan 2-Dec 31**
Credit Only Event
Sponsoring Club: AVA-VA, Virginia Volkssport Association
POC: Pat Mead, 540-342-0013. 1109 Clearfield Rd SW, Roanoke, VA 24015

Start Point: Roanoke Valley Convention & Visitors Bureau, 800-635-5535. 114 Market St. From I-81, exit 143 onto 581 south. Exit at Elm Ave. Follow Visitor Center signs.

Event Info: Daily 9-5. Closed Christmas and New Years. Trail is rated 1+ and is suitable for strollers and wheelchairs. Pets must be leashed. Heavy rainfall may result in flooding in South Park. Call the Visitors Bureau to check. This trail is along city and residential streets. Several parks and historical sections of Roanoke are also included.

Urbanna - 10km Walk (YR871) **Apr 1-Jun 30**
Credit Only Event
Sponsoring Club: AVA-365, Explorer Post 49
POC: Sam Tollett, 757-766-3065. 3 Delmont Court, Hampton, VA 23666

Start Point: Virginia Street Cafe. From US 17 South, turn left on Rt 602 to Remlik and Urbanna. Stay on Rt 602 until you reach Urbanna. Rt 602 ends and Rt 227 starts here. The Cafe is on your left at the corner where Rt 227 turns right. From US 17 North, cross the York River Bridge. Approximately 30 miles from the bridge, turn right on Rt 616 (this turn is a short distance north of Saluda). At the T-intersection, turn right on Rt 602 to Urbanna. Rt 602 ends and Rt 227 starts in Urbanna. Cafe if on your left at the corner where Rt 227 turns right.

Event Info: Mon-Sat 8-3; Sun 9-noon. Trail is rated 1 and is suitable for strollers and wheelchairs. Pets must be leashed. Follows sidewalks and shoulders of roads in town.

Vienna - 10km Walk (YR869) 25km Bike (YR870) **Jan 2-Dec 31**
A Awards available
Sponsoring Club: AVA-151, Northern Virginia Volksmarchers
POC: Dr. Charlene Agne-Traub, 703-250-4008. 10260 Quiet Pond Terrace, Burke VA 22015

Start Point: NOVA Cycling & Fitness, 703-938-7191. 214 Dominion Road. From north, east & west, take the Washington DC Metro Beltway (I-495/I-95) to exit 9, I-66 west. Take exit 62, Rt 243/Nutley St west towards Vienna. At the traffic light at Maple Ave (Rt 123) turn right. Turn left at stoplight on Center St and go one block, right on Church St 1/2 block, left on Dominion. Start across from the Red Caboose. From the south, take I-95 to exit 160, Rt 123 towards Occoquan. Turn left and continue north on Rt 123 for 20 miles. Turn left at Center St, right at Church St and left on Dominion.

Event Info: Jan-Mar & Oct-Nov: Mon-Fri 11-7; Sat 10-6; Sun 12-5. Apr-Sept & Dec: Mon-Fri 10-8; Sat 10-6; Sun 12-5. Closed New Years, Christmas and Thanksgiving. Trails are rated 1+, suitable for strollers and wheelchairs. Bikers must sign waiver. Helmets are recommended. The walk is along residential city sidewalks & through short natural trails in community park. A portion follows a paved rails to trails walk/bike path. The bike is along the Washington & Old Dominion railroad park paved bike/walk/rollerblade path. Path does cross some busy streets with stoplights available for safer crossings.

Virginia Beach - 10km Walk (YR468)   25km Bike (YR724) **Jan 1-Dec 31**
A Awards available
Sponsoring Club: AVA-013, Gator Volksmarsch Club
POC: Sandra Pittman, 757-497-6224. 4705 Wellingborough Rd, Virginia Beach, VA 23455

Start Point: Virginia Beach Resort Hotel & Conference Center, 757-481-9000. 2800 Shore Dr. 3.5 miles east of the Chesapeake Bay Bridge Tunnel on Rt 60 (Shore Dr). From the north, use the Bridge-Tunnel to Rt 60 East. From the NW, S & SW, use I-64 to Rt 13 North (Northampton Blvd) to Rt 60 East.

Event Info: Daily dawn to dusk. The events are rated 2 and are not suitable for strollers or wheelchairs. Pets are allowed. They follow paved sidewalks and established trails maintained & marked by First Landing State Park. Bikers must sign a waiver and should wear a helmet.

Virginia Beach - 10km Walk (YR1162) 11/16km Walk (YR1161) 26km Bike (YR1163) **Jan 2-Dec 31**   28km Bike (YR1165) **Jan 2-Apr 30**   28km Bike (YR1164) **Oct 1-Dec 31**
A Awards available
Sponsoring Club: AVA-013, Gator Volksmarsch Club
POC: Charley Seward, 757-427-0081. 2228 Margaret Dr, Virginia Beach, VA 23456

Start Point: Holiday Trav-l Food Mart, 757-491-2550. 909 General Booth Blvd. From I-64 to Norfolk, use exit 284A, Rt 44 east (to ocean front). Take exit 8 (Birdneck Rd). At Birdneck Rd, turn right and go 2.8 miles to General Booth Blvd. Turn right and start is 2nd building on the right side.

Event Info: Daily dawn to dusk. Both walks are rated 1 and are suitable for strollers & wheelchairs. Pets are allowed. They both follow city sidewalks & bike paths. YR1161 has an optional 5km loop. All three bikes are rated 1. They also follow city sidewalks & bike paths. Bikers must sign a waiver and should wear a helmet.

Warsaw - 10km Walk (YR873) **Oct 1-Dec 31**
Credit Only Event
Sponsoring Club: AVA-365, Explorer Post 49
POC: Sam Tollett, 757-766-3065. 3 Delmont Court, Hampton, VA 23666

Start Point: Warsaw Supermarket, US 360. Take your favorite route to US 17 at Tappahannock. Turn on US 360 East. Go approximately 6 miles to Warsaw. The Market is in the shopping center on your right as you come into town.

Event Info: Mon-Sat 8-3; Sun 9-3. Trail is rated 1 and is suitable for strollers and wheelchairs. Leashed pets allowed. This event that runs along sidewalks and shoulders of roads in town.

Williamsburg - 10km Walk (YR287)   27km Bike (YR486)   Swim (YR487) **Jan 1-Dec 31**
The walk has an A Award. The bike & swim are Credit Only Events
Sponsoring Club: AVA-142, Peninsula Pathfinders
POC: James Geith, 757-851-1829. 104 River Walk Court, Hampton VA 23669

VIRGINIA, cont. ━━━━━━━━━━━━━━━━━━

Start Point: Tazewell Fitness Ctr, Williamsburg Lodge, South England St. Take I-64 to exit 238, Williamsburg, Rt 143 East. At the top of the ramp, turn right onto VA Rt 143 East. Follow Rt 143 one mile to VA Rts 5 & 31. Turn right and go 1.3 miles. Continue straight thru the stoplight (VA Rts 5 & 31 turn right here). Go .6 miles and turn left on S England.

Event Info: Walk or bike Mon-Fri 6am-8pm; Sat 8-7; Sun 9-5. Swim times: Daily, 10-noon & 2-4. Swim is in an indoor pool. Walk trail is rated 2 and is not recommended for strollers or wheelchairs. It is on sidewalks, road shoulders and a dirt exercise trail through the historical area of Colonial Williamsburg and the William and Mary Campus. Pets must be leashed and are not allowed on the bike or swim. The bike trail is unrated. It goes through scenic neighborhoods and along part of the Colonial Parkway. A few short sections are along major roads. Bikers should wear helmets. Bikers & swimmers must sign a waiver.

Williamsburg - 11/15km Walk (YR286) **Jan 1-Dec 31**
A Award available
Sponsoring Club: AVA-142, Peninsula Pathfinders of Virginia
POC: James Geith, 757-851-1829. 104 River Walk Court, Hampton, VA 23669

Start Point: Gift Shop, Visitors Center, Jamestown Colonial National Historic Park. Take I-64 towards Williamsburg to exit 242A, Rt 199 West. Drive about 3.4 miles to the 2nd stoplight. Turn right onto S Henry St (Rt 132). Immediately turn right onto the Colonial Parkway towards Jamestown. Continue 7.4 miles to the Park Entrance. Pay entrance fee and go to the Visitors Center.

Event Info: Daily 9-5. Closed Christmas. This event is rated 1+ and is suitable for strollers and wheelchairs. Pets must be leashed. The trail is along the shoulders of the park roads and through the area where Jamestown was located. Part of the walk is on dirt pathways.

Winchester - 10km Walk (YR590) **Jan 2-Dec 31**
B Awards available
Sponsoring Club: AVA-151, Northern Virginia Volksmarchers
POC: Tom/Joyce Andrew, 703-369-0268. 8219 Thornwood Court, Manassas, VA 22110

Start Point: Winchester-Frederick County Visitor Center, 540-662-4118. 1360 S. Pleasant Valley Rd. From parts East: Take I-95/495 (Washington DC Metro Beltway) to exit 8, Rt 50 west (Arlington Blvd). Winchester is 60 miles west. Upon entering Winchester, watch for and follow signs to Visitors Center. Turn right onto Pleasant Valley Dr and the Center is immediately on your right. From points North: Use I-81 south to exit 313, Rt 50 west. At 1st light turn right. Follow signs to Visitors Center.

Event Info: Daily 9-5. Closed major holidays. Trail is rated 1+, suitable for strollers but not recommended for wheelchairs. Pets must be leashed. Route is primarily on sidewalks along city and residential streets and some natural surfaces around local lake and park. Winchester is near the Blue Ridge Parkway in the Shenandoah Valley.

Woodbridge - 10km Walk (YR1177) **Jan 1-Dec 31**
Credit Only Event
Sponsoring Club: AVA-306, Wood & Dale Wanderers
POC: Elaine Garcia, 703-680-7282. Larry Morris, 703-221-3588. PO Box 2422, Woodbridge, VA 22193-2422

Start Point: Leesylvania State Park, 703-670-0372. 16236 Neabsco Rd. From I-95 take exit 156 East, (Rt 784), which turns into Rt 638 (Neabsco Mill Rd). Turn right on US1 (Jefferson Davis Hwy). Turn left at first light onto Neabsco Rd (Rt 610). Turn right into Leesylvania State Park. Start/finish is located at the Visitor Center. There is an entrance fee to enter the Park. $2.00 per car on weekdays. $3.00 per car on weekends. (Subject to change)

Event Info: Daily, dawn to dusk. Trail is rated 2+ (3 in inclement weather). It is not suitable for strollers or wheelchairs. Pets must be on a leash. This route is on natural surface trails all within Leesylvania State Park. It will take walkers through the woods and along a boardwalk and beach area.

Yorktown - 10km Walk (YR285) 15km Walk (YR284) 25km Bike (YR485) **Jan 1-Dec 31**
Walks have A Awards available   Bike has B Awards available
Sponsoring Club: AVA-142, Peninsula Pathfinders of Virginia
POC: James Geith, 757-851-1829. 104 River Walk Court, Hampton, VA 23669

Start Point: Gift Shop, Visitors Center, Yorktown Battlefield, Colonial National Historical Park.

Event Info: Daily 8:30-5. Closed Christmas. An admission fee may be charged. Walks are rated 1+ and are suitable for strollers and wheelchairs. Pets must be leashed. These trails are along the shoulders of roads through the battlefield area and the historical town of Yorktown. The bike is not rated. It also follows trails through historic Yorktown and the battlefields. Bikers must sign a waiver and should wear a helmet.

WASHINGTON

Anacortes - Two 10km Walks (YR656 & YR658) 11km Walk (YR418) **Jan 1-Dec 31**
B Awards available
Sponsoring Club: AVA-482, Skagit Tulip Trekkers
POC: Jean/Larry Nelson, 360-293-4217. 4006 L Ave, Anacortes, WA 98221

Start Point: Island Hospital, 1213 24th St. From I-5 take exit 230 west. Follow Hwy 20 west to Anacortes. Turn left on 24th St. Hospital is on the left. Please use street parking.

Event Info: Daily dawn-dusk. **YR418** (Town Mural Walk)is rated 1+ and is suitable for strollers & wheelchairs. Pets are allowed. This walk is on sidewalks through industrial and residential areas and around town with views of Fidalgo Bay, Guemes Channel & murals.   **YR656** (Games Island) is rated 2 and is suitable for strollers & wheelchairs. Pets are allowed. Carry water on this walk as there is none available on the island. Trail follows country roads with wonderful views of the water and marvelous rural scenes. There is one moderate hill. **YR658** (Skyline) is rated 3 and is not suitable for strollers & wheelchairs. Pets are allowed. Walk the wide paved Loop Trail in Washington Park and some residential areas and Skyline Marina.

Auburn - 11/12km Walk (YR1292) **Jan 1-Dec 31**
Credit Only Event
Sponsoring Club: AVA-339, Auburn Trampers
POC: Jackie Myers, 206-735-6438. 1025 Pike NE, Auburn, WA 98002

Start Point: Best Western Pony Soldier Motel, 1521 D St, NE. Exit 142A (SR18) off I-5 to Auburn exit north onto Hwy 167 Valley Freeway interchange. Exit 15th St NW, turn east (right) at stop sign. Turn left at D St NE (2nd light) to start.

Event Info: Daily, dawn to dusk. Trail is rated 1 and is suitable for strollers & wheelchairs but there are some areas where you will be on the road. Pets are not allowed. Enjoy a day at the races after the walk. This trail is on city sidewalks to the road in front of the New Emerald Downs Race Track Grandstand and past the horse barn area. Then onto an interurban trail (12 km route) where you can stop and enjoy the new bird sanctuary.

Bainbridge Island - 10km Walk (YR1061) **Jan 1-Dec 31**
B Awards available
Sponsoring Club: AVA-359, die Bremertoner Stadtmusikanten
POC: Brian Bealle, 360-697-2783 (eves) 360-697-6311 (work). 25939 Circle Dr NW, Poulsbo, WA 98370

Start Point: Walt's Lynwood Market, 206-842-5808. 4569 Lynwood Center Rd NE. From I-5 north or south, take exit 132, Hwy 16/Bremerton. Follow Hwy 16 and 3 north past Silverdale to Hwy

WASHINGTON, cont.

305/Poulsbo exit. Follow Hwy 305 to Bainbridge Island. At High School Rd (12.5 miles) turn right (if arriving from Seattle/Bainbridge ferry, turn left). Continue 2 miles on High School Rd to end. Go left on Fletcher Bay Rd 1.4 miles to end. Right on Lynwood Center Rd for 1 miles. Walt's Market is in the Lynwood Business Center. Please park in the gravel lot past the businesses.

Event Info: Daily 7:30am-9pm. Trail is rated 1 with an alternate return rated 3. It is not suitable for strollers or wheelchairs. First 2km of this trail is along a busy road. Pets must be leashed. This route is on paved or firm surfaces along level waterfront (except alternate return). You will have views of Rich Passage, Bremerton ferries and old Fort Ward gun emplacements.

Battle Ground - 10km Walk (YR1240) **Jan 1-Dec 31**
Credit Only Event
Sponsoring Club: AVA-557, Vancouver USA Volkssporters
POC: Margie, 360-693-6430. PO Box 2121, Vancouver, WA 98668.

Start Point: Meyer's Marketplace, 915 West Main St. From I-205, exit 30, 500 East, toward Orchards/Battle Ground, 2 miles. Continue 11 miles on 503 East to Battle Ground. Turn right at stop light onto Main St. Turn right into Plaza parking lot.

Event Info: Daily, dawn to dusk. Closed Christmas. Trail is rated 1+. Strollers may have difficulty and wheelchairs are not allowed. Pets must be leashed. There is a Deli in Marketplace and no hotel/motel is available in town. Many antique shops. Walk on city sidewalks, streets and roads with some gravel shoulders.

Bellevue - 10km Walk (YR135) **Jan 2-Dec 31**
Credit Only Event
Sponsoring Club: AVA-638, Northwest Striders
POC: Larry Loudenback, 206-747-3358. 14429 SE 15th St, Bellevue, WA 98007-5603

Start Point: Quality Food Center, 549 156th Ave SE. I-90 exit 11B, north on 148th Ave, right on Lake Hills Blvd, left on 156th Ave. Registration is inside the right entrance. Please park away from the entrance.

Event Info: Daily dawn-dusk. Closed Thanksgiving, Christmas and New Years. Trail is rated 2 and is suitable for strollers but not wheelchairs. Pets are allowed but please follow the leash and scoop law. This is a totally new trail for '97. You will see the lake and the trails as well as the Mormon Temple. Watch for the coyotes and blue herons as well as many other animals and birds.

Bellevue - Two 10km Walks (YR638 & YR639) **Jan 1-Dec 31**
Credit Only Events
Sponsoring Club: AVA-638, Northwest Striders
POC: Larry Loudenback, 206-747-3358. 14429 SE 15th St, Bellevue, WA 98007-5603

Start Point: Red Lion Hotel, 300 112th Ave SE. Take I-405, exit 12. West on SE 8th, right on 112th Ave SE. Registration file cabinet is on the level below the main lobby next to the executive office. Latte stand is in the main lobby.

Event Info: Daily dawn-dusk. **YR638** is rated 3 and is suitable for strollers but not wheelchairs. Pets must be leashed with clean-up. The route goes up three hills and a set of steps. Walkers will pass through residential areas to Chism Park on Lake Washington, Old Bellevue, Downtown Park, Bellevue Square and through the new Pedestrian Walkway. **YR639** is rated 2 and is suitable for strollers but not wheelchairs. Pets must be leashed with clean-up. Walk on trails in Wilburton and Kelsey Greek Parks and the Bellevue Botanical Gardens. Kelsey Creek is a "city farm" with barns & farm animals. Bellevue Botanical Gardens are especially nice to walk in the spring when everything is blooming.

Carnation - 10km Walk (YR181) **Apr 1-Nov 30**
Credit Only Event
Sponsoring Club: AVA-503, Hopkins Telephone Pioneers Volkssport Club
POC: Ruth Kalies, 206-630-2728. 19905 SE 300th St, Kent, WA 98042

Start Point: Remlinger Farms, 32610 NE 32nd. From I-90 take exit 22 (Fall City-Preston). Turn right on the Fall City-Preston Rd through Preston and across the bridge at Fall City. Turn left onto Fall City-Carnation Rd (SR 203). Follow SR 203 approximately six miles & turn right on NE 32nd St at Remlinger Farms sign.

Event Info: Daily 9-6. Trail is rated 1+ and is not recommended for strollers or wheelchairs. Pets are allowed on the trail but not in any buidlings. This walk will take you along county roads, city streets and wooded or gravel trails. Course is flat with one short hill and passes the Tolt and Snoqualmie Rivers.

Cathlamet - 10/21km Walk (YR803) 25km Bike (YR804) **Apr 1-Sept 30**
B Awards available
Sponsoring Club: AVA-621, P.E.O. Pathfinders
POC: Liz Johnson, 206-838-3454/206-839-1892. PO Box 6164, Federal Way, WA 98063

Start Point: Island Market, 485 State Hwy 409. From I-5 southbound, take exit 39 (the Ocean Beach Hwy) at Kelso and follow State Hwy 4 along the Lewis and Clark Trail westbound to Cathlamet. From I-5 northbound take exit 36 (the Ocean Beach Hwy) at Longview and follow State Hwy 4 along the Lewis and Clark Trail westbound to Cathlamet. At Cathlamet, turn left off of State Hwy 4 onto State Hwy 409. Follow 409 southbound 2.4 miles through Cathlamet, over the high bridge across the Columbia River and all the way across Little Island to Puget Island. The Island Market is on the left, .3 miles from the bridge across Birnie Slough. From Portland and Astoria, take US Hwy 30 to Westport. Take the ferry across the Columbia River to Puget Island. Follow State Hwy 409 northbound 1.5 miles to the Market on the right.

Event Info: Daily 7-7. **Walk** is rated 1 and is suitable for strollers and wheelchairs. Pets are allowed. This is an easy 10 or 21km walk along quiet country roads through pastoral farmland and cottonwood groves and along picturesque Welcome Slough. Bring a camera! Only one event credit even if doing both distances. The **bike** is rated 1 and is an easy ride along country roads. Bikers must sign a waiver and ahould wear a helmet

Centralia - Two 10km Walks (YR1267 & YR1271) 26km Bike (YR1270) **Jan 4-Dec 31**
Credit Only Events
Sponsoring Club: AVA-754, The Over the Hill Gang Volkssport Club
POC: Bob Glover, 360-330-5094. 2805 Yahtahay Lane, Centralia, WA 98531

Start Point: Safeway, 1129 Harrison Ave. I-5 north or south - exit 82, Harrison Ave. Southbound turn right on Harrison to 1st traffic light, left into parking lot. Northbound turn left on Harrison to 2nd traffic light and left into parking lot.

Event Info: Daily, dawn to dusk. **YR1267** is rated 2 and is suitable for strollers & wheelchairs. Pets are allowed. Register at Safeway in Centralia and drive 3 miles to start. Park in outer slots at front entrance. This route is on city sidewalks and streets. There are some uncut curbs. **YR1271** is rated 1 and is suitable for strollers & wheelchairs. Pets are allowed. Park in outer slots. This route is on city sidewalks and streets with some uncut curbs. **YR1270** is rated 1. Bikers must sign a waiver and should wear a helmet. Park in outer slots and please practice safe cycling. This route is flat. There are wide shoulders in most areas.

Chelan - 10km Walk (YR785) 31km Bike (R1032) **Apr 1-Dec 1**
Walk has B Awards available   Bike is a Credit Only Event
Sponsoring Club: AVA-210, Bavarian Volkssport Assn
POC: Gary/Sandy Miller, 509-687-3598. 1961 Lakeshore Dr, Manson, WA 98831-9746

Start Point: Campbell's Resort Lodge, 104 W Woodin. From Wenatchee, take Hwy 97A going North to Chelan. Approaching Chelan at the first intersection take the road that continues around the lake and takes you past the Forest Service. Cross bridge, Resort is located directly on the opposite side. Please park outside resort.

Event Info: Daily dawn-dusk. Walk is rated 2+ and is not suitable for strollers or wheelchairs. Pets must be leashed and please obey scooper laws. This is a scenic walk at Lake Chelan, thru two parks, past a dam and murals with mountain & lake vistas. The **bike** is rated 1+ and follows a scenic lakeshore road from Chelan along the south shore to Lake Chelan State Park and returns. It is on wide shoulders with bike lane status. A very beautiful, easy ride. Bikers must sign a waiver and should wear helmets.

Eatonville - 10km Walk (YR407) **Jan 1-Dec 31**
Credit Only Event
Sponsoring Club: AVA-336, Daffodil Valley Volkssport Assn.
POC: Linda Holden, 360-832-4272. 200 Antonie, S. (PO Box 971), Eatonville, WA 98328

Start Point: Mill Town Chevron, 236 Center Street, East. From the north: Take SR 161 south out of South Hill, Puyallup for 25 miles to the blinker light in Eatonville. Turn left at blinker light onto Center St; Chevron station is just ahead on left. Park in spaces away from station. From the south: From I-5, take SR 512 just north of McChord AFB. Take 2nd off ramp, turn right and follow SR 7 south through Parkland and Spanaway to blinker light on SR 7 (16 miles from SR 512). Turn left and follow Eatonville Cut-Off Rd to BP gas station on SR 161 (a "T" intersection). Turn right and follow directions above to Chevron Station.

Event Info: Daily, dawn to dusk. Closed Thanksgiving & Christmas. Trail is rated 1+ and is suitable for strollers but wheelchairs may have difficulty with dirt surfaces. Pets are allowed. This walk is in historic Eatonville past one of the few existing sawdust burners in Washington State. Go past the Eatonville Lumber Mill superintendent's home and the mill foreman's home; past the town founder's home and through the pioneer cemetery on city sidewalks and rural country roads.

Edmonds - Two 10km Walks (YR204 & YR451) **Jan 2-Dec 30**
B Awards available
Sponsoring Club: AVA-403, Puget Sound Sloshers
POC: Lorrie Pederson, 206-542-8694. 24132-102nd Place W, Edmonds WA 98020

Start Point: Harbor Square Athletic Club, 206-778-3546. 160 Dayton. From I-5 take exit 177 and proceed west on SR 104 (Edmonds/Kingston Ferry). At the intersection of SR 104 and Dayton (at ferry ticket booth), turn left and go 1 block. Turn left into Harbor Square complex. Park between the Club and the Harbor Square Inn (north side of Club).

Event Info: Mon-Fri 5:30 to dusk; Sat/Sun 7:30 to dusk. Closed major holidays. Closure hours and days may vary. Call Athletic Club to verify. **YR204** is rated 3 (2 on alternate). Strollers but not wheelchairs should use alternate route. Pets are allowed. Route is rated 3 due to park paths & gradual hill approaching park. Use buddy system in park which is remote & use alternate route in winter months to avoid the park which will be very slippery. Alternate route will cover more of the waterfront. Only one event credit per year, even if doing both routes. **YR451** is rated 2+, suitable for strollers but not wheelchairs. Pets are allowed. This walk goes through rural-like parts of Woodway, and is especially pretty in May and June. It also passes through downtown Edmonds and along portions of the waterfront.

Enumclaw - 10km Walk (YR1076) **Jan 1-Dec 31**
Credit Only Event
Sponsoring Club: AVA-339, Auburn Trampers Volksmarch Club
POC: Karin Plagens, 360-825-7338. 1603 Griffin Ave, Enumclaw, WA 98022

Start Point: Best Western - Park Center Hotel, 1000 Griffin Ave. From I-5 take eastbound SR 18 to the Auburn Way exit. Go south 14 miles into downtown Enumclaw. Continue through two stoplights. The hotel is located one block further. Park across the street in the city parking lot. From I-405 take the SR 169 exit driving south out of Renton. Drive 25 miles into Enumclaw. At the stoplight (Griffin Ave) turn left and continue with directions above. Park across the street in the city parking lot.

Event Info: Daily dawn-dusk. Trail is rated 1, possible for strollers but not wheelchairs. Pets must be leashed and clean-up is required. This is a flat, wasy walk on residential streets. You will see over 25 historic homes dating back to 1888 and the new murals around town.

Everett - 10km Walk (YR786) **Jan 1-Dec 31**
Credit Only Event
Sponsoring Club: AVA-403, Puget Sound Sloshers
POC: Mary Tipping, 206-776-7195. 7924 212th SW, #213, Edmonds, WA 98026

Start Point: Providence General Medical Ctr, Colby Campus, 1321 Colby Ave. From I-5 northbound, take exit 192 (Broadway, exit on left) and proceed north on Broadway to 14th St. Turn left and continue 3 blocks to Rockefeller Ave. Turn right and proceed 1/2 block to parking garage entrance. From I-5 southbound, take exit 198 (N Broadway, Port of Everett) and proceed south, crossing the Snohomish River and entering Everett. Follow Broadway to 13th St. Turn right and continue three blocks to Rockefeller Ave. Turn left and go 1/2 block to garage. Start box is located in the 13th Street Lobby, next to the cash machine. Recommend parking in the parking garage as a two hour limit is enforced on the streets around the Medical Center.

Event Info: Daily dawn-dusk. Trail is rated 1+ and is suitable for strollers but wheelchairs may have difficulty with curbs. Pets must be leashed. Route is through quiet neighborhoods in North Everett, past majestic homes of city founders. Proceeds along bluff overlooking Port Gardner Bay and Naval Station Everett. Views of Hat, Camano & Whidbey Islands and Olympic Mountains. Around Legion Park with views of Mount Baker and the Cascade Mountain Range.

Gig Harbor - 10km Walk (YR1178) **Jan 1-Dec 31**
Credit Only Event
Sponsoring Club: AVA-133, Sea-Tac Volkssports Club
POC: Victor or Harriette Kring, 206-922-9147. 802 11th Ave, Milton, WA 98354

Start Point: Le Bistro Coffee House, 206-851-1033. 4120 Harborview Dr. I-5 exit #132 (Gig Harbor/Bremerton) on SR 16 to second Gig Harbor exit (City Center). Continue straight through stop light on Stinson Ave to third stop sign. Turn left on Harborview Dr to stop sign and turn left into Le Bistro Coffee House parking.

Event Info: Mon-Fri, 7-7:30; Sat & Sun, 6:30am-7:30pm. Mid June-Labor Day they Close at 9:30pm. Closed major holidays. Trail is rated 2 and is suitable for strollers but not wheelchairs. Pets are permitted with a leash and clean-up. This route is on sidewalks & road shoulders around scenic waterfront of Gig Harbor with views of Mt Rainier and Puget Sound. There are many unique small shops & eateries.

Gold Bar (Wallace Falls State Park) - 11km Walk (YR781) **Apr 1-Sept 30**
B Awards available
Sponsoring Club: AVA-534, Four Plus Foolhardy Folks
POC: Margaret Stewart, 206-347-6982. PO Box 2689, Everett, WA 98203

Start Point: Sultan Bakery, 390-793-7584. 711 Stevens (US 2). I-5 to exit 194 (City Center/Stevens Pass) near Everett. Head east on US2 to Sultan for registration point. At the Sultan Baker, register and pick up walk map. Continue driving on US2 to Gold Bar. Leave the highway at Gold Bar and follow signs north to Wallace Falls State Park for the start/finish point at the trailhead.

Event Info: Daily, 6-6. Must be back by 6pm to stamp books for credit. Sultan Bakery is closed on Christmas. Trail is rated 4 and is not suitable for strollers or wheelchairs. Pets must be leashed with clean-up. Appropriate hiking footwear recommended. Carry your own water. There is no water on the trail. Restrooms at trailhead. Views of spell-binding 250 foot Wallace Falls & Skykomish Valley. 1,380 foot net elevation gain. Falls are a 5-Star.

Greenwater - 10km Walk (YR711) **May 1-Sept 15**
B Awards available
Sponsoring Club: AVA-115, Evergreen Wanderers
POC: Chuck Repik, 360-582-7474. 15022 Washington Ave SW, Tacoma, WA 98498

Start Point: Wapiti Woolies Store, 58414- FR 14E (Hwy 410). From Enumclaw, take Hwy 410 east going to Chinook Pass 19.5 miles to start. If store is not open, pick up start card/map from the fast start mail box on the deck rail. Pickup start card and drive back to Federation Forest State Park entrance. Start is on the right hand side of Catherine Montgomery Interpretive Center.

Event Info: Daily 8-6. Trail is rated 2, not suitable for strollers, wheelchairs or wagons. Pets must be leashed. There are outstanding refreshments available at Wapiti Woolies. This trail is on natural paths through woods with a few tree roots across them. It could be muddy in damp weather. The Interpretive Center is very informative. Part of the trail follows the White River. Follow green arrows at every intersection. If no arrow, continue straight. (Note sample arrow on start cabinet).

Ilwaco - 10kmWalk (YR1209) **Apr 1-Sept 30**
Credit Only Event
Sponsoring Club: AVA-557, Vancouver USA Volkssporters
POC: Bill Byrd, 360-892-6758. 1100 SE 99th Ave, Vancouver, WA 98664

Start Point: Chic-A-Dee Bed & Breakfast, 360-642-8686. 120 NE Williams St. Take US 101 into Ilwaco. At Spruce St turn right (north) on Williams to end of street (1 block).

Event Info: Daily, 8-5. Trail is rated 2+ and is suitable for strollers & wheelchairs. Pets are allowed. Route is primarily on city streets and sidewalks with some gravel roads and paths with small hills.

Issaquah - Two 10km Walks (YR790 & YR1253) **Jan 1-Dec 31**
B Awards available
Sponsoring Club: AVA-536, Tri-Mountain Volkssport Club
POC: Jennifer Littke, 206-222-5715. 36002 SE 46th, Fall City, WA 98024

Start Point: Front Street Market, 80 Front Street, South. From I-90 take exit #17 and go south on Fron Street to 2nd traffic light, about 7/10 of a mile. Turn left on Sunset Way. Go one block and turn right on Rainier Avenue. Park in the Issaquah City Hall parking area.

Event Info: Daily 7-dusk. **YR790** is rated 2 and is not suitable for strollers or wheelchairs. Pets are allowed but not in buildings. Route is almost totally level on city streets and trails with two short hills. Highlights are Issaquah Salmon Hatchery, Historic Downtown Issaquah, Train Depot and remnants of the old mining town. Also see Gilman Village and Boehm's Homemade Candy shop. **YR1253** is rated 2+ and is not suitable for strollers or wheelchairs. Pets are allowed but not in buildings. Carry water as none is available. Do not start this walk unless you can complete it by dusk. Bring a flashlight. Some of the trails could be muddy after heavy rains but are generally well maintained. This route is on some of the most popular trails and logging roads in Washington State. They gradually rise 450 ft through old growth forests and around Tradition & Round Lakes. The decline is also gradual.

Kelso - 10km Walk (YR423) **Jan 1-Dec 31**
B Awards available
Sponsoring Club: AVA-530, Border Crossers
POC: James B. Gorman, 360-577-3404 (days)/360-425-5428 (eves). 11 Larry Ln, Longview WA 98632   Or: Pete Hauser, 360-577-7435. 2325 Nichols Blvd, Longview, WA 98632

Start Point: Red Lion Inn, 510 Kelso Dr. Southbound on I-5 take exit 39. At the stop light, turn left. Proceed under the interstate bridge two stop lights to Kelso Dr. Turn right on Kelso which is a frontage road, approximately 400 meters to the Red Lion on the left. From I-5 northbound, take exit 39. At the stop light turn right one light to Kelso Dr. Turn right on Kelso for approximately 400 meters. The start is on the left in the lobby. Park in the side or rear areas.

Event Info: Daily dawn-dusk. Trail is rated 2, suitable for strollers and wheelchairs with some difficulty from the gravel surface on the dike path. Pets must be leashed. The trail goes through some commercial areas along the interstate and then goes up a gradual hill to a road overlooking the Columbia River Valley. It then goes through some residential areas, across the Cowlitz River to West Kelso and back along a flat route through town to a dike maintained path. There are some historic sites in the downtown area.

Kennewick - 10km Walk (YR1036) **Jan 1-Dec 31**
B Awards available
Sponsoring Club: AVA-590, Tri-Cities Windwalkers
POC: Mona Bauman, 509-735-2304. 7901 W Clearwater #175, Kennewick, WA 99336

Start Point: Greenbrier Mobile Village, Private Residence, 7901 W Clearwater #175. From south and west exit 109 off I-82. Continue on five lane road (Clearwater) to mobile home park (approximately one block before Columbia Center Blvd). Right into park, then right at first street; start point is the fourth mobile home on the right. From the north and east, from Hwy 395 or 12 continue towards Kennewick, crossing blue bridge. Stay on Hwy 240 to Columbia Center Blvd. Go left on Columbia Center Blvd to intersection of Columbia Center Blvd & Clearwater. Go right on Clearwater; left into mobile home park and continue as above.

Event Info: Daily dawn-dusk. Trail is rated 1+, suitable for strollers and wheelchairs. Pets are allowed. This routewill take you through different housing divisions. part of the trail will be on county streets with no sidewalks.

Kent - 10km Walk (YR972) **Jan 1-Dec 31**
Credit Only Event
Sponsoring Club: AVA-754, The Over the Hill Gang Volkssport Club
POC: Jack Maxcy, 206-927-4580. PO Box 23057, Federal Way, WA 98093.

Start Point: QFC Grocery Store, 1301 W Meeker. I-5 (north or south) exit 149 southbound or exit 149B northbound. Go east down hill to Meeker St. Turn left on Meeker and go about four blocks past 64th St. Turn left into QFC parking lot. Hwy 167 South, take Willis St exit. Go right on Willis to Meeker, left on Meeker and right into parking lot. Hwy 167 North, take Willis St exit. Left on Willis, right on Washington and left on Meeker.

Event Info: Daily dawn-dusk. Closed Christmas & New Years. Trail is rated 1, suitable for strollers and wheelchairs. Pets are allowed. The walk is along interurban paths and urban areas. No dirt trails. About 6km is along the Green River Trail System and 2km is on a bike path which is kind of isolated. Some people might not want to do it alone.

Kirkland - 10km Walk (YR134) **Jan 1-Dec 31**
A Award available
Sponsoring Club: AVA-384, Interlaken Trailblazers
POC: Josie Jewett, 206-883-0217. 14024 NE 77th St, Redmond, WA 98052

Start Point: La Quinta Inn, 10530 NE Northrup Way. From I-5 north or south, exit to Rt 520 east to Bellevue. Exit 520 onto Lake Washington Blvd (Rt 908) heading north toward Kirkland. Turn right at light to Northup Way. Left to La Quinta. From I-405 north or south, exit to Rt 520 W to Seattle. Exit 520 immediately at light at 108th Ave NE. Right onto 108th and immediately left at light onto Northup Way. La Quinta is approximately two blocks on the right.

Event Info: Daily dawn-dusk. Trail is rated 2, and is not suitable for strollers or wheelchairs due to stairs. Leashed pets allowed. You will enjoy the Lake Washington waterfront; lake, mountain and Seattle skyline views. The downtown area is a charming mix of galleries, shops and eateries.

La Conner - 10km Walk (YR657) **Jan 1-Dec 31**
B Awards available
Sponsoring Club: AVA-482, Skagit Tulip Trekkers
POC: Ralph or Naomi Johnson, 360-466-2007. 430 Cayuse Place, La Conner, WA 98257

Start Point: Market Place Antiques, 106 South 1st. From I-5 exit on #230 west. Follow Hwy 20 west to intersection of Hwy 20 and Whitney-La Conner Rd south into La Conner. At the three way intersection with Morris & Chilberg, turn right onto Morris Rd. Go six blocks to the channel. Market is on the left. Please use street parking.

Event Info: Daily, 9-dusk. Closed Easter & Christmas. Trail is rated 2+, suitable for strollers but not wheelchairs. Pets are allowed. Walk on pavement and some wood trails with one moderate hill up to the museum. Walk on downtown streets of La Conner & cross Rainbow Bridge.

Leavenworth - 10km Walk (YR168) **Apr 1-Dec 1**
B Awards available
Sponsoring Club: AVA-210, Bavarian Volkssport Assn.
POC: Russ/Bobbi Ferg, 509-548-6112. PO Box 25, Leavenworth, WA 98826 or Sue Bull, 509-548-4477.

Start Point: Alpen Inn, 509-548-4326. 405 Hwy 2. Located at the west end of town on Hwy 2. Please park across Hwy 2 in the Public Parking Area, not in the hotel lot.

Event Info: Daily, 7am-dusk. Trail is rated 2 and is suitable for strollers but wheelchairs may have difficulty. Pets must be leashed. Walkers go through town, residential areas and the river park. Enjoy the beautiful parks and new city park which lets you see downtown Bavarian Leavenworth.

Longview - 11km Walk (YR227) 25/35km Bike (YR381) **Jan 1-Dec 31**
B Awards available
Sponsoring Club: AVA-530, Border Crossers
POC: James Gorman, 360-577-3404 days/360-425-5428 eves. 11 Larry Ln, Longview WA 98632

Start Point: St. John's Medical Ctr, 1614 E Kessler Blvd. From I-5, exit 36 northbound and follow road around and over I-5 for 3.4 miles to fourth traffic light at 15th Ave (AM/PM Market on right). Turn right and proceed to 2nd traffic light at Delaware St. Turn left on Delaware for 1 block. Turn left into Medical Center parking lot. Southbound, exit 40, turn right at stop sign and go to first traffic light. Turn right. Proceed over Cowlitz River bridge. The name of the road changes to Washington Way. Go straight ahead to 15th Ave. Turn 45 degrees left on 15th Ave. Proceed approximately 1 mile to Delaware St. Turn right and proceed one block. Turn left into parking lot. Enter medical center on lower level. Start point is just beyond counter, 50 feet inside the entrance.

Event Info: Daily, 8am-8pm. The **walk** is rated 1+, suitable for strollers and wheelchairs. Pets must be leashed. This is a flat, all weather course. Some residential streets and the Lake Sacajewea Park path system. 6km are on the park's natural paths. The **bike** is rated 1+. No strollers, wheelchairs or pets. Bikers must sign a waiver and must wear a Snell or ANSI approved bike helmet. Carry water. Water is available in Sacajewea Park at the beginning and end of 25km trail and at Willow Grove Beach at 16km on the 35km trail. Bike repair facilities in Longview: Bob's Merchandise at 12th Ave & Hudson or Byman's at 1165 Commerce. This is an all weather trail leading west of Longview. Some residential streets along Sacajewea Park. Some light traffic. Mostly flat. Two short (100-150 meters) with slight upgrades. All but approx 400 meters is paved surface. Approx 5km along the Columbia River. Some farm & dairyland views.

WASHINGTON, cont.

Mercer Island - 10km Walk (YR712) **Jan 1-Dec 31**
Credit Only Event
Sponsoring Club: AVA-447, Mercer Island Volkssport Club
POC: Clint Prescott, 206-232-1311. 8905 SE 54th St, Mercer Island, WA 98040

Start Point: Tully's Coffee, 7810 SE 27th. From Seattle I-90 East, exit 7A. Turn right at the stop sign. Go to SE 27th St and turn left. Tully's is down two blocks on the left. From the east, exit 7 to second stop light (80th Ave SE). Turn left on 80th Ave SE and turn right on SE 27th St. Tully's is on the right. Please park across the street.

Event Info: Daily, dawn to dusk. Trail is rated 2 and is suitable for strollers and wheelchairs. Pets must be leashed. Paved paths on the Mercer Island "Lid" park over I-90. Beautifully landscaped with views of Seattle & Bellevue.

Mt Rainier National Park (Ohanapecosh Campgrounds) - 10km Walk (YR683) **Jun 1-Sep 7**
B Awards available
Sponsoring Club: AVA-360, Yakima Valley Sun Striders
POC: Clarence Haupt, 509-965-4980. 2510 S 52nd Ave, Yakima WA 98903

Start Point: Visitors Center, Ohanapecosh Campground, Hwy 123. From Seattle/Tacoma, take Hwy 410 east towards Chinook Pass. At junction with Hwy 123 (Cayuse Pass) turn onto Hwy 123. Travel south on Hwy 123 approximately 12 miles to Campgrounds. Turn right into Campgrounds, turn left to Ranger Station and then right into parking area. Walk down road to Visitors Center. From Portland, take I-5 north to exit 68. Take Hwy 12 east past Parkwood to junction with Hwy 123. Turn left on Hwy 123 and follow to Campgrounds. Follow parking directions above. From Yakima/east, take Hwy 12 over White Pass and follow to junction with Hwy 123. Take 123 north to Campgrounds and follow above directions.

Event Info: Daily 9-6. Trail is rated 3 and is not suitable for strollers or wheelchairs. No pets. No entrance fee required. Park in Ranger Station parking area. Walk down road to Visitors Center (distance included in 10km). Trail winds through old growth forests, by hot springs and crystal clear waterfalls.

Mount Vernon - 10km Walk (YR1268) **Jan 1-Dec 31**
B Awards available
Sponsoring Club: AVA-482, Skagit Tulip Trekkers
POC: JanRoberts, 360-424-4987. 3704 Mohawk Ct, Mt Vernon, WA 98273 or Marie Weltz, 360-424-7490. 2810 Cherokee St, Mt. Vernon, WA 98273

Start Point: Section Street Market, 360-428-0272. 2323 East Section St. From I-5 take exit 226, turn right (east) on Broad St up hill and proceed to South 13th St. Turn right on South 13th St for two blocks to Section St. Turn left on Section and proceed east to LaVenture Rd.

Event Info: Daily, dawn to dusk. Trail is rated 2 and is suitable for strollers & wheelchairs. Pets are allowed. Walk on sidewalks through established residential and business areas. Views of Skagit River, Mt. Baker and Cascades.

North Bend - 10km Walk (YR1054) **Jan 2-Dec 31** 14km Walk (YR1014) **Jul 1-Sep 30**
Credit Only Events
Sponsoring Clubs: YR1054: AVA-638, NW Striders
YR1014: AVA-534, Four Plus Foolhardy Folks
POC: YR1054: Larry Loudenback, 206-747-3358. 14429 SE 15th St, Bellevue, WA 98007-5603
YR1014: Raymon Faurbach, 206-822-8156. PO Box 3267, Kirkland, WA 98083

Start Point: Quality Food Center, 460 East North Bend Way. Exit I-90 at exit 31. Proceed north on North Bend Blvd to North Bend Way. Go right on North Bend Way for 1/4 mile to store on the left. YR1054 starts here. You will drive 16 miles to the trailhead to begin YR1014. Latte stand inside left entrance.

Event Info: Daily dawn-dusk. Closed Thanksgiving & Christmas. **YR1054** is rated 1 and is suitable for large wheeled strollers. Pets must be leashed with clean-up and are not allowed in the store. Carry water. The trail follows an old railroad bed through farm country. There are many species of birds to be seen along with Mt. Si. The route returns through residential areas, past Si View Park and along the South Fork of the Snoqualmie River. **YR1014** is rated 5, no strollers or wheelchairs. Pets are allowed. Wear appropriate hiking footwear. No water is avaliable on the trail. Allow six hours for this hike. This is a difficult hike to the top of Granite Mountain. Elevation gain is 3800 ft. Lower trail is heavily forested and the upper trail includes alpine meadows with many varieties of wildflowers. Many rocks, roots and steep switchbacks. Spectacular views at the summit.

Olympia - 10km Walk (YR500) **May 1-Sept 30**
B Awards available
Sponsoring Club: AVA-115, Evergreen Wanderers
POC: Mary Halford, 206-759-1486. 3330 Narrows Drive, Tacoma, WA 98407

Start Point: Nisqually Plaza - Texaco Station, 10220 Martin Way E. (Walk will start at Nisqually Wildlife Refuge.) From North or South on I-5 take Exit 114. Southbound exit goes right into Martin Way. Northbound turns right at the end of the ramp and another right at Martin Way. Look for the Texaco Station on the right.

Event Info: Daily dawn-dusk. Trail is rated 1. Rock & gravel used to repair flood damage to this trail may have made it ve;y difficult for strollers and wheelchairs. The flood mad the Wildlife Refuge more beautiful. No pets allowed. There is an entrance fee of $2.00 per single or family. Kids under 16, holders of Golden Eagle, Golden Age, Golden Access Passports, or Federal Duck Stamps are free. Mosquito repellent might be needed. Water and restrooms are available at registration and the start point. Bring your binoculars and cameras. Trail is flat.

Olympia - 10km Walk (YR260) 11km Walk (YR820) **Jan 1-Dec 31**
B Awards available
Sponsoring Club: AVA-148, Capital Volkssport Club
POC: Terry Nordahl, 360-866-4089. 10244 Windward Dr NW, Olympia, WA 98502

Start Point: Bayview Thriftway Deli, 516 W 4th Ave. Southbound on I-5, exit 105B, Port of Olympia, merge into Plum St and go left on State St which turns into 4th St. Bayview is on the right. I-5 North: Exit 105 and follow Port of Olympica signs. Left on Plum St and continue as above.

Event Info: Daily, 8-dusk. Closed Christmas. **YR260** is rated 1+, suitable for strollers but difficult for wheelchairs. Pets are allowed but not in buildings. It will take you through the State Capital, Campus and surrounding historical area. **YR820** is rated 2+, suitable for strollers and wheelchairs. Pets are allowed but not in buildings. Visit Olympia Farmers Market, the boardwalk and Priest Port Park. Great views of the Olympic Mountains.

Olympia - 10km Walk (YR1059) **Jan 1-Dec 31**
B Awards available
Sponsoring Club: AVA-148, Capitol Volkssport Club
POC: Pat Lazar, 360-456-6562. 2413 West Lake SE, Lacey, WA 98503

Start Point: South Bay Chevron Grocery & Deli, 3444 South Bay Road. Northbound on I-5: exit 107. Turn right on Pacific Ave SE. Turn left on Lilly Rd SE which becomes Lilly Rd NE. Go 2.7 miles. Start is on your left at the corner of Lilly Rd NE & South Bay Rd. Southbound on I-5: exit 107. Left on Pacific Ave SE then left on Lilly Rd SE and continue as above.

Event Info: Daily 8- dusk. Trail is rated 1, suitable for large-wheeled strollers but not for wheelchairs. Pet are allowed. Water, restrooms & food at the start/finish only. This is a rails to trails walk along the old Chehalis Western Railroad line. Enjoy the meadows, the wind in the trees and the birds at the pond.

Orting - 10km Walk (YR1252) **Apr 1-Sept 30**
Credit Only Event
Sponsoring Club: AVA-336, Daffodil Valley Volkssport Assn.
POC: Sandra Dunterman, 206-845-8152. 12516 79th Ave E, Puyallup, WA 98373

Start Point: Orting Jackpot, 204 N Washington Ave. Take State Route 410 to Sumner. Exit south onto SR 162 to Orting. Jackpot/Exxon on your left. Look for wood file cabinet. Park on side street.

Event Info: Daily, 7 to dusk. Trail is rated 1 and is suitable for strollers & wheelchairs. Pets are allowed but not in buildings. Walk through quiet neighborhoods on sidewalks and trails through city parks with a gravel path beside the highway out to High Cedars Golf Course. Mountain views, weather permitting.

Pasco - 10km Walk (YR1264) **Jan 1-Dec 31**
B Awards available
Sponsoring Club: AVA-590, Tri-Cities Windwalkers
POC: Frank & Fay Thomasen, 509-783-9271. PO Box 453, Richland, WA 99352

Start Point: Shopping Spot, 148 South 28th St. From the south: Take exit 113 toward Kennewick and Pasco. Follow signs to Pasco, crossing blue bridge; exit left on Lewis St. Go right on 28th. From the west off 182, take 20th Ave exit; turn right to Lewis St. Right on Lewis to 28th. Get in left turn lane to turn left on 28th. From the east off 395, take 20th Ave exit. Turn left & continue to Lewis St. Continue as above.

Event Info: Daily, dawn to dusk. Trail is rated 1 and is suitable for strollers & wheelchairs. Pets are allowed. Walk on asphalt bike and pedestrian path along the Columbia River, past the historic Moore Mansion near the Blue Bridge and other beautiful riverfront homes.

Port Angeles - 10km Walk (YR361) **Jan 1-Dec 31**
B Awards available
Sponsoring Club: AVA-517, Olympic Peninsula Explorers
POC: Dick or Glenda Cable, 360-681-2504. 193 Twin Peaks Lane, Sequim, WA 98382

Start Point: Swain's General Store, 360-452-2357. 602 E 1st St. Westbound 101: Follow Hwy 101 (Front St) to Albert St and turn left. Proceed one block to First St and turn left. Swain's is on the right. Go 1/2 block to the parking lot on the right. Eastbound on 101: Follow Hwy 101 (First St) to Swain's on the right. Please park in the back lot.

Event Info: Mon-Sat, 8am-7pm; Sun 9-6. Closed New Years, Christmas and Thanksgiving. Trail is rated 2+ and is not suitable for strollers or wheelchairs. Pets must be leashed. Tour the town, Olympic National Park Hqs & Peninsula College. Mostly on city streets.

Port Orchard - 11km Walk (YR1251) **Jan 1-Dec 31**
Credit Only Event
Sponsoring Club: AVA-359, die Bremertoner Stadtmusikanten
POC: Brian L. Beagle, 360-697-6311 (days) 360-697-3782 (eves). 25939 Circle Dr NW, Poulsbo, WA 98370

Start Point: McCormick Woods Golf Course Pro Shop, 5155 McCormick Woods Dr SW. From Hwy 16 take the Old Clifton/Tremont exit. Turn left on Old Clifton Rd and drive two miles to mcCormick Woods Dr and follow signs to McCormick Woods Golf Course and Mary Mac's Restaurant. Registration box is located in the Pro Shop. Walkers are asked to park in the back row or on the unpaved area.

Event Info: Daily, dawn to dusk. Trail is rated 2; not suitable for strollers or wheelchairs. Pets are not allowed. Carry water & bring insect repellent. Walkers should allow at least two hours of daylight to complete the walk due to wooded trails. Walk on unpaved nature trails and paved roads around McCormick Woods Golf Course. Trail proceeds along several nature trails through a wildlife area.

Port Townsend - 10/11km Walk (YR421) **Jan 1-Dec 31**
B Awards available
Sponsoring Club: AVA-517, Olympic Peninsula Explorers
POC: Jean Cartwright, 360-385-5207. 211 Baycliff Dr, Port Townsend, WA 98368

Start Point: Port Townsend Athletic Club, 360-385-6560. 229 Monroe St (downtown). From northbound SR104: SR 104 from hood Canal Bridge. Right on Hwy 19 and follow to Monroe St and turn left. Entrance to the club is on Washington St. There is RV parking in the lot at Monroe and Washington Streets.

Event Info: Mon-Fri 6am-dusk; Sat 9-8; Sun 10-5. Closed major holidays and the third Saturday in May. Trail is rated 2+. Not suitable for strollers or wheelchairs. Pets must be leashed. Walk is on city streets in Victorian Port Townsend.

Puyallup - 10km Walk (YR242) **Jan 1-Dec 31**
Credit Only Event
Sponsoring Club: AVA-336, Daffodil Valley Volkssport Association
POC: Theola Swann, 206-840-0889 or send SASE to DVVA, PO Box 1488, Puyallup, WA 98371

Start Point: Safeway, 1405 E Main. From I-5 north or south take exit 127, (Puyallup) and go east on Hwy 512. Continue on Hwy 512 for approximately 11 miles. Exit Hwy 512 at Pioneer Ave, turn right on Pioneer and enter the left lane. Turn left at the light (15th St SE). Proceed thru the next light to the Safeway parking lot.

Event Info: Daily dawn-dusk. Closed Christmas. Trail is rated 1, suitable for strollers but not wheelchairs. Pets are allowed. This is an easy walk on city sidewalks through downtown Puyallup past many historical sites, antique stores and through two city parks.

Redmond - 10km Walk (YR784) **Jan 2-Dec 31**
Credit Only Event
Sponsoring Club: AVA-638, Northwest Striders
POC: Larry Loudenback, 206-747-3358. 14429 SE 15th St, Bellevue, WA 98007-5603

Start Point: Safeway, 630 228th Ave NE. From I-90, take exit 17. Go north on E Lake Sammamish Pkwy, right on SE 43rd Way which becomes 228th Ave. Registration file cabinet is next to customer service inside the store. Please park away from store entrance.

Event Info: Daily dawn-dusk. Closed Thanksgiving and Christmas. Trail is rated 3, suitable for strollers but not wheelchairs. Pets must be leashed and there is a scooper law. This walk is revised for '97. You will appreciate the elimination of the hill at the start. Views of the Cascade Mountains and beautiful homes all along the trail.

Redondo - 10km Walk (YR802) **Jan 1-Dec 31**
Credit Only Event
Sponsoring Club: AVA-133, Sea-Tac Volkssports Club
POC: Victor or Harriette Kring, 206-922-9147. 802 11th Ave, Milton, WA 98254

Start Point: Redondo Community Store & Post Office, 206-839-7854. 28200 9th Ave South. I-5 exit 147, South 272nd St westbound to 12th Ave, South/Marine View Dr South. Veer left on Marine View Dr South to Redondo Beach Drive South. Turn left to public parking lot on left. Public restrooms across street on pier (only restrooms on the walk). Do not park at the store -- round trip distance from the parking lot is included in the event distance.

Event Info: Daily, dawn to dusk. Closed Thanksgiving & Christmas. Trail is rated 3 and is suitable for strollers but not wheelchairs. Pets are allowed. No restrooms are available in the store (postal regulations). Walk on road shoulders and sidewalks along Redondo Beach seawall and public pier. Some steps and short, steep hills. Breathtaking panoramic views of Puget Sound, the Cascade & Olympic Mountain ranges, Poverty Bay & the Seattle skyline to the north.

Renton - 10km Walk (YR659) **Jan 1-Dec 31**
Credit Only Event
Sponsoring Club: AVA-561, Global Adventurers
POC: Larry Lehman, 206-271-3053. 2023 Aberdeen Ave SE, Renton WA 98055-4537

Start Point: Chevron Food Mart, 206-255-1774. 301 Grady Way. From I-405 east and west, take exit 2, (SR167) Rainier Ave to Grady Way. Turn right on Grady Way, go past Holiday Inn and turn into Chevron Food Mart.

Event Info: Daily dawn-dusk. Walk is rated 1 and is suitable for strollers but not wheelchairs. Pets must be leashed. This route is on the Cedar River Parkway, residential streets & city sidewalks.

Richland - 10km Walk (YR432) **Jan 1-Dec 31**
B Awards available
Sponsoring Club: AVA-590, Tri-Cities Windwalkers
POC: Eleanor Corley or Kitty Lund, 509-946-1539/509-946-0153. PO Box 453, Richland, WA 99352

Start Point: Best Western Tower Inn, 1515 George Washington Way. From the south on 240 and from 182, take the George Washington Way exits; continue on GW Way to Best Western Tower Inn on the left. After registration, turn left out of the parking lot on GW Way and drive to Newcomer Ave (Lutheran Church on the corner) and turn right. Continue to Davison and turn.left on Davison; continue to Park St and turn right to Leslie Groves Park.

Event Info: Daily, dawn to dusk. Trail is rated 2 and is suitable for strollers but not wheelchairs. Pets are allowed. This walk is on city streets and bike/pedestrian paths along the Columbia River. Trail takes you past north Richland homes, Hanford High School and Washington State University-Tri-Cities Campus.

Roslyn - 10km Walk (YR1208) **Apr 1-Oct 31**
Credit Only Event
Sponsoring Club: AVA-540, StarWalkers Volkssports Club
POC: Carolyn Dexheimer, 509-649-3099. 505 South A St, Roslyn, WA 98491

Start Point: The Dexheimer Residence, 505 South A Street. I-90 east or west take exit 80 following directional signs to Roslyn. Proceed on Bullfrog Rd 2.5 miles to the intersection of the Hwy 903 (1st stop sign). This is the intersection where the restrooms are available. Turn left to Hoffmanville Ave (Cruise Inn Restaurant is across the street). Turn right to South A Street and then turn left. Continue on South A St to start. (Right side of the street directly across from Carek's Meat Market.) Parking available on the street only and NOT in front of the meat market. Please do not block driveways.

Event Info: Daily, dawn to dusk. Trail is rated 1+ and will be difficult for strollers. Wheelchairs not recommended. Pets are allowed. The course rambles around Roslyn city streets, back roads and trails to Ronald and back through the many ethnic cemeteries. Water is available at the start/finish. Use the water faucet on the right hand side of the steps. Carrying your own water on the course is strongly advised.

Seattle - 10km Walk (YR351) 11km Walk (YR408) **Jan 1-Dec 31**
Credit Only Events
Sponsoring Club: AVA-373, Seattle Strasse Striders
POC: Jack W. Winter, 206-883-8536. PO Box 27573, Seattle, WA 98125-2573

Start Point: Crows Nest Marine Supplies, 206-632-3555. 1900 N Northlake Way, #155. From north or south on I-5, take exit 169, NE 45th St. Turn west on NE 45th. At the top of the hill, turn left onto Meridian Ave North, headed south. The start faces N 34th at the SW corner of Meridian Ave and N 34th St. Turn onto 34th for the best (on-street) parking. Do not park in the store lot.

Event Info: Mon-Fri, 9-8; Sat, 8:30-6; Sun, 10-5. Closed major holidays. **YR351** is rated 1+ and is suitable for strollers & wheelchairs. Pets are allowed on a leash with clean-up. This route tours the University of Washington campus. One section is without sidewalks and requires caution as vehicles are present. **YR408** is rated 2 and is not suitable for stroller or wheelchairs. Pets are allowed on leash and with clean-up. This is the Lake Union walk. It is 99% flat but has two sets of down stairs and graveled walks. It is on city sidewalks and other walkways around Lake Union.

Seattle - 10km Walk (YR655) **Jan 1-Dec 31**
B Awards available
Sponsoring Club: AVA-WA, Evergreen State Volkssport Association
POC: Pat Ellison, 206-863-5388. 7413D 142nd Ave East, Sumner, WA 98390

Start Point: 7-11 Store, 2429 Harbor Ave SW. From I-5 southbound take exit 163A, northbound exit 163. Proceed across the West Seattle Bridge to Harbor Ave (NOT Harbor Island) exit. Go right on Harbor Ave. 7-11 is on left one mile down. Do not park in store lot.

Event Info: Daily dawn-dusk. Trail is rated 1 and is suitable for strollers and wheelchairs. Leashed pets allowed. This is a flat easy walk on residential streets along Alki Beach. Experience spectacular views of the Seattle skyline across the Sound with ferry boats cruising, volleyball players in the sand, lots of walkers and beautiful sunsets.

Seattle - 10km Walk (YR054) 11km Walk (YR011) **Jan 1-Dec 31**
A Award available
Sponsoring Club: AVA-249, F.S. Family Wanderers
POC: Dorothy/Paul Steedle, 206-284-7560. 1627 4th Ave, West, Seattle, WA 98119

Start Point: The Seattle Inn, 225 Aurora Ave N. From I-5 take exit 167 "Mercer St-Fairview Ave", (coming from the south, this exit is on the left side of the freeway). On the exit ramp, keep to the left. Turn left at light onto Fairview Ave North. In five blocks turn right onto Denny Way. At 6th Ave North (one block beyond Aurora Ave), turn right. Go one block to John St and turn right again. Parking is available on the street or in nearby parking lots. Please do not park in the hotel's lot.

Event Info: Daily dawn-dusk. **YR011** is rated 2 but is not suitable for strollers and wheelchairs. Pets are allowed. Trail goes through Seattle Center, waterfront and downtown. It includes Pioneer Square, Freeway Park and Westlake Mall. **YR054** is rated 2+ and is not suitable for strollers or wheelchairs. Pets are allowed. Route passes through Seattle Center grounds, up Queen Anne Hill on sidewalks and park paths. Beautiful homes and gardens and sweeping views of Elliot Bay, Olympics, Cascades & downtown Seattle.

Seattle - 11/12km Walk (YR1074) 28km Bike (YR1075) **Jan 1-Dec 31**
Credit Only Events
Sponsoring Club: AVA-318, The Emerald City Wanderers
POC: Robert & Sharon Bruce, 206-282-8749. 3505 West Howe St, Seattle, WA 98199

Start Point: 7-Eleven Store, 5103 - 25th Ave. NE. From I-5 take exit 168 (NE 45th St). Turn east (right if northbound, left if southbound) on NE45th. Continue past University of Washington campus and down the viaduct, taking first right hand turn at the bottom, looping around under the viaduct onto 25th Ave NE. Turn right on 25th Ave. Continue north past University Village Shopping Center (on the right) to NE Blakley St. Turn left on Blakely and park on the street. Do not park in the store lot.

Event Info: Daily, dawn to dusk. The **walk** is rated 2 and is not suitable for wheelchairs. Strollers are possible. Pets must be on a leash and "scooper" laws are in effect. The walk is mostly on city streets along picturesque Ravenna Blvd and around scenic Green Lake on a paved walking path. (Construction on the path in 1997 may require some off-path detours in the park.) There are two moderate hills. The 1km option traverses Ravenna Park. The **bike** is rated 1. No pets allowed. Ride on a paved bike trail through a greenbelt area and along Lake Washington from Seattle (University area) to town center in Lake Forest Park. It is a former railroad right of way and is very level. Bikers must sign a waiver and wear a helmet.

Seattle - 12km Walk (YR1306) Jan 1-Dec 31
Credit Only Event
Sponsoring Club: AVA-373, Seattle Strasse Striders
POC: Sam Bess, 206-367-0728. PO Box 27573, Seattle, WA 98125-2573

Start Point: Cafe Aroma, 509 NE 165th St. From north or south 15, take exit 175 (NE 145th St). Turn east onto NE 145th St. At 5th Ave NE turn left. Parking is available in the gravel area of the Cascade Booster Club Bingo on the corner of 5th Ave NE & NE 165th St. Alternative parking is available on the 5th Ave NE side of the Cafe Aroma between the building and the fence.

Event Info: Daily, dawn to dusk. Closed major holidays. Trail is rated 2 and is not suitable for strollers or wheelchairs. Pets must be leashed and clean-up must be provided. This route is along city sidewalks and street shoulders with some travel on dirt or gravel paths. It includes several wood footbridges. There are some hilly areas.

Sedro-Woolley - 10km Walk (YR1269) **Jan 1-Dec 31**
B Awards available
Sponsoring Club: AVA-482, Skagit Tulip Trekkers
POC: Helen or Jim Neher, 360-856-2081. 812 Orth Way (PO Box 666) Sedro-Woolley, WA 98284

Start Point: Three Rivers Inn, 360-855-2626. 211 Ball St. From I-5 take exit 230 East. Follow SR 20 East about 6 miles to Sedro-Woolley to Ball St & start point.

Event Info: Daily, dawn to dusk. Trail is rated 1+ and is suitable for strollers & wheelchairs. Pets are allowed. Walk along deserted railroad bed, country roads and residential sidewalks. Views of Skagit River & Cascades.

Sequim - Two 10km Walks (YR640 & YR833) 12km Walk (YR641) **Jan 1-Dec 31**
B Awards available
Sponsoring Club: AVA-517, Olympic Peninsula Explorers
POC: Victor McAllister, 360-681-2560. 102 Louella Ridge Dr., Sequim, WA 98382.

Start Point: Econo-Lodge, 360-683-7113. 801 East Washington St (Hwy 101 & Brown Rd). Follow Hwy 101 to Sequim. From the east, Econ-Lodge is on the left as you approach Sequim. From Port Angeles or the west, go through Sequim and Econo-Lodge will be on the right as you are leaving Sequim. YR641 & YR833 start at the Econo-Lodge. For YR640, register at the Econo-Lodge and drive 2 miles east at John Wayne Marina. Directions at registration point.

Event Info: Daily dawn-dusk. **YR640** is rated 2 and is not suitable for strollers or wheelchairs. Pets are allowed. This event tours country lanes and Sequim Bay State Park trails. **YR641** is rated 3 and is not suitable for strollers or wheelchairs. Pets are allowed. Visit scenic Bell Hill along country lanes. Beautiful views of mountains, straits of Juan de Fuca & Canada. **YR834** is rated 2 and is suitable for strollers & wheelchairs. Pets are allowed. Walk around Sequim residential park and downtown areas. Visit free museum and area mastadon exhibit. The Econo-Lodge will give volkssporters a discount.

Spokane - 10km Walk (YR976) **Jan 1-Dec 31**
A Award available
Sponsoring Club: AVA-326, Lilac City Volkssport Assn.
POC: Dick or Geri Odell, 509-534-7056. 4254 East 22nd Ave, Spokane, WA 99223

WASHINGTON, cont.

Start Point: Deaconess Medical Center, 509-458-5800. 800 West Fifth Ave. Westbound on I-90, take exit 280 (Lincoln St). Turn right (east) on Third Ave, turn right (south) on Wall St and continue to Fifth Ave to Visitor Parking lot for Medical Center. Street parking is also available. Eastbound on I-90 take exit 280A (Maple St). Turn left (north) on Maple and then turn right (east) on Third Ave. Follow directions above.

Event Info: Daily dawn-dusk. Trail is rated 1, suitable for strollers and wheelchairs. Pets must be leashed. This walk is along paved sidewalks thru downtown and historical points in Spokane. It also goes along paved paths thru Riverfront park and along the Centennial Trail adjacent to the Spokane River.

Steilacoom - 11km Walk (YR635) **Jan 1-Dec 31**
B Awards available
Sponsoring Club: AVA-115, The Evergreen Wanderers
POC: Eugene W. Shaw, 206-588-8532. 7326 95th Ave, Tacoma, WA 98498

Start Point: Arco AM/PM, 3025 Steilacoom Blvd. Northbound on I-5, exit 119. Turn left, follow signs to Steilacoom (approximately 5.7 miles). Turn right on Rainier (5 blocks). Right on Puyallup (1 block), left on Steilacoom Blvd. One mile to Arco AM/PM on left side of road. Southbound on I-5, exit 129. Turn right on 74th St. 74th becomes Custer. Continue on Custer and turn right on 88th St. and go 2 blocks to Steilacoom Blvd. Arco AM/PM is at the corner of Steilacoom Blvd and Sentinel approximately 2.1 miles on Steilacoom Blvd.

Event Info: Daily dawn-dusk. Trail is rated 2 and would be difficult for wheelchairs and strollers due to one set of steps and one long hill. Pets are allowed. Route is on city sidewalks, bicycle lane and one easy 1000' trail, all bordering Puget Sound. Scenic views of the Olympic Mountains, Puget Sound and McNeil, Anderson and Ketron Islands.

Sumner - 10km Walk (YR159) **Jan 1-Dec 31**
B Awards available
Sponsoring Club: AVA-336, Daffodil Valley Volkssport Association
POC: Pat Ellison, 206-863-5388. 7413D 142nd Ave E, Sumner WA 98390

Start Point: Spartan Drive-In/Pepperoni Patch, 15104 E Main St. Southbound on SR 167 to SR 410: take second Sumner exit (Valley Ave) and turn left. Turn right on Main St for one block. Northbound I-5: take exit 127 (Hwy 512) to SR 410 and continue as above. Please park in the back of parking lot.

Event Info: Daily 9-9. Closed Easter, Memorial Day, Labor Day, 4th of July, Thanksgiving and Christmas. Trail is rated 1, suitable for strollers and wheelchairs but all curbs are not cut. Pets are allowed. Route goes through clean, quiet neighborhoods with lots of flowers and views of Mt. Rainier, up and down Main Street "USA", with many gift and antique shops. There are maps outside for early walkers.

Tacoma - 10km Walk (YR753) **Jan 2-Dec 31**
B Awards available
Sponsoring Club: AVA-809, Tacoma Easy Walkers Club
POC: Ethel Roy, 206-472-3236. 6210 S Sheridan Ave, Tacoma, WA 98408-4709

Start Point: Mary Bridge Children's Hospital, 317 S. Martin King Jr Way. On I-5 take the Bremerton/Gig Harbor exit #132. Take the Sprague Avenue exit to right. Follow Sprague for approximately 1 mile. Turn right onto Division Ave. Follow Division to Martin L King Jr. Way and turn right. Free parking at MultiCare garage. Enter at the Rose garden on your right.

Event Info: Mon-Fri 9-8; Sat 10-7; Sun noon-7. Holidays vary. Please call POC if in doubt. Trail is rated 2, Suitable for strollers but wheelchairs only with a companion walker. Pets are allowed. Walk through UPS College, Wright Park and Old Tacoma with large shade trees lining the streets. A walk that participants have wanted to repeat.

216

Tacoma - 10km Walk (YR694) **Jan 2-Dec 31**
Credit Only Event
Sponsoring Club: AVA-809, Tacoma Easy Walkers
POC: Ethel Roy, 206-472-3236. 6210 S Sheridan Ave, Tacoma, WA 98408-4709

Start Point: Boathouse Grill, 206-756-7336. Point Defiance Park. From I-5 take exit 132 (SR16/Bremerton). Take 6th Ave exit, staying in the middle lane. Turn left on 6th Ave and right on N Pearl St. Right turn on 54th going past Ferry Landing with a left turn to parking area.

Event Info: Daily dawn to dusk. Trail is rated 2 and is not suitable for strollers or wheelchairs. For your safety, you are encouraged to use the buddy system when walking the trail. Box lunches available at the Boathouse Grill for $6.50 each. Walk through old growth trees, along natural trails, paved roads and sidewalks. 95% of the walk is in the park.

Tacoma - 10/12km Walk (YR1291) **Jan 2-Dec 31**
Credit Only Event
Sponsoring Club: AVA-809, Tacoma Easy Walkers
POC: Ethel Roy, 206-472-3236. Tacoma, WA 98408-4709

Start Point: Antique Sandwich Company, 206-752-4069. 5102 N Pearl St. From I-5 take exit 132 (SR16/Bremerton). Take 6th Ave exit staying in the middle lane. Turn left on 6th Ave then a right on N Pearl St to start.

Event Info: Mon-Sat, 7-7; Sun 8-7. Open most holidays. Trail is rated 2 and is suitable for strollers but difficult for wheelchairs. Pets are allowed. Most of the walk will be residential, through Proctor District, a diversity of architectural style homes on Mason Ave with a pleasant view along Commencement Bay.

Tacoma - Two 10km Walks (YR1262 & YR1263) **Jan 2-Dec 31**
Credit Only Events
Sponsoring Club: AVA-115, Evergreen Wanderers
POC: Mary Halford, 206-759-1486. 3330 Narrows Drive, Tacoma, WA 98407

Start Point: Cicero's Coffee House, 2123 North 30th Street. From north or south on I-5: exit 133. Exit I-705, City Center. Stay in right lane, take Schuster Pkwy exit. Stay in left land, past Stadium Way, then stay in right lane to exit on N 40th, Old Town. Start is on the right corner at the traffic light (Intersection of North 30th & McCarver).

Event Info: SUMMER HRS: Memorial Day-Labor Day, Mon - Thurs & Sat & Sun, dawn to dusk. Closed Fridays. WINTER HRS: Sept 3-May 26, Mon-Fri, 6am-7pm; Sat & Sun 7:30-7. Closed Christmas, New Years & Thanksgiving. Early closing on Christmas and New Years Eve. **YR1262** is rated 3 and is not suitable for strollers or wheelchairs. Pets are allowed but must be leashed at all times with clean-up provided. Walk along the Schuster Parkway sidewalk with a scenic view of Commencement Bay. Continue on the sidewalks in downtown Tacoma, enjoy Broadway, Antique Ros, scenic & historic Tacoma and return past park, historical homes and views of Commencement Bay. **YR1263** is rated 1+ and is suitable for strollers and wheelchairs but there is one short hill with a gradual incline. Pets are allowed on a leash with clean-up. This is an easy, friendly walk on the sidewalk along scenic Ruston Way on beautiful Commencement Bay. The walk also covers some of the streets in historical Old Town Tacoma.

Tukwila - Two 10km Walks (YR799 & YR1293) **Jan 1-Dec 31**
Credit Only Events
Sponsoring Club: AVA-478, Cedar River Rovers
POC: Nancy Fairman, 206-235-7012. 3500 Shattuck Avenue S, Renton, WA 98055

Start Point: Kinko's Copy Center, 112 Andover Park East. From South: Take I-5 to Southcenter Pkwy exit. Turn right. Turn left on Strander Blvd and left again on Andover Park East. Turn right

WASHINGTON, cont. ━━━━━━━━━━━━━━━━━━━━━━━━━━

on Baker Blvd and left on Christensen Rd. From North: Take I-5 to Southcenter Blvd. Turn left on Southcenter and turn right at the light. Cross I-405 and turn left on Tukwila Pkwy. Turn right on Andover Park East, left on Baker Blvd and right on Christensen Rd. From East: Take I-90 to I-405 South to Southcenter Blvd. Follow directions above. Parking area is on Christensen Rd behind Kinko's.

Event Info: Daily dawn-dusk. **YR799** is rated 1 and is suitable for strollers and wheelchairs. Pets are allowed on a leash with clean-up. Walk on a flat, paved path that follows the Christensen Trail along the Green River to Brisco Park. **YR1293** is rated 2 and is not suitable for strollers or wheelchairs. Pet are allowed on a leash with clean-up. This walk takes place in Fort Dent & Tukwila Parks and along the Green River. You will find several references to Tukwila's past. There is one fairly steep hill and several stretches of gravel.

Vancouver - Two 10km Walks (YR424 & YR425) **Jan 1-Dec 31**
Credit Only Events
Sponsoring Club: AVA-551, All Weather Walkers
POC: Judy Noall, 360-737-6118 X4017. c/o Clark County Parks, PO Box 9810, Vancouver WA 98666-9810

Start Point: AM/PM Store, 39th & Main St. From I-5 north or south, take exit 2--39th St/Hospital (2 miles north of the Columbia River). Both directions exit onto 39th. Turn left on 39th St. Drive 4 blocks to Main. The Arco Station AM/PM store is on the SE corner of the intersection. Please park in surrounding residential areas, not in store lot.

Event Info: Daily dawn-dusk. **YR424** is rated 2. Strollers are possible but wheelchairs couldn't finish the trail. Pets are allowed. The course is on asphalt, sidewalks, and a little grass and short packed dirt pathway. The majority is residential with 2.5km in a greenway plus one park. There are vistas of the Vancouver Lake lowlands and one steep hill. **YR425** is rated 2, suitable for strollers but not wheelchairs. It is on asphalt and sidewalks through two parks, some residential areas and a school ground. Some natural trails.

Vancouver - Two 10km Walks (YR138 & YR632) **Jan 1-Dec 31**
A Awards available
Sponsoring Club: AVA-557, Vancouver USA Volkssporters
POC: Margie Bickford, 360-693-6430. PO Box 2121, Vancouver, WA 98668.

Start Point: Red Lion Inn at the Quay, 360-694-8341. 100 Columbia. From I-5 north or south, take exit 1C onto Mill Plain Blvd (from north turn right onto Mill Plain; from south turn left onto Mill Plain). Go west on Mill Plain Blvd which becomes 15th St to Columbia St. Turn left onto Columbia St to the Red Lion on the right.

Event Info: Daily dawn-dusk. **YR138** is rated 1+ and is suitable for strollers and wheelchairs. Pets are allowed. Trail goes through city streets and historical sites of the Cradle of the NW. **YR632** is rated 1 and is suitable for strollers & wheelchairs. Pets are allowed. This trail is along 14' wide concrete trail by theColumbia River, wetlands, overlook & Water Resource Center.

Vancouver - 10km Walk (YR116) 40km Bike (YR251) **Jan 1-Dec 31**
B Awards available
Sponsoring Club: AVA-557, Vancouver USA Volkssporters
POC: (Walk) Margie Bickford, 360-693-6430. PO Box 2121, Vancouver, WA 98668 (Bike) M L McKnight, 360-896-4069. PO Box 2121, Vancouver, WA 98668

Start Point: Health Experience Athletic Club, 360-696-9841. 5411 East Mill Plain Blvd. From I-5, take exit 1-C onto Mill Plain Blvd (from the north, turn left and from the south turn right onto Mill Plain Blvd). Go east to MacArthur Blvd. Turn right on MacArthur Blvd. Go one block to start on the left. From I-205 north or south, take exit 28. Go west to MacArthur Blvd and turn left for one block to start on the left.

Event Info: Weekdays dawn-dusk; weekends, 8-8. Closed all major holidays. **Walk** is rated 1 and is suitable for strollers and wheelchairs. Pets must be leashed. Route goes through neighborhoods by small parks and a cemetery. The **bike** is rated 3. Bikers must sign a waiver. Helmets are required. Route is on paved roads through East County neighborhoods to Lacamas Lake, circle and return.

Walla Walla - 10km Walk (YR654) **Jan 1-Dec 31**
Credit Only Event
Sponsoring Club: AVA-572, Walla Walla Volkssporters
POC: Sharyl Dill, 509-529-1682. 1540 Ruth Ave, Walla Walla, WA 99362

Start Point: St. Mary's Medical Center, 401 W. Poplar. From Hwy 12, take the 2nd Ave exit and turn right. Go 8 blocks to Poplar St and turn right. Go another 3 blocks and St Mary's Medical Center will be on your left between 5th & 7th Sts.

Event Info: Daily dawn-dusk. Trail is rated 1+ and is suitable for strollers and wheelchairs. Pets must be leashed. Trail will take you through historic areas of Walla Walla, past picturesque homes and parks. It is mostly on sidewalks but in a few places you will walk on the shoulder of the road.

Wenatchee - 10km Walk (YR298) 25km Bike (YR299) **Apr 1-Dec 1**
B Awards available
Sponsoring Club: AVA-210, Bavarian Volkssport Association
POC: Gib, Charlene Edwards, 509-663-3356. 2015 Overlook Dr, Wenatchee WA 98801or Gladys Albin, 509-662-2863. PO Box 1901, Wenatchee, WA 98801.

Start Point: Orchard Inn, 509-662-3443/800-368-4571. 1401 N. Miller St. From Seattle, take US 2, 110 miles to Wenatchee. From I-90 take US 97 to US 2, turn right and travel 15 miles to Wenatchee. From Spokane, take I-90 west to George, exit SR 281 north to Quincy. West on SR 28 to Wenatchee. Orchard Inn is on north end of Wenatchee Ave across from Denny's.

Event Info: Daily dawn-dusk. **Walk** is rated 1 and is suitable for strollers and wheelchairs. Pets are allowed. It is along paved trails in River Front Park and sidewalks along city streets. You will pass many art displays. The **bike** is rated 1+. This route is a paved walk/bike way along the shores of the Columbia River. It is a loop trail with a section of city streets to complete the distance. There are two short steep uphill sections on the bridge approaches. Be sure to follow all speed and caution signs. Bikers must sign waiver and wear a helmet.

Wenatchee - 10km Walk (YR297) **Apr 1-Dec 1**
Sponsoring Club: AVA-210, Bavarian Volkssport Association
POC: Gib/Charlene Edwards, 509-663-3356/Fran Taber, 509-782-1630. 2015 Overlook Dr, Wenatchee, WA 98801 or Gladys Albin, 509-662-2863. PO Box 1901, Wenatchee, WA 98801.

Start Point: Rivers Inn, 509-884-1474. 580 Valley Mall Parkway, East Wenatchee. From Seattle: US 2, 110 miles to East Wenatchee. From I-90: US 97 to US 2, turn right, travel 15 miles to East Wenatchee. Turn right on Sunset Hwy to first traffic signal at 9th St NE. Turn left ***one block to Valley Mall Pkwy. Turn right 1 1/2 blocks to Rivers Inn on your right. From Spokane: I-90 west to George, exit SR 281 north to Quincy, west on SR 28 to East Wenatchee. Drive straight to 2nd traffic light at 9th St NE, turn right and continue from *** above.

Event Info: Daily dawn-dusk. Trail is rated 1+, suitable for strollers but questionable for wheelchairs. Pets are allowed. This route follows city sidewalks and a paved walk/bike trail along the Columbia River with two short gradual uphill stretches.

Woodland - 28/34km Bike (YR821) **Jan 1-Dec 31**
B Awards available
Sponsoring Club: AVA-530, Border Crossers
POC: James Gorman, 360-577-3404 (days)/360-425-5428 (eves). 11 Larry Lane, Longview, WA 98632 or Pete Hauser, 360-577-7435. 2325 Nichols Blvd, Longview, WA 98632

WASHINGTON, cont. ━━━━━━━━━━━━━━━━━━━━━━━━

Start Point: Save-On-Foods Store, 1325 Lewis River Rd, SR 503. From I-5 Southbound, take exit 22 (Dike Access Rd). At the stop sign, turn left. Proceed under the interstate following North Goerig St (unmarked) around to the right to the stop sign at Scott St. Continue straight ahead to the junction with SR 503/Lewis River Rd. Bear right on SR 503 and proceed approximately 600 meters to the start on your right. From Northbound I-5, take exit 21 (SR 503). At the stop light, turn right for one block. Proceed on SR 503 for another 300 meters to start on your left. The start counter is in the front of the store between the entrance and the check-out stands.

Event Info: Daily dawn to dusk. Trail is rated 1+. Participants must sign waiver and wear a SNELL or ANSI approved bike helmet. Please carry your own water and tools. No local bike repair facilities. No restrooms on trail for 26km. Route is on flat, all weather paved roads. There may be some wind. Traffic is light. Beautiful views of dairylands, mountains, hills and forested lands, and farms along the Columbia & Lewis Rivers.

Yacolt - 10km Walk (YR570) **May 15-Oct 31**
Credit Only Event
Sponsoring Club: AVA-743, Pathways to Adventure
POC: Judy Berry, 503-244-7073 or Judy Noall, 360-699-2467. 7065 SW Hunt Club Rd, Portland, OR 97223

Start Point: The Pomeroy House, 20902 NE Lucia Falls Rd. Heading North on I-5 take exit 9 (Battle Ground), at end of ramp continue straight at light, NE 10th Ave (SR-502), proceed north (approx 2.3 miles) to 219th St (SR502). Turn right (east) approx 5.3 miles to stop light at intersection of Battle Ground Rd & Lewisville Rd (SR503). Turn left (north). Go approx 5.5 miles to NE Rock Creek Rd. Turn right (east) and follow winding Rock Creek Rd as it becomes NE 152nd Ave and then Lucia Falls Rd, approx 5.5 miles to the Pomeroy Farm. Only a small brown sign before the farm. Watch carefully for turn-in. Turn left at farm and proceed to the box outside the Gift Shop for check in. Heading South on I-5 take exit 14 (Ridgefield & Battle Ground). Turn east to NE 10th Ave, turn right (south). Proceed to 219th St (SR502) and turn left (east). Continue as above. After check in, proceed east (left) on Lucia Falls Rd to Moulton Falls Park.

Event Info: Mon-Sat, 8:30-2; Sun, 10-2. Finish by 4:30. Pomeroy House closes at 5pm. Trail is rated 2+ and is okay for strollers if they can negotiate stairs. Not suitable for wheelchairs. Pets must be leashed. This walk gives you the opportunity to experience the beauty of the East Fork of the Lewis River. The 334 acre park has many beautiful waterfalls on both the East Fork of the Lewis River and Big Tree Creek. There is a wealth of both evergreen and deciduous trees so the change in seasons is beautiful.

Yakima - 10km Walk (YR1077) **Apr 1-Oct 31**
B Awards available
Sponsoring Club: AVA-360, Yakima Valley Sun Striders
POC: Joe Cook, 509-966-3849. 4509 Summitview, Yakima, WA 98908

Start Point: Rio Mirada Motor Inn, 509-457-4444. 1602 Terrace Heights Road. Take I-82 to Yakima. Exit on exit 33 Yakima/Terrace Heights. Proceed east on Terrace Heights Dr. Rio Mirada is on the left side, one block east of freeway.

Event Info: Daily, 7:30 to dusk. Trail is rated 1, and is suitable for strollers but not wheelchairs. Pets are allowed on a leash. Trail is along Yakima Greenway and through the Arboretum. Mostly paved trails with some gravel.

West Virginia ═══════════════════════

Cairo - 11km Walk (YR878) **April 19- Sept 30**
B Awards available
Sponsoring Club: AVA-664, Riverfront Ramblers
POC: Karen Maes, 304-727-2699. PO Box 28, St. Albans, WV 25177.

Start Point: North Bend State Park, RR1 Box 221. From north or southbound I-77, take the US 50 Exit at Parkesburg and turn east. Take US 50 to the junction of WV 31. Turn south on WV 31 for four miles into and through Cairo. Outside Cairo, you will pick up a country road into North Bend; follow the signs. From north or southbound I-79, take the US 50 exit at Clarksburg and turn west. Take US 50 to the junction of WV 16 at Ellenboro. Turn left on WV 16 and drive to Harrisville where you will pick up the county road that will lead you into the park; follow the signs. The lodge is at the top of the hill near the park entrance.

Event Info: Daily, 9 a.m. to 5 p.m. Trail is rated 1+ and is suitable for strollers; wheelchairs may have problems. Pets allowed on leash, but pets are not permitted inside at start point. The walking trail is a Rails-to-Trails conversion. It is flat and well-marked. Note: From the lodge, you will have to drive to the start point which is approximately two miles away.

Charleston - 10km Walk (YR1020) **Jan 2- Dec 31**
B Awards available
Sponsoring Club: AVA-664, Riverfront Ramblers
POC: Karen Maes, 304-727-2699. PO Box 28, St. Albans, WV 25177.

Start Point: Mountain State Outfitters, 4112 MacCorkle Ave., SE. From eastbound I-64/I-77, take exit 98, the 35th Street Bridge exit. Move to the left lane. At the first light turn left on MacCorkle Ave. Drive six blocks to the start/finish point on the left side of the street. Parking is available on both sides of the street.   From westbound I-64/I-77, take exit 95 (MacCorkle Ave. exit). Go west on MacCorkle (61) to the start/finish.

Event Info: Mon- Sat, 10 a.m. to 5 p.m. Closed Sundays and major holidays. Trail is rated 1+ and is suitable for strollers and wheelchairs. Pets allowed on leash, but pets are not permitted inside at start point.   Trail is a combination of paved streets and sidewalks on level ground.   Includes a beautiful view of the West Virginia State Capitol Complex from across Kanawha River.

Charleston - 10km Walk (YR 879) **Jan 2- Dec 19**
B Awards available
Sponsoring Club: AVA-664, Riverfront Ramblers
POC: Karen Maes, 304-727-2699. PO Box 28, St. Albans, WV 25177.

Start Point: Coonskin Park Pro-Shop - Coonskin Park Clubhouse, 2000 Coonskin Dr. From I-64 through Charleston, take exit 99 - Greenbrier Street/Yeagei Airport.   Turn north on Greenbrier St./114.   When the road splits into a Y at the bottom of the hill, stay to the right. Look for signs to Coonskin Park. At the next stop light turn left onto Coonskin Dr.   In about 3/4 of a mile you will enter the park. Follow signs to the Clubhouse Pro Shop.

Event Info: Daily, 8 a.m. to dusk. Closed Dec 20 through Jan 2, 1998. Trail is rated 3 + with a 1+ option.   Strollers OK; not suitable for wheelchairs. Pets allowed on leash, but pets are not permitted at the start point. Trail is on a combination of paved park roads and gravel/dirt paths.   The last part of the trail climbs a fairly steep hill; however, there is a 1+ option, and the hill may be avoided.

Charleston - 10km Walk (YR 880) **April 19- Sept 30**
B Awards available
Sponsoring Club: AVA-664, Riverfront Ramblers
POC: Karen Maes, 304-727-2699. PO Box 28, St. Albans, WV   25177.

Start Point: D & M Stables, Kanawha State Forest. From I-64/I-77 through Charleston, take exit 58A/Oakwood Rd. At the light turn right onto Oakwood Rd./US 119 South. In one mile, at the 2nd set of stop lights, turn left onto Oakwood Rd. Stay on Oakwood Rd. when it turns left after ½ mile. In another 2/5 mile, turn right onto Bridge Rd. At the first stop sign, Bridge becomes Loudon Heights Rd. Stay on Loudon Heights. In 3/5 mile, turn right on Connell Rd. Left on Loudendale Rd. After 2 2/5 mile, you will enter the State Forest. The stables are two miles from the entrance.

Event Info: Mon- Fri, 10 a.m. to 5 p.m. Sat - Sun, 9 a.m. to 5 p.m. Closed major holidays. Trail is rated 1 + and is suitable for strollers, not wheelchairs. Pets are allowed on leash, but pets are not permitted at the start point. Trail is on paved and dirt path roads. A second trail is offered and is rated 2. Only one event credit allowed, even if doing both trails.

Davis - 10km Walk (YR1016) **April 19- Sept 30**
Credit Only Event
Sponsoring Club: AVA-664, Riverfront Ramblers
POC: Karen Maes, 304-727-2699. PO Box 28, St. Albans, WV 25177.

Start Point: Canaan Valley Resort - registration desk at the lodge, Rt. 1, Box 330. From I-79, take exit 99 at Buckhannon/Weston. Then Rt 33 east through Elkins and into Harman. At Harman, take Rt. 32 north to Canaan Valley Resort.

Event Info: Daily, 8:30-5:30. Trail is rated 1 +, suitable for strollers and wheelchairs. Pets must be leashed. Route is on paved park roads.

Davis - 10km Walk (YR1171) **April 19-Sept 30**
Credit Only Event
Sponsoring Club: AVA-664, Riverfront Ramblers
POC: Karen Maes, 304-727-2699. PO Box 28, St. Albans, WV 25177.

Start Point: Blackwater Falls State Park, registration desk at the lodge. From I-79, take exit 99 Buckhannon/Weston. Take Rt. 33 east through Elkins and into Harmon. At Harmon take Rt. 32 north to Blackwater Falls/Davis.

Event Info: Daily, 8:30-5:30. Trail is rated 1 +, suitable for strollers and wheelchairs. Pets allowed on leash. Route is on paved roads and has gentle hills.

Harpers Ferry - 10km Walk (YR1019) **Jan 2-Dec 31**
Credit Only Event
Sponsoring Club: AVA-664, Riverfront Ramblers
POC: Karen Maes, 304-727-2699. PO Box 28, St. Albans, WV 25177.

Start Point: Appalachian Trail Conference Office, 799 Washington St. From I-81, take exit 12 - the US 45/US 9 East exit to Charles Town. Follow signs toward Charles Town. At the US 9/N340 Intersection turn left. At the second set of stop lights turn left into the towns of Bolivar and Harpers Ferry - do not go into the park entrance. Stay on the main road until you get to the second Jackson/Washington intersection. Conference center is on this corner.

Event Info: Nov 1- Jun 1, daily 9-5. Closed weekends. Jun 2-Nov 1, daily 9-5 and open weekends, 9-4. Closed all major holidays. Trail is rated 3, not suitable for strollers or wheelchairs. Pets must be leashed and are not allowed in the start point. Route is a combination of sidewalks, stone and wooden steps and dirt paths. There are significant hills and the sidewalks can be slippery when wet.

Huntington - 10km Walk (YR877) **April 19-Sept 30**
B Awards available
Sponsoring Club: AVA-664, Riverfront Ramblers
POC: Karen Maes, 304-727-2699. PO Box 28, St. Albans, WV 25177.

WEST VIRGINIA, cont. ━━━━━━━━━━━━━━━

Start Point: Ritter Park Tennis Club, 8th Street and Cadwell Rd. From I-64, take exit 11 - Hal Greer Blvd. and turn north. After 1.8 miles, be sure you are in the left lane. Go through two sets of stop lights and, just past McDonalds and across from Cabell-Huntington Hospital, turn left on Boulevard Ave. After three blocks, Boulevard Ave. becomes Washington Blvd. After four blocks, cross a tricky intersection and turn left into the park; the tennis courts are on your right.

Event Info: Daily, 9-5. Trail is rated 1+ and is suitable for strollers or wheelchairs. Pets are allowed on leash, but pets are not permitted at the start point. This walk is on a dirt and fine gravel, well-marked pathway and city sidewalks.

Parkersburg - 10/15km Walk (YR375) **June 3-Oct 26**
A Award available
Sponsoring Club: AVA-804, Flusstalvolk
POC: Sandia Sommer, 614-373-8685. 519 Seventh St, Marietta, OH 45750

Start Point: Blennerhassett Museum, Second & Juliana Streets. From I-77 north or south, take US 50 west into Parkersburg. Turn left on Ann St. Take Ann to Second (do not follow Rt 68 over the bridge). Go left on Second one block to Museum. From Ohio take US 50 across the bridge at Belpre. Stay in right land on Ann St.

Event Info: June-Aug, 10-5; Sept-Oct, 12-4. June through August they are closed on Mondays and Sept & Oct they are closed Monday through Wednesday. Trail is rated 1+ (2 if you do the 15km). Only one event credit even if doing both distances. These trails are not suitable for strollers or wheelchairs. Pets are allowed but must be muzzled on the boat. The 10km begins with a ferry ride to Blennerhassett Island. Walk the Island and return to the Museum and walk Parkersburg with views of historic buildings and homes. The optional 5km climbs Quincy Hill to Overlook Park.

South Charleston - 10km Walk (YR1015) **Jan 2-Dec 31**
B Awards available
Sponsoring Club: AVA-664, Riverfront Ramblers
POC: Karen Maes, 304-727-2699. PO Box 28, St. Albans, WV 25177.

Start Point: Farm Table Restaurant, 419 D. Street. From eastbound I-64, take exit 56 and turn left at the top of the ramp. From westbound I-64, take exit 56 and turn right at the top of the ramp. Move to the left lane. At the T intersection (at the light), turn left on MacCorkle/US 60. At the next light (the Indian mound is on your left), turn left and then drive to the right, around the mound. At the stop sign, turn left on D St. Drive two blocks; the start/finish is on your right at the corner of 5th and D.

Event Info: Mon-Sat, 9-5. Closed major holidays. Trail is rated 3 and is not suitable for strollers or wheelchairs. Pets are allowed on leash, but are not permitted at the start point. Trail is on sidewalks and side streets and contains some short hills.

St. Albans - 10km Walk (YR881) **Jan 2-Dec 31**
Credit Only Event
Sponsoring Club: AVA-664, Riverfront Ramblers
POC: Karen Maes, 304-727-2699. PO Box 28, St. Albans, WV 25177.

Start Point: Universal Health Club, 808 B Street. From I-64 take exit 44, the St. Albans/Hwy 35 exit. Turn right on Hwy 35. After three miles (at the first stop light), Hwy 35 intersects Hwy 60. Cross Hwy 60 and immediately turn left onto Main St. West. After two miles you will cross Coal River and turn right onto one-way Kanawha Terrace. Move immediately to the far left lane and pull into the first parking lot on the left. Universal is across the street.

Event Info: Mon-Fri, 6 a.m. to 7 p.m.; Sat, 10-3; Sun, 10-2. Closed major holidays. Trail is rated 2+, suitable for strollers but not wheelchairs. Pets must be leashed.

WISCONSIN

Cedarburg - 10km Walk (YR136) **Apr 1-Oct 31**
B Awards available
Sponsoring Club: AVA-490, Deutschstadt Volkssporters
POC: W. R. Breen, 414-375-0383. W51 N176 Fillmore Ave, Cedarburg, WI 53012

Start Point: Washington House Inn. W62 N573 Washington Ave. From I-43 take exit 89 to Pioneer Rd (Hwy C) and drive west on Pioneer to Washington Ave (Hwy 57). Turn right on Washington Ave and go about 5 blocks north to the Inn on the left side of the street at the intersection of Washington Ave and Center. Street parking is available and there are municipal parking lots in the area. Do not park in the rear lot of Inn as it is reserved for Inn guests.

Event Info: Daily 9-2. Off trail by 5. Trail is rated 1. Strollers and wheelchairs may have some trouble with short stretches of gravel and grass. No pets are allowed. The route will take you through the historic main street district of Cedarburg and through many of the city's lovely parks.

LaCrosse - 10km Walk (YR1250) **Apr 1-Sept 30**
B Awards available
Sponsoring Club: AVA-068, Grandad Bluffers Volkssport Club
POC: Charlene Keith, 608-783-2165. 918 Well St, Aralaska, WI 54650

Start Point: KwikTrip #761, 500 Cass St. Located on the corner of 5th & Cass. Two blocks east of the Mississippi River Bridge (Big blue bridge).

Event Info: Daily, dawn to dusk. Trail is rated 1 and is suitable for strollers & wheelchairs. Pets must be leashed. This is a city walk through historic housing district and downtown district of LaCrosse.

Madison - 10km Walk (YR763) **Jan 1-Dec 31**
A Award available
Sponsoring Club: AVA-835, Madison Area Volkssport Association
POC: Bonnie Hamer, 414-563-1417. W6898 Hwy 12, Ft Atkinson, WI 53538

Start Point: Inn on the Park, 1-800-279-8811. 22 South Carroll St. Located on the SW corner of the Capital Square. From the Beltline (Hwy 12-14-18-151) exit Hwy 151 (Park St). You will travel north on Park St about 2 miles and take a diagonal right onto West Washington (at stop light). Proceed on West Washington to the Capital Square and the start.

Event Info: Daily dawn to dusk. Trail is rated 2, not suitable for strollers or wheelchairs. Pets are not allowed. The trail takes you on city streets along beautiful lake shore homes, through city parks and on the University Campus.

Madison - 11km Walk (YR1248) **Mar 1-Nov 30**
A Award available
Sponsoring Club: AVA-835, Madison Area Volkssport Assn
POC: Jo Sparks, 608-273-9904. 4209 Wanetah Trail, Madison, WI 53711

Start Point: Best Western Inn Towner Motel, 2424 University Ave. From I-90 take exit 142 and go west on US 12, 18 to Midvale Blvd. Go north (right) on Midvale to University (approx 2.5 miles). Go east (right) on University and stay to the right. One block after the Campus Drive-University Ave split, turn left on Highland. Start will be on the right.

Event Info: Daily, dawn to dusk. Trail is rated 2 and strollers & wheelchairs may have difficulty. No pets are allowed. Motel parking may occasionally be limited. Two hour metered street parking is available. This route (the Picnic Point Walk) is on sidewalks and campus lake shore paths offering panoramic views of the Capitol and Lake Mendota, concluding through a wooded, residential area.

WISCONSIN, cont. ─────────────────────

Madison - 10km Walk, (YR1246) **Jan 1-Dec 31**
A Award available

Sponsoring Club: AVA-835, Madison Area Volkssport Assn.
POC: Angie Sparks, 608-249-2379. 205 North Third, Madison, WI 53704

Start Point: Madison Bagel Company, 2044 Atwood Ave. From I-90 take State Hwy 30 exit (Left exit). Go west on 30, exit onto North Fair Oaks Ave. Turn left (south, under Hwy 30) onto North Fair Oaks. Turn right at 2nd light onto Atwood Ave (approx 3/4 miles). Start is on the right approx 1/2 mile down.

Alternate Start Point: Monty's Blue Plate Diner, 2089 Atwood Ave. Follow directions above but Diner is on the left approx 1/2 mile down.

Event Info: Mon-Sat 8-4; Sun 8-2. Closed Christmas. Trail is rated 1 and is suitable for strollers & wheelchairs. No pets are allowed. There is two hour metered parking available 1/2 block from Madison Bagel Co. On Atwood or free unlimited street parking in the neighborhood north of Madison Bagel on Rusk or Linden Ave. This walk (Historic Eastside) follows the Isthmus to one of Madison's earliest neighborhoods and its first city park. Continues along Lake Monona and features a visit to Olbrich Botanical Gardens. The walk brochure includes a brief history of several of the historical buildings & sites.

Madison - 10km Walk (YR1247) **Jan 1-Dec 31**
A Award available
Sponsoring Club: AVA-835, Madison Area Volkssport Assn.
POC: Thomas Charkowski, 608-221-1698. 5406 Spicebush Lane, Madison, WI 53714

Start Point: Bluephies Restaurant, 2701 Monroe St. From Hwy 12 (West Beltline Hwy) take the Midvale Blvd exit north. Proceed one block north to Nakoma Rd intersection. Turn right and proceed on Nakoma Rd for approx 1.25 miles. Stay on Nakoma as it curves right and becomes Monroe St. Proceed on Monroe St 9 blocks to Knickerbocker St. Turn right on Knickerbocker and right again into Bluephies parking lot.

Event Info: Jun-Aug, daily, 9:30-8; Jan-May & Sep-Dec, 9:30-5. Closed major holidays. Call if in doubt. Trail is rated 1 and is suitable for strollers & wheelchairs. No pets are allowed. This is a beautiful, scenic walk around Lake Wingra, through Madison's Henry Vilas Zoo and the University of Wisconsin Arboretum. A wonderful walk with something for the entire family.

St Croix Falls - 10km Walk (YR720) 25km Bike (YR1005) **Apr 15-Oct 31**
Walk has B Awards available   Bike is a Credit Only Event
Sponsoring Club: AVA-796, St. Croix Valley Volkssporters
POC: Dianne Hoffman, 715-483-3918. 684 Moody Rd, St. Croix Falls, WI 54024

Start Point: Polk County Information Ctr, 715-483-1410. Intersection of Hwy 35 & Hwy 8. 55 miles NE of Minneapolis and St. Paul. Take I-35 to US Hwy 8 east to Wi Hwy 35. Start is at the intersection o;f Hwy 35 & Hwy 8.

Event Info: Daily 9-2. Finish by 5. Closed Easter. **Walk** is rated 3 and is not suitable for wheelchairs. Okay for strolllers. Pets are allowed on a leash. Route provides mixed multiple terrains of pavement, sidewalks, grass and gravel trails. It includes the historic St Croix River Dalles Gorge. The **bike** is not rated. Trail fee of $3.00 per day required. Bikers must sign waiver and should wear a helmet. It is on the Gandy Dancer Bike Trail which is an 8' wide limestone surfaced trail on an old railroad bed. It has a very minimal 1-2% grade.

WYOMING

Buffalo - 11km Walk (YR835) **May 1-Sept 30**
A Award available
Sponsoring Club: AVA-806, Clear Creek Volkssport Assn.
POC: Frank Schleicher, 307-684-2739. 213 High St, Buffalo, WY 82834

Start Point: Super 8 Motel, 655 East Hart (junction of Hwy 16 & I-25). From I-90 exit #56b to I-25 southbound. Then exit at #299. Turn right at stop sign at bottom of off ramp. From I-25 northbound, exit at #299. Turn left at stop sign at bottom of off ramp. Turn left immediately after Col. Bozeman's Restaurant. From Hwy 16 west, turn left at Main St (2nd stoplight). Go to Hart St (next light) and turn right. Turn right before Col. Bozeman's.

Event Info: Daily dawn to dusk. You must finish before sunset. Trail is rated 2. Not for strollers or wheelchairs. No pets allowed. The trail is on paved bike paths, city sidewalks and graveled trails.

Casper - 10km Walk (YR024) **Apr 1-Sept 30**
A Award available
Sponsoring Club: AVA-093, Cheyenne High Plains Wanderers
POC: Rita Livingston, 307-237-8378. 1301 Manor Dr, Casper, WY 82609

Start Point: Parkway Plaza Hotel, 307-235-1777. 123 West E St. From I-25 exit 188A at Center St South (toward mountain) on Center. Turn right, almost immediately, from Center. Start is the registration desk of Parkway Plaza Hotel.

Event Info: Daily, dawn to dusk. Trail is rated 2 and is suitable for strollers but not wheelchairs. Pets must be leashed. Route is paved and much of it is along the North Platte River with views of Casper Mountain. Some parts parallel historic trails. There are displays of historic interest. There are no books available at the start. RV parking is available.

Casper - 10km Walk (YR040) **May 1-Sep 30**
A Award available
Sponsoring Club: AVA-501, Wyoming State Parks & Historic Sites
POC: Pat Thompson, 307-577-5150. Edness Kimball Wilkins State Park, PO Box 1596, Evansille, WY 82636

Start Point: Entrance Fee Booth, Edness K. Wilkins State Park, 307-577-5150. Off I-25, north or south, exit Evansville, WY, just south of Casper, Follow signs for the park about 2 miles south.

Event Info: Daily 8-4. Finish by 4. Trail is rated 1 and is suitable for wheelchairs & strollers. Pets are allowed on a leash. Please carry water and use sun protection. Half of trail is paved and the remainder is on sand and gravel.

Cheyenne - 10km Walk (YR002) **Jan 1-Dec 31**
A Award available
Sponsoring Club: AVA-093, Cheyenne High Plains Wanderers
POC: Mike/Carol Jennings, 307-632-9072. 1600 Kopsa Ct, Cheyenne, WY 82007

Start Point: Wrangler Western Wear Store, 307-632-9072. 1518 Capitol Ave. From I-25 take West Lincolnway Exit 9 to Lincolnway (which is 16th St downtown). From I-80 take Central Ave exit 362 to Lincolnway. Go left to the red building on the corner of 16th St and Capitol Ave (2 blocks).

Start (During Frontier Days-July 18-27): Brown's Shoe Fit Companpy, 1802 Dell Range Blvd. From I-25 take I-80 east and then go to exit *364 which is East Linconway. At top of exit go left on College Dr to Dell Range and left on Dell Range to the corner of Bllue Grass Cr. From I-80 take the *364 exit and from the west turn left on College and from the east turn right on College and follow the same directions. RV parking is available in the area.

Event Info: May-Sep 8am-9pm. Sep-May 9-5. Closed New Years, Easter, Thanksgiving and Christmas. Trail is rated 2 with an altitude of 6062 ft. Strollers & wheelchairs will find some high curbs. Pets must be leashed. Route is on city streets and sidewalks with about a mile through a city park. No books are available at the start.

Cheyenne - 11km Walk (YR015) **Jan 1-Dec 31**
B Awards available
Sponsoring Club: AVA-093, Cheyenne High Plains Wanderers
POC: Mike/Carol Jennings, 307-632-9072. 1600 Kopsa Ct, Cheyenne, WY 82007

Start Point: Brown's Shoe Fit Company, 1802 Dell Range Blvd. From I-25 take I-80 east and then go to exit *364 which is East Linconway. At top of exit go left on College Dr to Dell Range and left on Dell Range to the corner of Blue Grass Cr. From I-80 take the *364 exit and from the west turn left on College and from the east turn right on College and follow the same directions. RV parking is available in the area.

Event Info: Mon-Sun 9-8:30. Closed major holidays. Trail is rated 2 and is suitable for strollers and wheelchairs. Pets are allowed on a leash. 99% of the trail is on the Cheyenne Greenway.

Cheyenne - 10km Walk (YR1009) **May 1-Sep 30**
A Award available
Sponsoring Club: AVA-501, Wyoming State Parks & Historic Sites
POC: Dan Allen, 307-632-7946. Curt Gowdy State Park, 1351 Hynds Lodge Rd, Cheyenne, WY 82009

Start Point: Curt Gowdy State Park, Fee Booth, 307-632-7946. Take Happy Jack Road (Hwy 210) from Cheyenne for 23 1/2 miles. Get off at Fee Booth by Granite Reservoir or 24 miles from Laramie, WY by taking I-80 to 210 East.

Event Info: Daily 7:30am-5 pm. Trail is rated 3 and is not suitable for strollers or wheelchairs. Pets are not allowed. You must carry water. Good shoes and a walking stick are recommended. This trail goes over low lying meadows, gentle rolling hills and around massive granite formations. You will see wild and domestic animals in the area

++Devils Tower - 10km Walk (YR497) **May 1-Sept 30**
Sponsoring Club: AVA-177, Northern Hills Walking Club
POC: Cindy Waller, 307-283-2310. PO Box 912, Sundance WY 82729

Start Point: Devils Tower Trading Post. Located on your left just before entrance to Devil's Tower Nat'l Monument. From I-90 take Hwy 14 to Devils Tower Junction. Follow signs to Devils Tower National Monument. The Trading Post is on your left across from Devils Tower KOA. There is an entry fee to walk or drive into the Monument.

Event Info: Daily, 8-8. Trail is rated 3 and is not suitable for strollers or wheelchairs. Pets are allowed on a leash. This is a beautiful trail through our First National Monument. Includes the trail around the base of the Monument. Goes through "Prairie Dog Town".

Evanston - 10km Walk (YR042) **Apr 1-Sept 30**
A Award available
Sponsoring Club: AVA-501, Wyoming State Parks & Historic Sites
POC: AllenCowardin, 307-789-6547. 601 Bear River Dr, Evanston, WY 82930

Start Point: Bear River Travel Information Center, Bear River State Park. Just south of exit 6 on I-80.

Event Info: Daily, 8-5. Trail is rated 1 and is suitable for strollers or wheelchairs. The only obstacle to wheelchairs is 200' incline. All curb cuts in downtown Evanston are ADA accessable. Pets must be leashed. Start point is on 5' wide trail in the park. It goes into downtown Evanston and through historic Depot Square area.

Ft Bridger - 10km Walk (YR507) May 1-Sep 30
A Award available
Sponsoring Club: AVA-501, Wyoming State Parks & Historic Sites
POC: Jolene Pale, 307-684-7629. Ft Bridger State Historic Site, PO Box 35, Ft Bridger, Wy 82933

Start Point: Ft. Bridger State Historic Site. 307-684-7629. Going east on I-80, get off at Ft Bridger exit. Drive about two miles to start. Driving west on I-80, take the Mountain View exit and drive about 5 miles to start. Follow signs.

Event Info: Daily 9-5:30. Closed Labor Day Weekend. Trail is rated 1 and is suitable for strollers and wheelchairs if they can negotiate some grassy areas. Pets are allowed on a leash. Carry water. Trail goes through Historic Fort and the town of Ft. Bridger. Grass trails in Fort and paved roads in town. Contact Ron Green, 611 Rodeo Ave, Cheyenne, WY 82009 for brochures.

Guernsey - 10km Walk (YR041) May 1-Sep 30
A Award available
Sponsoring Club: AVA-501, Wyoming State Parks & Historic Sites
POC: Guernsey State Park, Museum Attendant. 307-836-2334. PO Box 429, Guernsey, WY 82214

Start Point: Museum, Guernsey State Park, 307-836-2334. 15 miles E of I-25, 4 miles N of Guernsey. Enter Park and follow signs to the Museum.

Event Info: Daily 10-6. Early start box is available in front of Museum. Trail is rated 4. Not suitable for strollers or wheelchairs. No pets are allowed. Please carry water. Good shoes and a walking stick are recommended. Sunscreen is helpful. Route is mostly on dirt trails. Some areas are paved and you will climb over the spillway. Good views of the lake and sometimes wildlife.

Guernsey - 11km Walk (YR388) Jan 1-Dec 31
A Award available
Sponsoring Club: AVA-501, Wyoming State Parks & Historic Sites
POC: Manager, 307-836-2356. Hwy 26, Guernsey, WY 82214

Start Point: Bunkhouse Motel, 307-836-2356. Hwy 26. Downtown Guernsey. Just off Hwy 26, 15 miles east of I-25.

Event Info: Daily dawn to dusk. Trail is rated 2+. Not suitable for strollers or wheelchairs. An alternate trail is available. No pets are allowed. Please carry water, wear good shoes and use sunscreen. Trail goes over the Oregon Trail ruts and out to Register Cliff.

Lander - 10/15km Walk (YR039) May 24-Sept 1
A Award available
Sponsoring Club: AVA-501, Wyoming State Parks & Historic Sites
POC: Darrel Trembly, 307-332-6333. Sinks Canyon State Park, Sinks Canyon Rd, Lander, WY 82520

Start Point: Visitor's Center, Sinks Canyon State Park, 307-332-6333. 3079 Sinks Canyon Rd. From center of Lander, follow Wyoming 131 about nine miles southwest to the State Park. The Visitors Center is on the left side of Hwy 131.

Event Info: Daily 9-5. You must finish by 7. Trail is rated 3+. There is an optional 5km trail to the Popo Agie Falls which is rated 4. None of this event is for strollers or wheelchairs. Pets are not allowed. Carry water, wear good shoes and use sunscreen. A walking stick is helpful. There is much wildlife in this area. Route is mostly on trails. Goes over the river on a bridge, through mixed forest and meadows. Uphill for the initial half.   An additional 5km route is available for individuals who walk up to the Falls.   This part of the walk is rated 4 due to a 600 ft gain in elevation.

Moorcroft - 10km Walk (YR140) **May 1-Sep 30**
A Award available
Sponsoring Club: AVA-501, Wyoming State Parks & Historic Sites
POC: Ron Siefort, 307-756-3596. Keyhole State Park, 353 McKean Rd, Moorcroft, WY 82721

Start Point: Keyhole State Park, Fee Booth. 307-756-3596. 353 McKean Rd. Take I-90 east or west and exit at Keyhole State Park entrance sign. Go 9 miles to Park Fee Booth.

Event Info: Daily 8-6. Trail is rated 2+ and is not suitable for strollers or wheelchairs. Please carry water and wear good shoes. Pets are not allowed. Trail goes along the lake on trails.

Newcastle - 10km Walk (YR028) **Apr 5-Oct 26**
A Award available
Sponsoring Club: AVA-763, Newcastle Area Chamber of Commerce Volkssports
POC: Allan Ward, 13 1/2 W Wentworth, Newcastle WY 82701 or call Chamber Office 307-746-2739.

Start Point: Sundowner Inn, 451 W Main. Two blocks west of downtown on Main St.

Event Info: Daily 7 to dusk. Trailis rated 2, suitable for strollers and wheelchairs. Pets must be leashed. The route wanders through town past points of historical interest and civic pride.

Pine Bluffs - 10km Walk (YR318) **May 1-Dec 31**
B Awards available
Sponsoring Club: AVA-093, Cheyenne High Plains Wanderers
POC: Emma Fosdick, 307-638-8538. 1415 Madison Ave, Cheyenne, WY 82001

Start Point: Gator's Travelyn Motel, 307-245-3226. 7th & Parsons (515 West 7th). Take the Pine Bluffs exit from I-80 and turn into the town area. Go 2 blocks to 7th and turn right for one block. RV parking is available in the area.

Event Info: Daily 6am-10pm. Trail is rated 3. No wheelchairs or strollers. Pets must be leashed. Altitude is 5047 ft. Route covers some city streets and some along dirt paths in the cliff areas. There are some hills and inclines. No books at the start. The trail is not open if snow is in the area. The route may be slippery in the cliff areas.

Sundance - 10km Walk (YR522) **May 1-Sept 30**
A Award available
Sponsoring Club: AVA-177, Northern Hills Walking Club
POC: Susan Worthington, 307-283-1182 (wk) 283-1677(hm). Box 189, Sundance WY 82729

Start Point: Country Cottage and Yogurt Garden, 423 Cleveland St. Exit 187 from I-90. Turn toward Sundance. At stop sign at the corner of Cleveland and 6th St turn left. Cottage is on the corner of Cleveland and 5th.

Alternate Start Point: Bear Lodge Motel, 218 Cleveland. One block west of Country Cottage on left.

Event Info: May & Sept: 8-6; June, July & Aug; 8-8. Closed Sundays, use alternate start point. Trail is rated 2 and has one long hill. It is not suitable for strollers or wheelchairs. Pets are allowed. Route goes through the town and out into the countryside. You will have a hilltop view of Sundance Mountain, Green Mountain and Inyan Kara Mountain.

Thermopolis - 10km Walk (YR038) **Apr 1-Sept 30**
A Award available
Sponsoring Club: AVA-501, Wyoming State Parks & Historic Sites
POC: Monica Hamilton/Todd Stevenson, 307-864-2176. 220 Park St, Thermopolis, WY 82443

Start Point: Hot Springs State Park Bath House, 307-864-3765. 220 Park St. Just north of Thermopolis off Hwy 20.

Event Info: Daily, 8-6. Trail is rated 1 and is suitable for strollers & wheelchairs. Pets must be leashed. It is recommended that you walk this event in the morning due to very little shade on the route. Walk goes on trails and through town. Contact Ron Green, 611 Rodeo Ave, Cheyenne, WY 82009 for brochures.

NOTES

NOTES

VOLKSSPORTS ASSOCIATE

Yes, I want to support volkssporting across the United States. Please sign me up as follows: (circle choice)

Individual-$20 per year   Family-$25 per year (List names below)   Corporate-$200 per year

Foreign-$30 per year

Enclosed is my check for $_____ made payable to Volkssports Associate.

Please charge my(circle one)   VISA   MASTERCARD   DISCOVER   AMERICAN EXPRESS

OTHER (fill in type of card): _____

Card No.:_____Exp date:_____

Signature:_____

I belong to the following AVA Club(s):_____

_____

_____

Please rush my membership packet to:

Name:_____Phone:_____

Address:_____

City/State/Zip:_____

Additional Family Members (for family memberships):_____

_____

_____

232